D1259477

MOLECULES
AND
CRYSTALS

MOLECULES AND CRYSTALS

IN INORGANIC CHEMISTRY

A. E. VAN ARKEL

Professor of Inorganic Chemistry
University of Leiden

NEW YORK
INTERSCIENCE PUBLISHERS INC.

LONDON
BUTTERWORTHS SCIENTIFIC PUBLICATIONS
1956

BUTTERWORTHS PUBLICATIONS LTD.
88 KINGSWAY, LONDON, W.C.2

U.S.A. Edition published by
INTERSCIENCE PUBLISHERS INC.
250 FIFTH AVENUE, NEW YORK 1

First Edition in English 1949
Second Edition in English 1956

The original work *Moleculen en Kristallen* published by
W. P. van Stockum & Zoon
The Hague

Printed in Northern Ireland at The Universities Press, Belfast
by Sir Isaac Pitman & Sons, Ltd.

June 59 DuPont

CONTENTS

PREFACE

ALTHOUGH the general scope of the second English edition has remained the same, there are considerable changes in many chapters. The chapter on the stability of ionic compounds has been enlarged, a new chapter on compounds of variable composition has been added, and that on complexes changed insofar as more attention is paid to complexes with non-isolated groups. For the second part, dealing with non-ionic compound formation, more space has been given to the non-ionic complexes, and a new chapter on interstitial compounds has been added. The author hopes that, with these additions, the second edition will more completely cover the whole field of inorganic chemistry.

A. E. VAN ARKEL

October, 1956

Chapter I

INTRODUCTION

1. PROBLEMS OF CHEMISTRY

THE famous discovery by LAVOISIER that metals increase in weight when calcined marked the beginning of a new era in chemistry. Combustion could be considered no longer as a loss of material, but as a process involving the taking up of oxygen; the phlogiston theory was, in fact, dead. Stimulated by the atomic theory of DALTON, in 1807, chemistry now developed very swiftly along entirely new lines. The discoveries at the end of the eighteenth and the beginning of the nineteenth century constituted the first great turning point in chemistry. The second was BOHR's theory of the atom, which led to the development of chemistry along lines previously followed in physics. Lavoisier's discovery resulted in all the old ideas being discarded, whereas Bohr's atomic theory brought new light to bear on existing knowledge and gave to chemistry a newer and wider perspective.

In broad outline, the picture of chemical science about 1900 was as follows: With the exception of some elements, principally the rare earths, qualitative and quantitative analyses no longer represented any major problems. Organic chemistry was forging ahead and the structural formulae of complicated compounds, such as sugars and alkaloids, had been worked out.

The physical chemist, meanwhile, had concentrated his attention on a number of important thermodynamic relationships between different properties, such as freezing point and latent heat of melting, vapour pressure and temperature, and the heat of reaction and electromotive force of a galvanic cell; such relationships were of particular importance in applications of the phase rule to equilibria between different phases. It was, nevertheless, impossible to give an answer to the question of why a particular material has properties different from those of another. In the scientific literature of those days this kind of problem is seldom mentioned, and the impression is given that the possibility of answering such questions was never envisaged. There was, for example, no speculation on the differing volatilities of HCl and NaCl, nor why NaCl is an electrolyte and CCl_4 is not, nor why $Th(OH)_4$ is a base and $Si(OH)_4$ an acid. Therefore, there is missing from the chemistry of 1900 any consideration of the problem of how the properties of a substance depend on its composition; it is, moreover, obvious why such problems at that time were insoluble, for without knowledge of the properties of the atoms composing the molecules it is impossible to correlate the properties of a substance with its chemical structure.

It appears paradoxical that at a time when it was known in great detail how atoms were arranged in complicated molecules, almost nothing was known about the atoms themselves, for in 1900 only the relative atomic weights of atoms were known, and not the absolute values. It is, therefore, hardly surprising that some scientists of repute still doubted the reality of atoms. One of them was OSTWALD. He finally accepted the implications of the investigations of SVEDBERG on the Brownian movement of colloidal particles, which provides a visual demonstration of the thermal movement of small particles as the direct result of their bombardment by surrounding molecules.

The evidence for the reality of atoms, provided by the Brownian movement, was greatly strengthened by the results of research in radioactivity and x-rays. By means of interference phenomena, which occur when x-rays fall on a crystal, it is possible to determine with great accuracy the position of atoms in a crystal, making it difficult to doubt any longer the reality of the atoms.

It is really remarkable that the series of experimental discoveries, which at the end of the nineteenth century had provided such strong evidence for the reality of atoms, should at the same time have destroyed the early concept of the atom. They revealed that atoms are physical realities, but, on the other hand, they also proved that these atoms are certainly not indivisible, and, in fact, must possess a complicated structure consisting of a positively-charged nucleus and negatively-charged electrons. The abandonment of the idea of indivisibility of atoms, and the recognition of the possibility of transmutation, has changed the aspect of chemistry very little indeed, because in most chemical processes the atom can still be regarded as indivisible, inasmuch as the nucleus is not affected. The knowledge which has been gained of atomic structure has, however, greatly broadened the scope of chemistry. The atomic theory has led to an understanding of the forces acting between atoms and has opened up the possibility of finding the relationship between the constitution and properties of substances, so that it is now possible to answer such questions as:

1. What compounds will be formed when two elements react with one another?
2. Why has a given compound its particular properties?

3. What properties will hitherto unknown compounds have?
4. What atoms must react together, and in what way, in order to produce compounds with given properties?

2. BOHR'S MODEL OF THE ATOM

RUTHERFORD's experiments on the bombardment of thin layers of metals by α-particles showed that the mass of the atom is concentrated in a very small, positively-charged nucleus. Thus, the idea arose that the atom consists of a positive nucleus and a number of electrons. If the nucleus has a charge n then there must also be in the atom a number of electrons, together possessing the same charge n, since the atom as a whole must be electrically neutral. If we express the charge of the nucleus, in terms of the charge of an electron, as unity, then this so-called 'atomic number' is equal to the number of electrons. The question now arises as to how to reconcile the simultaneous existence of positive and negative charges in one atom.

What, in fact, prevents the negative electrons from joining with the nucleus? This question was partially answered in the theory of the atom published by Bohr in 1913, which was based on the experiments of Rutherford, and the resulting model of the atom has properly been called the Rutherford-Bohr model. Although this original picture of the atom has been modified to a large extent, it is still, for the purpose of this book, of the greatest use*. According to Rutherford and Bohr the atom consists of a positively-charged nucleus around which a number of electrons revolve under the influence of the electrostatic forces which the nucleus exerts on the electrons. The whole system can be likened to a solar system in which the planets revolve around the sun in defined orbits, but an essential difference between the planetary system and the atom is that in the former all velocities are possible, while in the latter the movements of the electrons are confined to definite velocities. The quantum theory explains how these velocities are determined.

The hydrogen atom has a nuclear charge of unity and therefore has one electron. According to Bohr this electron will have one velocity so that it moves in a circular path with a radius of

* In the modern model of the atom, based on wave mechanics, the conception of electronic orbits in the old model is replaced by the idea of the probability of the occurrence of an electron at a given point. The conclusions, however, which can be drawn from the older model remain the same in the newer conception, and it is important to remember that in this new model the essential points of Bohr's theory have not been discarded, but merely interpreted differently and very greatly refined.

$0{\cdot}532 \times 10^{-8}$ cm; it can further describe a path with a radius of $4 \times 0{\cdot}532 \times 10^{-8}$ cm and, in general, paths of radii $n^2 \times 0{\cdot}532 \times 10^{-8}$ cm in which n is a whole number, but no intermediate values can occur. Corresponding to each of these paths there is a certain energy of the system which we can call E_1, if the electron is in the first orbit, and E_2 when it is in the second, and so on.

If the electron is now brought from the first into the second orbit, then an amount of energy must be expended, equivalent to $E_2 - E_1$. If, on the other hand, the electron moves from state 2 to state 1, then an amount of energy $E_2 - E_1$ is set free, which, according to Bohr, is released as monochromatic radiation of a frequency given by the relationship $\nu = (E_2 - E_1)/h$, in which h is Planck's constant.

If an electron in a hydrogen atom moves from one orbit to another of lower energy, radiation will be emitted, the frequency of which indicates the energy difference between initial and final states. From studies of spectra we can then, in principle, calculate in what energy states an atom can occur; and, even more important for our purpose, we can calculate the energy required to move an electron from the orbit of lowest energy to an infinite distance from the atom. Such a process leads to splitting the atom into a positive ion and an electron. The energy needed for this procedure is called the *ionization energy* or, less accurately, the *ionization potential.*

Now an atom can, in general, lose more than one electron, and work must be performed to remove each of these electrons from the atom. Each subsequent electron will then have its own ionization energy, which will be greater for the second electron than for the first, because during the removal of the second electron it is being attracted by a positively-charged ion. If an atom normally contains n electrons, then during the removal of the first electron, this electron is attracted by the charge $+e$ of the ion that is being formed. The second electron is attracted by a charge $+2e$, and the more electrons the atom has lost, the greater will be the ionization energy for subsequent electrons.

3. PERIODIC SYSTEM OF THE ELEMENTS

In addition to the methods applied by Rutherford there are others for determining the magnitude of the nuclear charge. From the study of spectra it appears that hydrogen, helium and lithium possess one, two and three electrons, respectively, and thus the nuclear charges, or atomic numbers, are known. The x-ray spectra, which are much less complicated than light spectra, can be used to determine the atomic numbers of all elements with higher nuclear charges. The elements occurring in nature can now be arranged in a series of increasing atomic number, or, what amounts to the same thing, in a series with an increasing number of electrons per atom. In this way an almost continuous series is obtained, starting with hydrogen, nuclear charge one, and finishing with uranium at 92. When the first measurements of the nuclear charges were performed there were still six gaps in this series, corresponding to the atomic numbers 43, 61, 72, 75, 85 and 87. Two of these were filled by the discovery of the elements hafnium (72) and rhenium (75). The series of the natural elements has since been enlarged to one hundred by the synthesis of new elements from nuclear reactions. These trans-uranium elements are unstable: under certain conditions their nuclei will break up into two smaller ones, and the four elements missing in the series of the natural elements have been observed among the fission products of the artificial trans-uranium elements. Elements (85) and (87) have been observed only in minute quantities, too small for their chemical properties to be studied.

The arrangement according to increasing atomic numbers gives almost the same order as the series based on atomic weight and put forward by MENDELÉYEV as the basis of his periodic system of the elements. The periodic system based on atomic number does not show any of the irregularities which occur in Mendeléyev's system where, as a result of the properties of the element, the noble gas argon must be placed before potassium, and tellurium before iodine, although the atomic weights of argon and tellurium are greater than those of potassium and iodine. Further, there is one group of elements, when arranged in a periodic system according to atomic number, into which one gets a clearer insight than when it is arranged in a system according to atomic weight. In Mendeléyev's system there is a series of elements, after the element barium, the properties of which are so similar that their separation constitutes one of the most difficult problems in analytical chemistry. As long as the elements were arranged according to atomic weight, it was not known precisely how many of these 'rare earths' existed. When Bohr published his theory it became known with certainty that barium had an atomic number of 56 and that the next known element, tantalum, had an atomic number of 73, so that there should be sixteen additional elements between these two. Bohr then showed that, of these sixteen, fifteen must have the properties of the rare earths, while the properties of the sixteenth should resemble those of the element zirconium, and therefore should be looked for not among the rare earths, but among the zirconium minerals, where in fact it was soon found. The way in which Bohr reached his conclusion can be best understood by further consideration of the periodic system.

Table I—The Periodic System of the Elements

	1st main group alkali metals	*2nd main group alkaline-earth metals*	*3rd main group*	*4th main group*	*5th main group*	*6th main group*	*7th main group*	*8th main group transition metals*			*1st subgroup*	*2nd subgroup*	*3rd subgroup*	*4th subgroup*	*5th subgroup*	*6th subgroup chalcogens*	*7th subgroup halogens*	*8th subgroup noble gases*
1st period																	H	He
																	1	2
2nd period	Li	Be	B											C	N	O	F	Ne
	3	4	5											6	7	8	9	10
3rd period	Na	Mg	Al											Si	P	S	Cl	Ar
	11	12	13											14	15	16	17	18
4th period	K	Ca	Sc	Ti	V	Cr	Mn	Fe	Co	Ni	Cu	Zn	Ga	Ge	As	Se	Br	Kr
	19	20	21	22	23	24	25	26	27	28	29	30	31	32	33	34	35	36
5th period	Rb	Sr	Y	Zr	Cb†	Mo	Tc	Ru	Rh	Pd	Ag	Cd	In	Sn	Sb	Te	I	Xe
	37	38	39	40	41	42	43	44	45	46	47	48	49	50	51	52	53	54
6th period	Cs	Ba	*	Hf	Ta	W	Re	Os	Ir	Pt	Au	Hg	Tl	Pb	Bi	Po	At	Rn
	55	56	57–71	72	73	74	75	76	77	78	79	80	81	82	83	84	85	86
7th period	Fr	Ra	**															
	87	88																
****rare-earth metals***			La	Ce	Pr	Nd	Pro	Sm	Eu	Gd	Tb	Dy	Ho	Er	Tu	Yb	Lu	
			57	58	59	60	61	62	63	64	65	66	67	68	69	70	71	
*****actinides***			Ac	Th	Pa	U	Np	Pu	Am	Cm	Bk	Cal			Md			
			89	90	91	92	93	94	95	96	97	98	99	100	101	102	103	

The division into main and subgroups is only of significance for the fourth and subsequent periods. In the first three periods all the elements properly belong to the main groups.

The names of the elements are given in the table on page 262.

† *Alternatively, niobium* (Nb).

The expression 'periodic system' indicates that there is a definite connection between the properties of elements and their positions in the series; certain properties will recur after a certain number of positions. Sodium, eight places after lithium, has properties strongly resembling those of lithium, while eight places farther on occurs potassium, which again has similar properties. In order to bring out these similarities, the elements with similar properties are arranged in vertical order in the periodic system (*see Table I*). The last column or group, contains the elements helium, neon, argon, krypton, xenon and radon, the so-called noble gases, which do not form molecules with any other elements. They are, in fact, monatomic gases at ordinary temperatures, and can be liquefied only at low temperatures.

The first group contains the alkali metals, lithium, sodium, potassium, rubidium, caesium and the element (87), of which very little is known. They are all univalent metals which react readily with a variety of other substances such as oxygen, water and chlorine. The next group contains the alkaline-earth metals which are all divalent, while the penultimate group contains the halogens—fluorine, chlorine, bromine and iodine. The similarities in properties of these elements, especially the latter three, had already been noted long before the entire table of the periodic system was constructed, the halogens thus having been one of the pillars of the periodic system. Also in this group is element (85), whose unknown properties can easily be predicted from those of the other halogens. The elements of the sixth group strongly resemble one another, particularly sulphur and selenium. The elements in this group are called 'calcogens'*; oxygen forms, with metals, the so-called 'calces', chalks, an old name for oxides, just as the halogens plus metals form 'salts', so called after NaCl, Latin *sal*.

Bohr's atomic theory gives a very satisfactory explanation of the periodicity in the natural system of elements, and in order to understand its full implications one must consider the models of atoms with more than one electron. The electrons in an atom cannot all be considered as equivalent. Thus, while a fairly small amount of energy is sufficient to remove the first of the three electrons from the lithium atom, the energy necessary for further ionization is fourteen times greater (*see Table VI*, Section 10). If both electrons were equivalent, then the ionization energy for the second would be about twice as great as that for the first. From this it can be argued that the first electron is bound less strongly than the second, that the orbit of the first electron is farther away from the nucleus than

* From the German *Chalcogenen*.

that of the other two. Similarly, for the next element, beryllium, two electrons are fairly easily removed, the remaining two being more strongly bound and thus apparently closer to the nucleus than the first pair. It appears, therefore, that there is a group of two electrons whose orbits are closest to the nucleus, which are held more strongly than any of the other electrons. This group of two electrons occurs in all elements, with the exception of hydrogen, and is called the K group, or shell.

In the sodium atom there is, again, one electron which can be removed easily, and in magnesium two of this kind, and in both elements there are ten other electrons of which two belong to the K shell, while the remaining eight correspond to a new group called the L shell. In fact, the atomic theory has postulated that the electrons are distributed among the K, L, M, N, O and P shells which, when complete, contain 2, 8, 18, 32, 50 and 72 electrons, respectively. The number of electrons contained in each of the shells is given by the formula $2n^2$, where n has the values 1, 2, 3, 4, 5 and 6 corresponding to shells K, L, M, N, O and P.

The first element, hydrogen, contains one electron belonging to the K group, the K shell being filled in the next element, helium, which contains two electrons. In the subsequent element, lithium, there are again two electrons of the K group, plus a third electron, which is the first of the L group. Proceeding in this way to elements of higher atomic numbers, the groups L, M and N are formed. If, while going through the whole series of elements from (1) to (100), each new group was started only when the preceding one was completed, there would be no electrons of the O, P and Q shells, since an atom with completely filled K, L, M, N and O shells would have $2 + 8 + 18 + 32 + 50 = 110$ electrons. In actual fact, an atom may contain an electron of, say, the O group, before the N group is completed; in this way it becomes possible for P and Q group electrons to occur, although the maximum number of electrons observed in an atom does not exceed one hundred.

With elements other than hydrogen and helium, the electrons in the second, or L shell, begin to develop after completion of the K shell, and this process continues until, in neon, the L shell is complete with eight electrons, the elements from lithium to neon forming the second period.

The M shell begins to develop with the elements which follow neon, and after eight places in the table, argon occurs with eight electrons in the M shell, and is, like neon, a noble gas. Argon is the last element in the third period, and although the M shell is not yet complete, the next electron shell begins to develop in the elements which follow. However, in scandium, the third element after argon, normal growth of the *N* shell stops because further electrons begin to fill the still incomplete *M* shell. This shell already contains eight electrons, so that one would expect that after a further ten elements, viz. in the element zinc, the *M* shell, with eighteen electrons, would be completed. However, after vanadium, one of the electrons of the *N* shell goes over to the *M* shell, and thus the latter is completed in the element before zinc. In copper there is only one electron in addition to the completed *M* shell, containing its complement of eighteen electrons.

As seen in *Table II*, the outer shell, which in copper has one electron, now proceeds to develop in the subsequent elements until, with krypton, it again has eight electrons and the properties of a noble gas. The completion of the *M* shell, and the growth of the *N*

Table II

elements	*K*	*L*	*M*	*N*	*O*	*P*	*Q*	
H→He	1→2							*1st period*
Li→Ne	2	1→8						*2nd period*
Na→Ar	2	8	1→8					*3rd period*
K→Ca	2	8	8	1→2				
Sc→Ni	2	8	8+(1→8)	2				*4th period*
Cu	2	8	18	1				
Cu→Kr	2	8	18	1→8				
Rb→Sr	2	8	18	8	1→2			
Y→Pd	2	8	18	8+(1→8)	2			*5th period*
Ag	2	8	18	18	1			
Ag→Xe	2	8	18	18	1→8			
Cs→Ba	2	8	18	18	8	1→2		
La→Lu (*rare earths*)	2	8	18	18+(0→14)	8+1	2		*6th period*
Hf→Pt	2	8	18	32	8+(2→8)	2		
Au	2	8	18	32	18	1		
Au→Rn	2	8	18	32	18	1→8		
Fr→Ra	2	8	18	32	18	8	1→2	*7th period*
Ra→Th	2	8	18	32	18	8→8+2	2	(*incomplete*)
Th→Cm	2	8	18	32	18→18+7	8+1	2	

shell to eight electrons comprises the fourth period of the system with eighteen elements, from argon to krypton, in contrast to the two previous periods which contain only eight elements each. In the subsequent period, after krypton, the *O* shell begins to grow, although the *N* shell is not yet complete. With the element yttrium, the *N* shell begins to fill until, in silver, it again contains eighteen electrons, whereas there is one electron in the *O* shell. This development temporarily ceases, although the *N* shell, with only eighteen electrons, is not complete. As in the previous period, so with the following elements, an expansion of the outer *O* shell takes place until, in xenon, it contains eight electrons which give to it, as to all the previous elements which have eight electrons in their outer shell, the characteristics of a noble gas. In the sixth period there occurs the same phenomenon as in the previous ones. In the first place, the *P* shell starts to grow, but with the third element after xenon, namely lanthanum, filling of the *O* shell begins. However, the *N* shell of the previous period has still not completed its development of thirty-two electrons, containing at this stage only eighteen electrons. After the start of the growth of the *O* group, beginning in lanthanum, this is temporarily interrupted, and the development of the *N* group now proceeds to completion, for which fourteen additional electrons are necessary. There is, thus, after barium, a series of fifteen elements, all of which have the same electronic structure in their two outer electron shells, forming the group of rare earths. This group, which constituted one of the greatest difficulties in the construction of a logical periodic system of the elements as long as they were arranged in order of atomic weight, fits perfectly into the scheme based on the Bohr atomic model. It is obvious that the group of rare earths, or lanthanides, must contain fifteen elements, all of which are now known since the discovery of element (61), promethium, among the fission products of the trans-uranium elements. With lutecium (71) the *N* shell is finally complete and the next electron, occurring in hafnium, now goes into the *O* shell, which develops in the same manner as the *N* shell of the previous period until it contains eighteen electrons. This process is complete in the element gold, and now a start is made with the development of the penultimate, or *P* shell. Just as in the development of the other shells, this is temporarily terminated when, in the noble gas radon, it contains eight electrons.

Now a start is made with the *Q* group and, by analogy with the previous periods, one should expect this growth to be interrupted while the incomplete *O* and *P* groups are built up, not to their full number, but to thirty-two and eighteen electrons, respectively.

One cannot go further into the development of the periodic table beyond this point, because one soon comes to the end of the series of known elements. However, it appears fairly certain that the elements following uranium have some resemblance to actinium, which means that this element marks the beginning of a second series of rare earths, the actinides.

In *Table II* the distribution of the electrons in all the atoms in the different groups is shown. In the long periods, between the elements scandium and copper, yttrium and silver and lanthanum and gold, there are a few elements which have only one electron in the outermost shell, e.g. palladium, with only one *O* electron and eighteen *N* electrons. As the differences in energy between the two states of an atom with one or two *O* electrons may be very small, this state can be changed under the influence of neighbouring atoms, and in the gaseous state be different from that in the solid. The distribution of the electrons is not always exactly known.

The periodic system developed from Bohr's atomic theory is of the greatest importance in chemical science because it demonstrates that the properties of the elements depend on their positions in the system. It is immediately apparent that chemical valency depends on the number of loosely-bound electrons in the atom. Thus, the alkali metals have one such electron while the divalent alkaline-earth metals have two, etc. Valency is therefore closely connected with electronic structure and provides the foundation for the modern theory of the chemical bond, the basis of which is to be found in the coupling or transfer of the valency electrons.

Chapter II

THE CHEMICAL BOND

4. ENERGY CHANGES IN CHEMICAL REACTIONS

In chemistry the only useful kind of atomic model is one which will give information on the forces which act between atoms. Of these forces there are, in the first place, the forces of attraction, which lead to the formation of molecules, but, in addition, there are also forces which come into play between molecules when a gas condenses to a liquid or a solid. In contrast to the former 'chemical forces', the latter are generally denoted as 'cohesion', or van der Waals forces, named after the man who first took them into consideration. A sharp distinction cannot be made between these two kinds of forces, and, in fact, 'chemical' forces sometimes play a part in condensation, while 'cohesion' forces can also play a part in holding together the atoms in a molecule. In addition to forces of attraction there are also forces of repulsion; two atoms at a certain distance in a molecule *AB* could never be in equilibrium if there were only attractive forces. The repulsive forces manifest themselves when a liquid or solid is compressed. We shall return later to consideration of these forces of repulsion and shall first consider the role of the forces of attraction in the formation of chemical compounds, and what data are required to understand how and why these compounds are formed.

The formation of a compound between two elements is generally associated with the development of heat and the resultant increase in kinetic energy of the molecules taking part in the reaction. Let us first imagine sodium and chlorine reacting in a space which is completely isolated from its surroundings so that no heat can enter or leave the system, and the reacting substances can perform no external work. It then follows that, in such a system, the total energy must remain constant, and, since the kinetic energy increases during the process, it also follows that the potential energy must decrease. The potential energy is the result of mutual attraction of the atoms. It is apparent that if the sum of the potential energies of two gram atoms of sodium and one gram molecule of chlorine is greater than that of two gram molecules of NaCl, the attraction between the Cl and the Na atoms in the NaCl is greater than that between the Cl atoms in the chlorine molecule and that between the Na atoms in the solid sodium.

We should be able to calculate the potential energy of atoms in elements and compounds, once we have determined the magnitude of the forces acting between the atoms as a function of the distance by which the atoms are separated from each other in the elements and

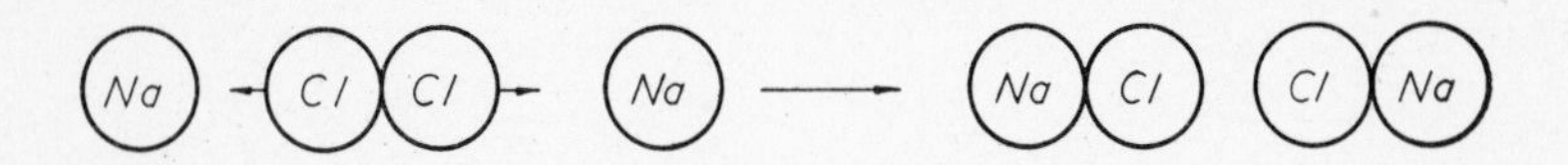

compounds. Such a calculation should be analogous to that of the change of potential energy of a body when it falls toward the earth; or, to take another example, to that of the change of potential energy which occurs when two bodies, carrying electrical charges of opposite sign, attract each other and move from a distance b to within a distance a of each other. Let us take the second example and carry out the calculation. Imagine that we have two spheres with charges e_1 and e_2 at a distance r apart. Then, from Coulomb's law, it follows that these bodies exert an attractive force on each other equivalent to $f = -e_1 . e_2/r^2$. If the bodies are displaced through a very small distance dr, sufficiently small for the force to be regarded as constant, the mutual distance being increased from r to $r + dr$, then the work performed over this distance dr is $-f . dr$ and the change of potential energy is $+f . dr$. If we wish to calculate the change of potential energy when the bodies, originally at a distance b from each other, come to within a distance a, then we must divide the distance a—b into a sufficient number of small parts over which the force can be considered to be constant, and the work done for each can be calculated and then totalled. To obtain the real value when the parts are infinitely small, integral calculus is employed and gives the result $e_1e_2/a - e_1e_2/b$. This result has a simpler form when the original distance b is equal to infinity. The change of potential energy is then $+e_1 . e_2/a$. If two small bodies with charges $+e$ and $-e$ are brought from an infinite distance to a distance a from each other, the change in potential energy is $-e^2/a$. We can also arrive at this result without the use of integral calculus in the following manner. The distance b—a is divided into n equal parts p. The work over the first part is greater than $(e_1 . e_2/b^2)p$ and smaller than $\{(e_1 . e_2)/(b - p)^2\}p$. If p is small, then we can obtain a good approximation, if the work is put equal to the geometric mean of the two values, or

$$\frac{e_1 \cdot e_2}{b(b-p)} p = -\frac{e_1 \cdot e_2}{b} + \frac{e_1 \cdot e_2}{b-p}$$

Thus, it follows that, for the second part, the expression is

$$-\frac{e_1 \cdot e_2}{b - p} + \frac{e_1 \cdot e_2}{b - 2p}$$

for the third

$$-\frac{e_1 \cdot e_2}{b - 2p} + \frac{e_1 \cdot e_2}{b - 3p}$$

and for the last

$$-\frac{e_1 \cdot e_2}{b - (n - 1)p} + \frac{e_1 \cdot e_2}{b - np}$$

$$= -\frac{e_1 \cdot e_2}{b - (n - 1)p} + \frac{e_1 \cdot e_2}{a}$$

If the values for the work are now added together for all the small parts, then we obtain the result $-e_1 \cdot e_2/a + e_1 \cdot e_2/b$; and with $b = \infty$ and $e_1 = -e_2$ we obtain again $-e^2/a$ for the change of potential energy.

There may be forces acting between atoms which vary with distance in a manner differing from that of the coulomb forces, but as soon as we know how these forces change with distance then we can calculate how much energy is released when a molecule is formed from two atoms which are at a distance a apart in the molecule. We shall then have to investigate what these forces are, and how closely the atoms in a molecule can approach one another.

We have considered, so far, only the energy changes occurring in a physical process without any knowledge of the absolute value of the energy involved. However, this knowledge is not necessary, since only energy changes can be measured. We can arbitrarily choose a state corresponding to zero energy from which all energy changes are measured. By definition, the potential energy of two particles will be taken as zero when they are at infinite distance. When the particles attract one another the energy of any other state will have a negative value.

If the value for the energy of a given system is positive, then it cannot be a stable system; the particles will either try to separate to an infinite distance from one another corresponding to zero energy, or they will take up an entirely different configuration, with negative energy. An example of a system with positive energy is that of two particles of equal charge e at a distance r, the energy being e^2/r.

A linear system of three particles $2e$, $-e$, $-e$ in points 1, 2, 3, at distances $a_{1\cdot2} = a$, $a_{1\cdot3} = 2a$, $a_{2\cdot3} = a$, respectively, has an energy

$$-\frac{2e^2}{a_{1\cdot2}} - \frac{2e^2}{a_{1\cdot3}} + \frac{e^2}{a_{2\cdot3}} = -\frac{2e^2}{a} - \frac{2e^2}{2a} + \frac{e^2}{a} = -\frac{2e^2}{a}$$

which, if the order is altered to $-e$, $2e$, $-e$, changes into

$$-\frac{2e^2}{a} - \frac{2e^2}{a} + \frac{e^2}{2a} = -\frac{7e^2}{2a}$$

5. INFLUENCE OF TEMPERATURE ON THE STABILITY OF CHEMICAL COMPOUNDS

If potential energy, alone, is considered, then it can be concluded that, under all circumstances, atoms will combine in such a way that the potential energy E is as small as possible. Sodium and chlorine will form the compound NaCl because the Na and Cl atoms have a lower energy in the compound than as separate elements. It is, however, noteworthy that there are not only processes known which occur with diminution of E or with development of heat, but also reactions in which heat is absorbed with a consequent increase of potential energy. This can, perhaps, be made clearer by considering the phenomenon of the condensation of a gas to a liquid. Molecules of a gas attract one another, for it is known that at sufficiently low temperatures all substances condense to a liquid and finally solidify. By this process heat is given out corresponding to the latent heats of evaporation and fusion, or to the heat of sublimation when a gas condenses directly to a solid. If such a condensed gas is heated then the kinetic energy of its molecules increases. Even at low temperatures there are some molecules which, as a result of their thermal movement, have a sufficient velocity to move towards the liquid surface, overcome the attraction of their neighbours and escape, with a certain velocity, from the liquid itself. In the space above a liquid such molecules are always found, and every liquid, or solid substance, at a fixed temperature has a constant vapour pressure resulting from the fact that an equilibrium is soon established in which as many molecules escape from the substance as return to it. As the temperature rises, the molecular velocity in the liquid increases and more molecules escape, the vapour pressure increasing with increasing temperature. A given quantity of liquid at a fixed temperature, in a sufficiently large volume, will evaporate completely.

Let us imagine that a liquid is evaporated in this way, and that we proceed to heat the vapour. The mean velocity of the molecules of the gas will increase and, as a result of their collisions, they will begin to rotate and oscillate; when the oscillations increase in intensity the attractive forces between the atoms in the molecule will cease to be sufficient to hold it together and the molecule will split into atoms, or dissociate. At any given temperature such dissociation will be greater, the smaller the attractive forces between the atoms in the molecule. Finally, if the temperature is raised high enough, all the molecules will dissociate into atoms; but this dissociation will depend on the concentration, according to the law of GULDBERG and WAAGE, because at high concentrations the chance of recombination of atoms is greater and the dissociation will be correspondingly reduced.

If two gases, at a given temperature and pressure, are compared, the degree of dissociation will give some indication of the forces between the atoms or of the potential energy of the molecule. As has been already stated, at high temperatures all molecules will be completely dissociated into atoms and it is known, from astronomical observations, that at temperatures above 4000°C practically no chemical compounds exist. Although we are not in a position to study gases under such conditions, we can imagine the temperature being increased and ask ourselves what will happen to the atoms. As an atom is not indivisible, it must break up into its constituent parts, and this is indeed what happens, for it is known that at very high temperatures electrons are produced from atoms. While one cannot heat large quantities of gases to such high temperatures, one can, by means of electric discharges, bring small quantities up to these temperatures. From the study of the resulting spectra it is known that dissociation into electrons and positive ions does occur. As will be seen later, dissociation of the atom into ions and electrons plays an important part in the formation of chemical compounds. Usually, the cohesion between molecules is less than that between the atoms in the molecules, so that, if heated sufficiently, the latter will first evaporate and then dissociate; but the order of sequence may also be reversed. For example, $CaCO_3$ and NH_4Cl each decompose on heating into two compounds CaO and CO_2 and NH_3 and HCl, respectively, before evaporation of the original compound can be observed; in the vapour, the molecules $CaCO_3$ and NH_4Cl, as such, do not occur in any measurable concentration.

We can, at this point, consider two well-known examples of dissociation of compounds: At a pressure of one atmosphere, mercury forms an oxide below 300°C, but above this temperature the compound decomposes, while at lower oxygen pressures the decomposition temperature is lowered. Iodine atoms form iodine molecules at low temperatures, while at high temperatures the molecules dissociate into iodine atoms. The fact that at the same temperature and pressure chlorine molecules are dissociated to a much lesser degree than those of iodine shows that the potential energy of the Cl atoms in the molecule, as compared with the energy of the free atoms, is lower than that of iodine atoms in the iodine molecule.

So far, in connection with the formation and decomposition of compounds, we have only considered the implications of potential energy and temperature, but a complication does occur when, as often happens, the reaction velocity between two substances is so small that the ideal state is not reached. In order to increase the velocity of the reaction, the temperature of the system must be raised. The fact that mercury and oxygen do not react at −100°C, but do react rapidly at 200°C, is not because HgO is not stable at low temperatures, but because the reaction velocity is then so low that chemical combination cannot be observed.

These examples can now be summarized. Solid substances which can always occur at low temperatures can be transferred, by different processes, into other states; as a rule, the molecules are first dissociated from one another; this process happens in *evaporation*, and when the solid substance changes directly into vapour this is called *sublimation*. At still higher temperatures, the single molecules will dissociate into atoms or molecules of the elements which compose them. This process is called *chemical dissociation*. In exceptional conditions, the molecules can undergo an additional break-down into charged particles, or ions. These processes are illustrated in the following diagram:

$$\left.\begin{array}{l}\textit{solid}\\ \textit{liquid}\end{array}\right\} \rightarrow \left\{\begin{array}{l}\textit{free molecules (evaporation)}\\ \textit{elements or different compounds (chemical decomposition)}\\ \textit{ions (electrolytic dissociation)}\end{array}\right.$$

So far, the discussion of the influence of temperature on the stability of chemical compounds has shown, in a qualitative way only, that, on increasing temperature, compounds stable at low temperature will first decompose into compounds with smaller molecules, secondly into atoms and finally into ions and electrons.

An exact description of the effect of temperatures on chemical processes, which allows an accurate calculation of the degree of decomposition, is given by thermodynamics. In every system there are always two tendencies. Under the influence of the attractive forces between the atoms the latter tend to approach each other closely, with the effect that the atoms will arrange in a rigid, ordered pattern, in which the interatomic distances are minimal, and the potential energy is also at a minimum. However, except at the absolute zero point, the thermal agitation of atoms and molecules always tends to disturb this order. In the absence of attractive forces between the molecules the system would be completely disordered: the substance would spread over the entire available space, and two kinds of molecules would not separate into two well-ordered solid phases, but form a mixture, with a random distribution of the molecules. In thermodynamics this tendency to disorder is accounted for by the so-called entropy S, that, like both potential and kinetic energy, is a function of temperature and volume or pressure. The entropy is greater, the greater the disorder: for a single substance, therefore, the entropy is minimal in a solid, greater in the liquid state, which is less strictly ordered than a solid, and greatest in the vapour, where the disorder is combined with a large volume. The competition order : disorder, expressed in energy : entropy, is described in thermodynamics by a function called free energy, which is the combination of the total energy U, entropy S, and absolute temperature T

$$F = U - TS$$

A system at constant temperature will not be stable if, under the given conditions, F can take a lower value, either by a decrease of U or an increase of S. The system cannot undergo further change if F is at its minimum value under the prevalent conditions; at this stage the system is said to be in a state of equilibrium.

Strictly speaking, the minimum of F determines the equilibrium state only if the volume of the system is constant. If it is not, but the pressure is constant, the equilibrium is determined by a function G, the free *enthalpy*, that contains the volume V.

$$G = U - TS + PV = H - TS$$

where $H = U + PV$ is the enthalpy.

Since the change in the term PV in all transitions that occur at normal or lower pressures is small as compared with the others, for all practical purposes the differences in enthalpy $H_2 - H_1$ can be set equal to differences $U_2 - U_1$ in energy.

Fusion

Let the indices S and L denote the solid state and the liquid state, respectively. For any substance

$$S_S < S_L \qquad \text{and} \qquad H_S < H_L$$

because the solid is ordered to a higher degree than the liquid, and the attractive forces in the solid are greater than in the liquid, the former usually being the denser of the two. At very low temperature the term TS becomes very small, and the formula for the free enthalpy approaches $G = H$. It follows that, at low temperatures, $G_S < G_L$ and that the solid is, therefore, the stable phase. On the other hand, at very high temperatures, TS becomes much greater than H, and G approaches $-TS$. It is easily seen that, in this case, $G_S > G_L$; in other words, the liquid is the stable phase. Somewhere between the two extremes there is a temperature where $G_S = G_L$. At this temperature the free enthalpy G will not change when one system is transformed into the other, the two being in equilibrium with each other. At the temperature at which water and ice can be stable when in contact with one another, the melting, or fusion, point T_F is given by the equation

$$G_S = H_S - TS_S = G_L = H_L - TS_L$$

or

$$T = \frac{H_S - H_L}{S_S - S_L}$$

Liquid-gas transition

Because $S_L < S_G$ and $H_L < H_G$, a liquid will form a gas at higher temperature, the transition point being given by

$$T = \frac{H_L - H_G}{S_L - S_G}$$

Now the difference in entropy between the two phases is to a great extent due to the large volume of the gas. The entropy of a pure solid can be expressed by a formula that connects it with the specific heat C

$$S_{T_2} - S_{T_1} = \int_{T_1}^{T_2} \frac{C}{T} \, \mathrm{d}T$$

If the specific heats are constant, this formula reduces to

$$S_{T_2} - S_{T_1} = C \ln \frac{T_2}{T_1}$$

The formula for the entropy of an ideal gas is

$$S = R \ln V + C_V \ln T + S_0$$

where S_0 is the entropy for $V = 1$ and $T = 1$.

Since, in the difference $S_L - S_V$, by far the largest term is $R \ln V$, this difference is almost constant for all 'normal' liquids. In actual fact, it is ~20 units for liquids that have their boiling points in the range 100°–200°C, and is slightly lower for lower boiling points and increases to ~25 for compounds with very high boiling points. It follows that the boiling point is given by a formula

$$T_B = \Theta(H_G - H_L)$$

or

$$= \Theta L$$

where $L = H_G - H_L$ is the latent heat of vaporization. The magnitude Θ is called Trouton's constant. In an abnormal liquid, like water, there is an unusual order, caused by a very special kind of attraction between molecules, that leads to a lower value of S_L and thereby to a higher value of Θ.

Chemical decomposition of a solid, producing a gas

If palladium dichloride is heated, it decomposes, and at 1195°K its chlorine pressure reaches 1 atmosphere. This decomposition point is determined by an equation similar to that for the boiling point. In this case, too, a gas, with a very high entropy, is formed from a solid that always has a relatively low entropy. Here, again, the change in entropy per mol of gas formed is almost independent of the decomposing compound and its decomposition products.

The entropy changes in the reactions

$$CuCl_2 \rightarrow Cu + Cl_2$$
$$K_2PdCl_6 \rightarrow K_2PdCl_4 + Cl_2$$
$$CaCO_3 \rightarrow CaO + CO_2$$
$$KBF_4 \rightarrow KF + BF_3$$
$$2K_2O_2 \rightarrow 2K_2O + O_2$$

are nearly equal, ~35 cal/degree for each mol of gas formed. If, therefore, the heat effects of the reactions are known, either by experiment or calculation, the decomposition point can be easily calculated, and it is then known that up to that temperature the compound is stable, provided that the pressure of the gas formed in the reaction is greater than 1 atmosphere, or that the compound is kept in a closed vessel, in order to prevent the formation of the vapour. It is to be noted that since H and S are both functions of temperature, the formulae derived are only approximate, and can be used only for a rough estimate of the stability of a compound if its heat of formation from the components into which it decomposes is known.

The situation is quite different for compounds that do not form a gas on decomposition, e.g. CSi and $CaSiO_3$. Although CSi has a heat of formation lower than $PdCl_2$, and the heat of formation of $CaSiO_3$ from CaO and SiO_2 is smaller than that of $CaCO_3$ from CaO and CO_2, the decompositions

$$CSi \rightarrow C + Si$$

and

$$CaSiO_3 \rightarrow CaO + SiO_2$$

can be observed at very high temperature only, because the change in entropy in these cases is very small, no gaseous phase being formed. In a reaction between solids

$$A(s) + B(s) \rightarrow AB(s)$$

the change in entropy is

$$\Delta S = -S(A) - S(B) + S(AB)$$

that is equal to

$$\int_0^T (-C_A - C_B + C_{AB}) \, dT$$

Now according to the rule of DULONG and PETIT the specific heat of a compound is usually nearly equal to that of the sum of its components. The change in entropy ΔS, in a reaction between solids only, is usually, therefore, very small, and even if the heat effect is relatively low, the temperature will not cause the compound that is stable at low temperatures to decompose at higher, the decomposition point given by $T_D = \frac{\Delta H}{\Delta S}$ being very high. The course of a reaction between solids, at moderate temperatures, will be determined by the change in energy alone. This holds true for reactions of a more complicated type as well, e.g. double decompositions. If the change in energy can be calculated or determined by experiment, the course of the reaction

$$NaCl(s) + KF(s) \rightarrow NaF(s) + KCl(s)$$

is determined: the reaction will go in that direction in which the energy decreases.

Two solids usually will not form an endothermic compound; the change in entropy will be so small that it cannot compensate for the change in energy, except at a very high temperatures: a solid endothermic compound at high temperature can become stable, only if the compound has the greater entropy

$$\int^{T} \frac{(-C_A - C_B + C_{AB})\,\mathrm{d}T}{T}$$

then being positive. A reaction in which a solid endothermic compound is formed from a solid and a gas is an impossibility. It can be shown by calculation (*see* Section 19) that the (unknown) compound $FeCl_7$ has a lower heat of formation V than $FeCl_3$. The reaction

$$FeCl_3(s) + 2Cl_2 \rightarrow FeCl_7(s)$$

therefore is endothermic and can proceed only if it is connected with a sufficient increase of entropy to compensate for the increase in energy. Since, however, two mols of gaseous Cl_2 disappear in the reaction, the entropy decreases, and the reaction is impossible.

Endothermic gaseous compounds, however, may be stable at high temperature. Since $V(CrCl_3,s) > V(CrCl_4,s)$ there is no stable solid $CrCl_4$. If, however, $CrCl_3$ is heated in chlorine at a temperature at which $CrCl_4$ is gaseous and $CrCl_3$ is still solid, the reaction is

$$2CrCl_3(s) + Cl_2(g) \rightarrow 2CrCl_4(g)$$

two mols of gas ($CrCl_4$) being formed from one (Cl_2). The entropy of the $2CrCl_4(g)$, therefore, is greater than that of $2CrCl_3(s) + Cl_2(g)$, and gaseous $CrCl_4$ is formed, although its heat of formation is lower, or its energy higher, than that of solid $CrCl_3$ + chlorine. If, as in this case, the systems contain two gases, the concentration of both Cl_2 and $CrCl_4$ have to be calculated by means of a Guldberg-Waage equilibrium equation.

Solubility

Two substances, A and B, that do not react with each other to form new molecules may form a solution. As the solution is disordered, the two kinds of molecules being distributed at random, the entropy of the solution is larger than that of the components.

On the other hand, it can be shown that the energy of the solution is also greater, energy being required to form the solution. So at low temperatures, where the entropy is ineffective, solutions are not formed and the two compounds are completely immiscible. With increasing temperature, the solubility will increase, more rapidly the smaller the change in energy which impedes the formation of a solution.

When two gases are brought together they always will form a 'solution' (mixture) because there is no change in energy when two gases are mixed: gases are miscible in all proportions. Two liquids will be miscible when the molecules A and B are not very different in physical and chemical properties. Solids also can form solutions, so-called *solid solutions*, or *mixed crystals*.

In solid solutions, part of the molecules A, in a crystal, are substituted by molecules B. If the two kinds of molecules are not very similar, the introduction of molecules B in the crystal A will lead to a distortion of the latter, by which the energy is increased. Unless, therefore, the molecules are very similar, the solid miscibility will be restricted at low temperature, becoming appreciable only at high temperature.

Solutions of electrolytes in water do not belong to the group of solutions under discussion, since, in the formation of aqueous solutions of electrolytes, there is a chemical reaction between the ions formed and the water molecules, which changes both the enthalpy and the entropy of the solution.

If chemical reactions occur in a gas or in a solution the entropy will be a function of the concentrations of all the products formed in these reactions. The dissociation of hydrogen iodide HI at a given temperature T and pressure p

$$2HI \rightarrow H_2 + I_2$$

proceeds until an equilibrium, characterized by a minimal value of G, is reached. The calculation of the equilibrium concentrations is a problem of thermodynamics, and will not be discussed here. It is found that, from the change of equilibrium with temperature, the heat effect of the reaction can be calculated. In Sections 10 and 16 a number of heat effects are given that have been determined by this method. From the change of equilibrium, with changing temperature, between a gas and a solid, can be calculated the heat of sublimation, the heat of dissociation from the equilibrium

$$Cl_2 \leftrightarrows 2Cl$$

and the electron affinity from the equilibrium between atoms, ions and electrons

$$I^- \leftrightarrows I + e$$

6. TWO TYPES OF CHEMICAL BONDS DERIVED FROM ATOMIC DISTANCES

We have seen in the previous section that the energy of a chemical reaction can be calculated once we know the forces acting between the atoms and how closely the atoms can approach one another. The fact that the atoms do not coalesce as a result of the forces of attraction, but remain at a definite distance from one another, shows that there are forces of repulsion acting as well. The Bohr atomic model seems to give an immediate idea as to why these should operate, for at first sight it is apparent that forces of repulsion will come into play as soon as the electron clouds are in contact with one another, since both clouds have negative charges. The explanation, however, cannot be quite as simple as this, since, for noble gases, it can be shown that the electronic charge is spherically symmetrical, so that each atom behaves as if its whole charge were concentrated at the centre, completely compensated by the charge on the nucleus. When, therefore, one says that a Na^+ ion acts with respect to a Cl^- ion as if it were a point charge e, then one has already taken into account the repulsive action of the electrons. Were it not for these electrons, the ion would act as a particle with a charge of $11e$. Against the attractive charge of $11e$ is the repulsive charge of ten electrons, giving the resultant attractive charge e.

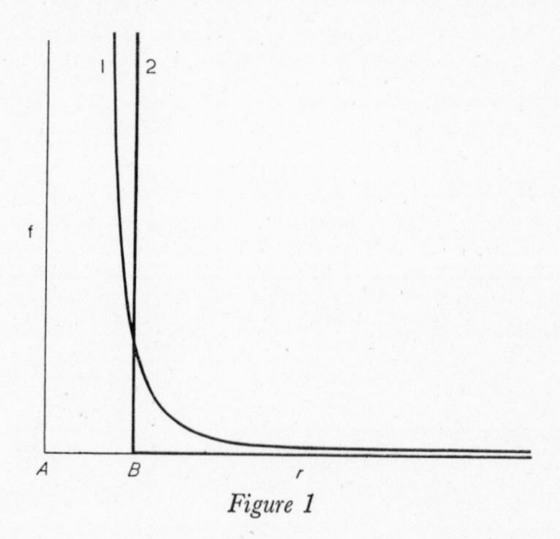

Figure 1

Therefore we must not continue using the electron charge to explain the repulsive forces between the Na^+ and Cl^- ions. If there is a repulsion, its cause must lie deeper, and in fact it has only been possible to give a theoretical explanation of it in a later phase of the atomic theory by the application of quantum mechanics, which will not be discussed here. We are, however, concerned with the result of this treatment, namely that the forces of repulsion are very small as long as the electron clouds are not in contact, but that at the moment of contact or actual penetration of one by the other, they suddenly increase very rapidly. This result is shown graphically in *Figure 1*, in which the small repulsion at the greater distance is neglected and the assumption made that at actual contact the forces do not increase rapidly, but suddenly become infinitely great. In place of the actual repulsive forces as a function of the distance r, which is given by line 1, is the repulsion, given by line 2. This method of representation asks that the atom be pictured as a completely hard sphere, the distance AB, which is the nearest to which the two atoms can approach, then becoming equal to the sum of the radii of the two spheres. Such a picture is not strictly accurate, and it would be better to regard the atoms as fairly hard rubber balls, using the formula for the repulsive forces represented by curve 1, but the introduction of such a refinement would make all the calculations decidedly more complicated and would not markedly affect the end result. We will therefore continue with the conception of hard, spherical atoms, noting that in Section 71 a compressibility correction is given. The radii of such hard spheres can be calculated from the shortest distance to which the atoms can approach each other. Important data regarding such distances are obtained from x-ray studies of crystal structures.

Crystals result when a solid substance is precipitated, under appropriate conditions, from a vapour or solution. It was suspected for a long time that the geometrical forms of crystals were due to a regular arrangement of atoms or molecules. Experimental verification of this idea was provided in 1912 by VON LAUE, who demonstrated that crystals showed interference phenomena with x-rays and, further, that it was possible to determine the structure of the crystal so accurately that sometimes the positions of atoms in the crystal could be given in one part in 100,000. It thus became possible to find the distance between the atoms in crystals, and it is important that it is not necessary to have well-formed crystals for this purpose. Nearly all substances are crystalline, even the silver chloride flocculent precipitate which is obtained when Cl^- and Ag^+ ions are brought together.

Later it became possible, again with the help of x-rays, to determine the structure of molecules in gases and liquids as well, and here, once more, interference phenomena are used, from which the positions of atoms in the molecule can be determined. Such structures are, however, more difficult to resolve than those of crystals, but the technique has been greatly developed in the last few years and, instead of x-rays, electron beams have been used which produce similar phenomena but are in practice easier to control. The present position is that the distances between atoms in compounds can be determined in the gaseous as well as the solid state.

In our first simple picture of atoms as hard spheres the shortest distance between any two identical atoms will be equal to their diameter, and one-half of this distance will be the atomic radius. In fact, in any compound *AB*, where the atoms can be regarded as hard spheres, the distance between *A* and *B* will be $r_a + r_b$ and it

Table III

compound	*radius* $\times 10^8$ (*calculated*)	*radius* $\times 10^8$ (*observed*)
CS_2	1·62	1·54
CO_2	1·24	1·13
CF_4	1·50	1·36
CCl_4	1·76	1·755
CBr_4	1·91	1·93
$SiCl_4$	2·03	2·00
$SnCl_4$	2·39	2·30
ICl	2·33	2·30
Cl_2O	1·65	1·68
SO_2	1·52	1·45
PCl_3	2·09	2·00
$AsCl_3$	2·20	2·16
ClO_2	1·47	1·53
$TeBr_2$	2·51	2·49

is found that this additivity applies to many cases. One can then determine the atomic radii for a number of elements and, with the help of the values so obtained, calculate the distance between them in a compound of any two of these elements. *Table III* contains a number of calculated atomic distances together with experimentally determined values and, as can be seen from this particular group of compounds, the agreement is sufficiently good to justify this approach.

We will now consider an important group of compounds, namely the halides of the alkali metals. Assuming that the atoms behave as completely hard spheres, one would expect that the shortest distance between two atoms in a crystal of NaCl will be equal to the sum of the radii of the Cl and Na atoms. The radius of the Na atom could then be found from the shortest distance between two atoms in a Na crystal. If, however, one proceeds in this way to calculate the distances in the alkali halides, one finds large discrepancies between the calculated and experimental values. In fact, the shortest distance between Na and Cl atoms in NaCl is *not* equal to the sum of the atomic radii of the elements, and *Table IV* gives the experimentally determined shortest distances in these compounds.

Table IV

Shortest Atomic Distances in the Alkali Halides

	F	$r_{Cl} - r_F$	Cl	$r_{Br} - r_{Cl}$	Br	$r_I - r_{Br}$	I
Li	2·02	0·55	2·57	0·17	2·74	0·26	3·00
$r_{Na} - r_{Li}$	0·29		0·24		0·24		0·23
Na	2·31	0·50	2·81	0·17	2·98	0·25	3·23
$r_K - r_{Na}$	0·36		0·33		0·31		0·29
K	2·67	0·47	3·14	0·15	3·29	0·23	3·52
$r_{Rb} - r_K$	0·14		0·15		0·14		0·14
Rb	2·81	0·48	3·29	0·14	3·43	0·23	3·66
$r_{Cs} - r_{Rb}$	0·20		0·27		0·28		0·29
Cs	3·01	0·55	3·56	0·15	3·71	0·24	3·95

It can be seen at once that there is a fairly constant difference between the distances of the corresponding Li and Na, Na and K salts, etc., and, equally, a fairly constant difference between all the chlorides and bromides, and between the fluorides and the iodides, etc. These constant differences show that the atoms of which the alkali halides are composed again behave approximately as hard spheres, but that these new spheres appear to have different dimensions from those of the elements; they are, in fact, in a different state. If one assumes, however, that the elements are composed of atoms then one must assume another state of affairs for the alakli halides.

At this point it is wise to examine a new hypothesis, attributed in the first instance to LEWIS and later to KOSSEL, who put forward the theory that these compounds are not composed of atoms but of ions. The determination of atomic distances in molecules and crystals leads to the very important result that there are apparently two kinds of chemical compounds, one in which the sizes of the atoms are nearly equal to their size when they occur in the element, and the other in which the dimensions are quite different. In the first kind, the state of the atoms in the compound is supposedly not essentially different from that in the element, and the chemical link between the C and Cl atoms in the compound CCl_4 is of the same kind as that between the carbon atoms in elementary carbon, and between the Cl atoms in the molecule Cl_2. In a compound of the second kind, NaCl for example, the bond is different from that between Na atoms in metallic sodium, and Cl atoms in a molecule of Cl_2. It has already been pointed out, and will be shown again later, that there is every reason to assume that the atoms in NaCl are present as ions. Both constituents in the compound have different charges, and a chemical bond of this kind is called a *heteropolar* bond, or, equally well, an *ionic* or *electrostatic* bond. In compounds of the first type there is no reason to assume different charges for the constituent parts of the molecule, for it would lead to the assumption that Cl_2 has one negative and one positive ion, thus producing a somewhat artificial picture. It will be shown later that the atoms in the molecule Cl_2 do not have different charges, their bond being called a *homopolar*, *atomic* or *covalent* bond.

The simple theory of the heteropolar bond was developed rapidly in contrast to the theory of the homopolar bond where great difficulties were encountered. Nevertheless, in the last decades important advances have been made, but the enormous mathematical difficulties encountered have resulted in the strict theory being applied only to the simplest examples of chemical combination. The theory of the ionic bond has no difficulties of a mathematical kind and in consequence can be used for more complicated compounds. In the following pages this theory will be treated first, and later a very elementary, schematic presentation of the theory of the homopolar bond will be given.

Chapter III

THE IONIC BOND

7. THE THEORY OF KOSSEL

In order to explain the electrical conductivity of aqueous solutions of inorganic salts and their effect on the freezing and boiling points of water, Arrhenius assumed that the molecules must be dissociated into electrically-charged particles to which he gave the name ions. The alkali- and alkaline-earth metals are present in all their compounds as ions, and the halogens in nearly all their compounds as ions. Fluorine, chlorine, bromine and iodine occur in solutions almost exclusively as negative ions with single charges and, since from the examination of the separation distances of the atoms in solid NaCl it appears that the state of the Cl atoms is different from their condition in the Cl_2 molecule, it is probable that the Cl atoms in solid salt are also present as ions. Kossel was the first to show that a great number of the properties of chemical compounds can be easily explained if it is assumed that crystals and molecules of simple inorganic compounds are composed of ions in which the electrical attractions of these ions supply the forces which hold the atoms together. Before proceeding to use these ideas to explain the properties of compounds the following difficulty must be dealt with.

At first sight it appears inexplicable that two charged particles, ions, do not discharge when they come in contact. This difficulty arises, however, when the properties of macroscopic bodies are applied to atoms, without further qualification. Although two oppositely-charged metal spheres will discharge when brought into contact if the charges are equal, it by no means follows that any two ions with equal and opposite charges will behave in the same way. This is borne out by study of the behaviour of solutions of electrolytes. Two charged ions brought into contact with each other need not necessarily discharge, and it will be seen later that the total potential energy of a Cl atom and a Na atom at the shortest distance of separation is greater than that of a Na^+ ion and a Cl^- ion, also at the shortest distance from each other. Thus, if a Na atom and a Cl atom are brought close to each other, the charge of the Na atom will go over to the Cl atom, thereby forming two ions, because the potential energy decreases in such a process. It is a well-known phenomenon that uncharged macroscopic bodies in contact with each other may become charged. Two metals in an electrolyte solution will show a potential difference, and must, therefore, have exchanged charges. Also, the occurrence of electrical charges when a rod of ebonite is rubbed with fur shows that charged bodies do not discharge under all circumstances, but that the reverse process can also take place. There is, therefore, no objection to assuming that ions can exist in contact with one another without a discharge taking place.

In aqueous solutions the following simple negative ions are known: F^-, Cl^-, Br^-, I^-, S^{2-}, Se^{2-}, in which the first four have a charge of unity and the last two a charge of two. At first, electricity was known only in the form of electrons, but subsequently it was discovered that, in addition to electrons, positrons also exist. As positrons and other particles, e.g. the antiprotons, do not occur under the conditions in which chemical reactions are carried out, an atom can only acquire a negative charge by taking up electrons. The ions F^-, Cl^-, Br^- and I^- all contain one electron more than the free atoms of these elements; that is to say, they have just as many electrons as the atoms of the elements known as noble gases, which follow the halogens in the periodic system.

Sulphur and selenium, both of which form divalent ions, possess two more electrons in the ionic than in the atomic state, and consequently have the same number of electrons as the elements which occur two places farther along in the periodic system, occupied by the noble gases argon and krypton. It thus appears that when negative ions are formed, the atoms take up sufficient electrons to correspond to the number in the succeeding noble gas. This phenomenon must be due to the fact that the structure of a noble gas is very stable, which is not surprising when one remembers the large amount of energy needed to break up their electronic configuration, demonstrated by the high ionization potentials of these gases (*see* Section 10).

Other atoms which do not have the stable structure of the noble gas, tend to change their number of electrons in such a way that the ion can take up the electronic structure of a noble gas, and it is therefore not merely fortuitous that all simple negative ions have this particular structure. The electrons which are taken up by the negative ions have been withdrawn from other atoms, and positive ions thus are formed simultaneously with negative ones.

Many more positive than negative ions are formed in aqueous solutions. All alkali metals have a single positive charge, that is, they lose one electron per atom, and in the ionic state have the same number of electrons as are possessed by the preceding noble gas.

All alkaline-earth metals, Be, Mg, Ca, Sr, Ba and Ra, form positive divalent ions. From each of these, two electrons are lost and the ion formed will again have the same number of electrons as the preceding noble gas. This is also true for aluminium, which forms tervalent ions, and for zirconium and thorium, which form tetravalent ions. Further, in those instances where free ions are not known, as for example in boron, it is assumed that the ions are present in the molecule as a result of the atom losing a sufficient number of electrons to give it the structure of a noble gas. It now becomes possible to foretell the combinations in which the elements will occur. Silicon occurs four places after neon and, in consequence, possesses four more electrons than neon; it can thus form tetravalent positive ions when it reacts with an element that can take up electrons, as for example fluorine or chlorine. Four F^- ions can accept the four electrons from the silicon atom, and thus silicon and fluorine give one Si^{4+} ion and four univalent F^- ions, which, together, can give the neutral combination SiF_4. The same method of approach leads to the expectation of the formation of compounds PF_5 and SF_6. In the latter, the S ion has six positive charges and the F ions one negative charge, so that the formula can be written as $S^{6+}F_6^-$.

But sulphur not only forms positive ions. As may be readily expected from its position in the periodic system where it occurs two places before and six places after a noble gas, it also forms divalent negative ions, as in K_2S. It is the general rule that, in principle, all elements can form both positive and negative ions. However, only some of the combinations which can be written in this manner will actually occur as molecules because, as was seen in Section 4, a compound will only be formed if the potential energy decreases during the process, and this occurs only when ions of fairly low valency are formed. There are no compounds known that contain positive ions with a valency of nine; the valency of negative ions is certainly never greater than four, and it is therefore quite easy to see why there is a limit to the number of compounds theoretically possible.

8. LIMITED VALENCY OF IONS

Let us suppose that a molecule of NaCl is formed from free atoms of Na and Cl. We can imagine a process in which an electron is first removed from a Na^+ atom and is then transferred to the Cl^- atom, and the two ions so formed allowed to approach each other to within a distance given by the sum of their radii. The potential energy of the system will change in such a process and can be readily calculated. Such a process is, in a sense, fictitious, in so far as it cannot be carried out physically, but this is immaterial for the purpose of calculating the total energy change. From the law of conservation of energy, or the law of Hess as it is called when applied to chemical processes, it follows that the total change of potential energy is independent of the way in which the process is carried out, being a function only of the initial and final states. The total change of potential energy will then be equal to the sum of the energy required to form a Na^+ ion from a Na atom, plus the value for transferring the electron to the Cl atom, together with the energy released when the ions approach to within a distance $r_{Na} + r_{Cl}$ from one another. The energy for the removal of the electron from the Na atom is the *ionization energy* I_{Na} (*see Table VI*, Section 10) and the energy of the system is thereby increased by an amount $+I_{Na}$. In transferring the electron to the Cl atom, an amount of energy, the *electron affinity* E_{Cl}, is given out. This can easily be understood if one considers that the uncharged Cl atom is attracted by the charge of the electron as a result of electrical induction, in the same way as an uncharged pith ball is attracted by a charged one. In addition to this induction energy, the union of the electron with the Cl atom will also result in the release of a much larger amount of energy, since the electron shell of the Cl^- ion now has the stable noble-gas structure. The total energy change is therefore $I_{Na} - E_{Cl}$. If, now, the ions approach to within the distance $r_{Na} + r_{Cl}$, the energy released will be $e^2/(r_{Na} + r_{Cl})$. The total energy change is therefore $I_{Na} - E_{Cl} - e^2/(r_{Na} + r_{Cl})$, and the process will result in the formation of a molecule NaCl if this quantity is negative, that is, when $e^2/(r_{Na} + r_{Cl}) > I_{Na} - E_{Cl}$.

It was shown in Section 2 how very rapidly the energy rises in order to remove subsequent electrons from an atom. The ionization energy for highly-charged positive ions rises so steeply that it outweighs the increased energy released when the ions combine. In consequence, compounds with highly-charged positive ions are not formed; iron, occurring as it does eight places after a noble gas, forms no compound $FeCl_8$. A positive ion with a valency of eight is very rare and higher valencies never occur at all. The valency of negative ions is also limited, because the electron affinity, which is positive for the first electron, becomes negative for subsequent ones (*see* Section 10) and still more so for the higher valencies. As a result, tervalent negative ions are seldom encountered and higher negative valencies almost never. It has already been noted that single negative ions always have a noble-gas structure; this arises from the fact that the energy decrease in the formation of negative ions is largely the result of the formation of the noble-gas structure.

The position is different for positive ions, since here a number of loosely-bound electrons are removed until the noble-gas structure is reached, and for further electron removal very large energies are required. It does not follow that the removal of electrons will proceed to the point of a noble-gas structure, since the latter represents only a limit to the valency and does not determine it as it does for negative ions. Iron, occurring eight places after a noble gas, does not have a valency of eight but is divalent in ferro, tervalent in ferri compounds and hexavalent in the ferrates, as, for example, in $BaFeO_4$.

Cobalt, as a result of its place in the periodic system, should have a valency of nine. It is, however, mostly divalent and occasionally tervalent. Phosphorus can be tervalent as well as pentavalent; sulphur is hexavalent in SO_3 and tetravalent in SO_2. At low temperatures the valency is such that the energy is a minimum, and which compounds will be formed can only be predicted when the energy can be calculated accurately.

The reason for the formation of chemical compounds is therefore essentially the formation of negative ions, and only secondarily that of positive ones. From what has been said, it follows that the elements in the long periods, where they occur more than eight places past a noble gas, can never show 'normal' valencies, in the sense that they will lose sufficient electrons to give the structure of the preceding noble gas. After these so-called transition metals there is a series of elements in which the valency rises from one to six, in the fourth period

Cu, Zn, Ga, Ge, As, Se

and from one to seven in the fifth period

Ag, Cd, In, Sn, Sb, Te, I

Examining the distribution of the electrons among the different shells in these atoms, it will be seen that the electronic structures show some similarities with those of the elements at the beginning of the long periods, in that there are one, two and three isolated electrons in the outer shells. The difference between Cu, Zn and Ga on the one hand, and K, Ca and Sc on the other, is that in the latter group of atoms the shell next to the outer one has eight electrons, but in the former, eighteen electrons. This group of eighteen electrons, like the 8-electron structure of the noble gases, has a high stability. Electrons can be removed easily as long as the 18-electron structure is not disturbed, but if more are removed then a large energy is required. The 18-electron structure puts a limit on the removal of electrons, but not such a sharp limit as does the noble-gas structure.

Exceptions do occur, in that copper and silver form not only the ions Cu^+ and Ag^+, which is to be expected, but also Cu^{2+} and Ag^{2+} ions, and gold also forms tervalent ions Au^{3+}. A further difference between the two structures is that the 18-electron structure is never reached by the taking up of electrons, so that negative ions with such a structure are unknown. The elements which form ions with an 18-electron structure are called elements of the *subgroups*. Ions with 18-electron structure are to be expected in the fourth, fifth and sixth periods, beginning with Cu, Ag and Au, and ending with the heptavalent positive halogen ions. However, the Br^{7+} ion is unknown, and accurate calculations of energies would be required to explain such instances.

For a detailed calculation of the energy of an ionic molecule from its component atoms the following data are necessary:

1. Ionization energy.
2. Electron affinity.
3. The distance by which the ions are separated from one another, which will be equal to the sum of the ionic radii when the ions are regarded as hard spheres.

9. IONIC RADII

Atomic radii can be calculated by measuring the shortest distance between two atoms in a molecule or a crystal, and in the same way ionic radii can be determined by measuring the shortest distance between two ions with the aid of x-rays or electron diffraction. Concerning ionic radii the same assumption can be made as for the determination of atomic radii, namely that the ions be regarded as hard spheres which will have the same radius in whatever compound they occur, provided they have the same charge. The positive ion S^{6+} in SF_6 will not have the same radius as the negative ion S^{2-} in Na_2S because the sulphur is in different states in the two compounds. Corresponding to each valency, an ion will have a certain ionic radius and it is easy to see that with increasing positive charge the radius of the ion must decrease. The S^{6+} ion has the same nucleus as the S^{2-}, with a charge of $16e$, but the S^{6+} ion has lost six electrons while the S^{2-} ion has taken up two. Thus, in S^{6+}, ten electrons are attracted by a nuclear charge of $16e$, while in S^{2-} the same charge attracts eighteen electrons. Because in the negative ion the mutual repulsion of the electrons is much greater, they will be farther from the nucleus than in the positive ion, the electron cloud consequently being larger in S^{2-} than in S^{6+}, which means that it will have a larger ionic radius.

Without further data, it should thus be possible to make some predictions regarding sizes of ions, and for this purpose we will confine our attention to ions with noble-gas structures. In any period the radii of the ions must decrease with increasing positive charge, as in the following series:

$$Na^+, Mg^{2+}, Al^{3+}, Si^{4+}, P^{5+}, S^{6+}, Cl^{7+}$$

These ions all have the same number of electrons as the neon atom, as is true of the negative ions of the previous period N^{3-}, O^{2-}, F^-. From N^{3-} to Cl^{7+} the nuclear charge rises from seven to seventeen, resulting in a steady contraction of the electron cloud, or, in other words, a contraction of the ionic radius. Now let us compare the ions in a column of the system, for example, the alkali metals

$$Li^+, Na^+, K^+, Rb^+, Cs^+$$

or the halogens

$$F^-, Cl^-, Br^-, I^-$$

Proceeding down the column, the number of electrons increases, and it is to be expected that, as a result of the increasing mutual repulsion of the electrons, the electron clouds will increase in size. We may therefore expect the following rules to hold:

1. For the same configuration, that is to say, for an equal number of electrons, negative ions will be considerably larger than positive ions, e.g. $r_{F^-} > r_{Na^+}$.
2. The ionic radius will decrease from left to right in a period for positive ions of the same structure.
3. In a column of ions of equal charge, the radius will increase in a downward direction.
4. If positive ions of an element with different charges are known, then the ionic radius decreases with increasing positive charge.
5. The largest ion that any element can form is the negative one, e.g. $r_{S^{2-}} > r_{S^{6+}}$.

In *Table IV* the shortest distances in the alkali halides and the differences between two subsequent compounds were given. If the ions could be regarded as completely hard spheres, then the difference should be the same, independent of the combined halogen, between a Li^+ and a Na^+, a Na^+ and a K^+, or a K^+ and a Rb^+ compound, and, furthermore, the difference between a fluoride and a chloride should be independent of the metal. In fact, the differences are not quite constant, but the deviations are sufficiently small to be neglected in the first rough approximation.

If one could determine the ionic radius of one single element, then the values for the other elements would be known. Assuming that the radius of the chlorine atom is 1·81 Å, then, from the shortest distance between two particles in KCl, for which the value 3·14 Å has been found, the radius of the K^+ ion is 1·33 Å, and, similarly, from the shortest distance in KBr is obtained the radius of bromine, and so on. The determination of the single radius is made in the following manner.

All alkali halides, except the salts CsCl, CsBr and CsI, have the same structure as NaCl (*see Figure 8*, Chapter IV) in which each particle is surrounded by six others of opposite charge. If the particles

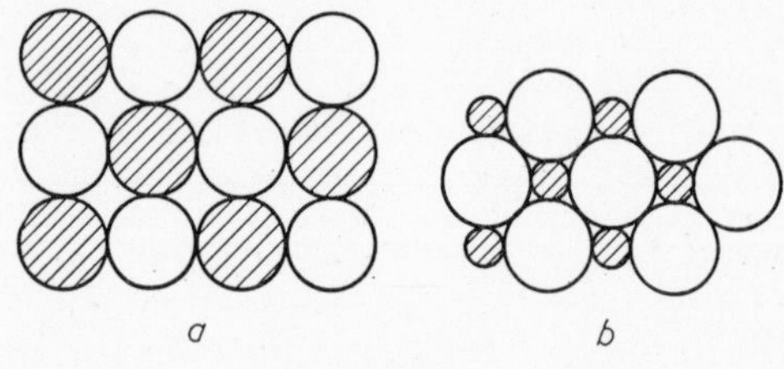

Figure 2

are the same size, as they are in KF, then the K^+ ion will only be in contact with the six surrounding F^- ions (*see Figure 2a*), but if the F ion is replaced by a much larger ion, say an iodine ion, and the K^+ by the smaller Li^+, then, as is shown in *Figure 2b*, the I^- ions will be in contact with one another. If the distance between the iodine ions is now determined directly by x-ray analysis, one-half this distance equals the radius of the iodine ion. With the help of this value all the other radii can be calculated.

From measurements of the shortest distances in crystals of a very large number of compounds, GOLDSCHMIDT has constructed a table for all noble-gas ions. PAULING also determined ionic radii by measuring the shortest distance in certain compounds, and from these calculated the values for other compounds containing ions of the same structure. The results of these two independent investigations show very good agreement. In *Table V* are the values of ionic radii, as determined by Pauling, for noble-gas ions and for ions with 18-electron structure, the so-called subgroup ions. The table confirms the predictions made as to the changes of the ionic radii in the rows and columns of the periodic system. The radii of ions which possess neither noble-gas nor 18-electron structures cannot be calculated by Pauling's method, and only the method of Goldschmidt

Table V

Ionic Radii in Å according to Pauling

		H^-	Li^+	Be^{2+}	B^{3+}	C^{4+}	N^{5+}	O^{6+}	F^{7+}
		2·08	0·60	0·31	0·20	0·15	0·11	0·09	0·07
N^{3-}	O^{2-}	F^-	Na^+	Mg^{2+}	Al^{3+}	Si^{4+}	P^{5+}	S^{6+}	Cl^{7+}
1·71	1·40	1·36	0·95	0·65	0·50	0·41	0·34	0·29	0·26
P^{3-}	S^{2-}	Cl^-	K^+	Ca^{2+}	Sc^{3+}	Ti^{4+}	V^{5+}	Cr^{6+}	Mn^{7+}
2·12	1·84	1·81	1·33	0·99	0·81	0·68	0·59	0·52	0·46
			Cu^+	Zn^{2+}	Ga^{3+}	Ge^{4+}	As^{5+}	Se^{6+}	Br^{7+}
			0·96	0·74	0·62	0·53	0·47	0·42	0·39
As^{3-}	Se^{2-}	Br^-	Rb^+	Sr^{2+}	Y^{3+}	Zr^{4+}	Nb^{5+}	Mo^{6+}	
2·22	1·98	1·95	1·48	1·13	0·93	0·80	0·70	0·62	
			Ag^+	Cd^{2+}	In^{3+}	Sn^{4+}	Sb^{5+}	Te^{6+}	I^{7+}
			1·26	0·97	0·81	0·71	0·62	0·56	0·50
Sb^{3-}	Te^{2-}	I^-	Cs^+	Ba^{2+}	La^{3+}	Ce^{4+}			
2·45	2·21	2·16	1·69	1·35	1·15	1·01			
			Au^+	Hg^{2+}	Tl^{3+}	Pb^{4+}	Bi^{5+}		
			1·37	1·10	0·95	0·84	0·74		

Ionic Radii in Å of Ions with Abnormal Valencies

NH_4^+	Mn^{2+}	Ti^{3+}
1·48	0·80	0·69
Tl^+	Fe^{2+}	V^{3+}
1·44	0·75	0·66
	Co^{2+}	Cr^{3+}
	0·72	0·64
	Ni^{2+}	Mn^{3+}
	0·70	0·62

can be used. *Table V* also gives values, which are not too reliable, for a number of frequently occurring ions with abnormal valencies.

10. IONIZATION ENERGY AND ELECTRON AFFINITY

Table VI gives the values of ionization energies which, together with the values of ionic radii and electron affinities, make it possible to calculate the energy changes which occur in the formation of ionic molecules, and to determine which ionic compounds of two elements

Table VI
Ionization Energies in kcal

He	Ne	Ar	Kr	Xe	Rn
567	494	361	322	279	248
Li	**Na**	**K**	**Rb**	**Cs**	—
123	118	99	96	89	—
1,731	1,083	728	628	538	—
Be	**Mg**	**Ca**	**Sr**	**Ba**	**Ra**
215	175	140	130	119	121
417	344	272	252	229	232
3,519	1,834	1,171	974	816	—
B	**Al**	**Sc**	**Y**	**La**	—
190	137	154	152	129	—
575	431	294	283	262	—
868	651	566	469	439	—
5,935	2,746	1,709	—	—	—

Cu	Ag	Au
177	175	213
464	504	283?
670	673	—
Zn	**Cd**	**Hg**
215	206	239
411	387	429
908	874	966
Ga	**In**	**Tl**
137	132	140
470	432	467
704	642	683
1,467	1,329	—

$I_H = 313$

can exist. One can immediately deduce important qualitative results from the table of ionization energies; for every element there is an enormous rise in ionization energy when an electron is removed from an electron shell with a noble-gas structure, and a smaller rise for the removal of one from a shell of eighteen electrons. This explains why ions are very seldom formed in chemical processes, if, by so doing, a noble-gas structure is disturbed; and that only in a very few elements, Cu, Ag and Au, the 18-electron configuration can be broken up. The table also shows how the energy for the removal of each succeeding electron increases, and that, roughly speaking, twice as much energy is required for the removal of the second valency electron as for the first. This is associated, as was seen earlier, with the instability of very highly-charged ions.

If the ionization energies of elements in a single column are compared, it will be noticed that the values decrease in a descending order in the first six columns; this is explained by the fact that the ionic radii steadily increase down the columns. For the same structure, an atom will have a smaller ionization energy, the larger its radius. A substantial part of the ionization energy goes to overcoming the coulomb forces between the ion and the electron which is being removed; and the farther the electron is, initially, from the nucleus, the smaller is this attraction, and the smaller therefore the ionization energy. The decrease in the ionization energy with increasing radius leads one to suppose that the compound will have a smaller energy than the ion and thus be more stable, the larger is the radius of the positive ion. In practice, this supposition is usually found to be correct.

Further important information on the chemical behaviour of the atoms can be obtained by relating their ionization energies to the electronic configurations. In order to get the maximum of information, the electronic configuration shall be described in more detail. The two electrons in the K group are equivalent: they have exactly the same energy, the only difference between the two being that they have opposite spin moments, i.e. that in the picture of the older Bohr theory, the two electrons revolve in opposite directions around a fixed axis. In all groups K, L, M, etc., the electrons can be divided into two groups with opposite spin moments, the factor 2 in the number $2n^2$ of electrons in each group being due to this effect. The $2n^2$ electrons are said to belong to n^2 orbitals, each orbital in a complete shell being occupied by two electrons. In each shell the energies in the different orbitals are not exactly equal; they can be divided into different groups, called s, p, d, f, etc., the orbitals in the K groups being s orbitals, the four orbitals in the L group forming two groups, one of one *s* orbital and one of three *p* orbitals. In the older Bohr theory the *s*, *p*, *d* . . . orbitals were distinguished by their different shapes, *s* orbitals being circular and *p*, *d* and *f* elliptical, with increasing axial ratio. It is useful to describe the different groups of electrons by symbols, denoting the number of the electrons in the group and their specific state. This symbol is $1s^2$ for the *K* group; the index 1 denoting that the two *s* electrons form a *K* group. The symbol for the complete *L* group becomes $2s^2 . 2p^6$; the first two electrons in the *L* shell of beryllium will be notated by $2s^2$, the four electrons in the *L* group of carbon by $2s^2 . 2p^2$. The complete *M* shell has ten *d* electrons, its symbol being $3s^2 . 3p^6 . 3d^{10}$, that of the incomplete *M* shell with eight electrons $3s^2 . 3p^6$. The symbol for the normal gallium atom becomes

$$\underset{K}{1s^2} \quad \underset{L}{2s^2 2p^6} \quad \underset{M}{3s^2 3p^6 3d^{10}} \quad \underset{N}{4s^2 4p^1}$$

There are three electrons outside the complete *M* shell: these three electrons have relatively low ionization energies, and gallium is, therefore, trivalent. Since, however, the $4p$ electron has a somewhat lower ionization energy than the two $4s$ electrons, the first electron is more easily removed than the next two, and thus gallium can also be univalent. From the values of the first, second and third ionization energies, it is not at once apparent that the *s* and *p* electrons have a slightly different energy, because if one electron is already removed, the energy to remove a second electron, that originally had the same energy, will be twice that value, and the energy to remove the third will be three times the original value.

Small differences in different ionization energies I_1, I_2, I_3, etc., will become apparent if the values of the ionization energies divided by the charge $I_1/1$, $I_2/2$, $I_3/3$, . . . I_n/n are considered. These values can be expected to be nearly equal for electrons of the same type, e.g. for all *p* electrons in the outermost shell, but not for *p* and *s* electrons.

Table VIIa contains all the known values for I_n/n. It shows that, indeed, this value is almost a constant for electrons of the same type, and that it is greater for *s* electrons than for *p* electrons, and greater for *p* electrons than for *d* electrons. From these table one can get important information as to the possible valencies of the elements. All elements at the ends of the long periods have an outer shell of *s* and *p* electrons, only. The two *s* electrons, with their higher ionization energy, form a more stable group, and all elements that contain these two electrons can form ions with a configuration s^2. All elements at the end of the long periods have two valencies:

Table VIIa

*Values I_n/n in kcal**

Li	124														
Be	210	215													
B	291	289	191												
C	371	368	281	260											
N	451	446	366	341	335										
O	528	525	445	424	404	314									
F	606	601	527	502	481	403	402								
Na	118														
Mg	173	176													
Al	219	217	138												
Si	260	257	189	188											
P	300	296	232	226	253?										
S	337	287?	272	270	269	239									
Cl	374	[372]	313	314	307	274	299								
Cu	178							K	100						
Zn	207	216						Ca	137	141					
Ga	236	236	138					Sc	190	148	154				
Ge	263	263	183	187				Ti	249	211	157	158			
As	289	289	210	233	242			V	295	279	204	164	155		
Se	313	337?	247	262	250	225		Cr	(346)	336	294	[247]	192	156	
Br	[335]	[335]	[277]	(288)	276	(262)	273	Mn	391	[387]	350	[308]	[261]	180	171
Ag	175							Rb	96						
Cd	195	207						Sr	127	131					
In	215	217	133					Yt	158	143	152				
Sn	235	236	169	169				Zr	196	185	161	160			
Sb	257	254	191	~214	199			Cb	231	217	187	161	156		
Te	277	277	218	236	248	208		Mo	258	282?				170	
J	[295]	295	[240]	[240]	[241]	219	241	Tc							
Au	213							Cs	90						
Hg	216	240						Ba	115	120					
Tl	229	235	141					La	147	131	129				
Pb	225?	247	173	171											
Bi	259	261	196	192	(167)?			Ra	117	122					

* *The sequence of $I_1, I_2, \ldots I_n$ is from the right to the left.*
As in Table VIIb, the I_n/n values for p electrons are divided into two groups, and the I_n/n values are slightly higher for the last three p electrons.

Table VIIb
*Ionization Energies in kcal**

H	313											
He	1254	567										
Li	2822	1743	124									
Be	5019	3547	420	215								
B	7843	5978	874	579	191							
C	(11240)	9037	1486	1103	562	260						
N	(15300)	(11660)	2256	1784	1097	683	325					
O	(20000)	(16960)	(3170)	2624	1781	1271	809	314				
F		(21880)	(4244)	(3606)	2633	2009	1444	806	402			
Ne		495										
Na		1090	118									
Mg		1847	346	176								
Al		2766	656	434	138							
Si		3838	1040	772	377	188						
P			1499	1184	695	453	253					
S			(2020)	[1670]	1090	808	539	239				
Cl			(2622)	[2232]	1563	1255	920	549	299			
Ar		362										
K		733	100									
Ca		1180	274	141								
Sc		1704	571	~297	~154							
Ti		2301	997	~634	~313	158						
V		(3061)	~1475	~1118	~611	327	155					
Cr		(3867)	(2075)	~1682	(1176)	[741]	385	156				
Mn		(4759)	(2738)	[2323]	~1752	[1232]	[784]	361	171			
Fe			(3470)					705	374	181		
Co										401	182	
Ni											420	176
Cu	680	467	178									
Zn		915	414	216								
Ga		1478	708	473	138							
Ge		2154	1053	789	367	187						
As		(2926)	1443	1155	629	466	242					
Se		(3818)	(1878)	[1565]	989	786	500	225				
Br		[4814]	[2345]	[2010]	[1387]	(1154)	827	(524)	273			

* *The sequence $I_1, I_2, \ldots I_n$ is from the right to the left.*
Values in [ ] are extrapolated; those in ( ) are uncertain.

Table VIIb, cont.
Ionization Energies in kcal

Kr		322										
Rb		634	96									
Sr			254	131								
Yt			473	286	152							
Zr			783	556	323	160						
Cb			1153	(870)	561	323	156					
Mo								170				
Tc							(677)					
Ru								(660)		173		
Rh								(716)		(417)	177	
Pd								(1125)		(770)	(459)	192
Ag	832	506	175									
Cd		881	390	207								
In		1338	646	435	133							
Sn		1870	939	707	337	169						
Sb		(2471)	1284	1018	572	429	199					
Te		(3149)	(1661)	1389	872	706	497	208				
J		(3901)	[2081]	(1772)	[1200]	[960]	[723]	438	241			
Xe		279										
Cs		548	90									
Ba			200	120								
La			442	263	129							
Hf						—						
Ta							—					
W								184				
Re									180			
Os										201		
Ir											212	
Pt											445	207
Au		463	213									
Hg		795	432	240								
Tl		1171	687	471	141							
Pb		1607	(967)	740	347	171						
Bi		(2168)	1291	1044	589	385	(195)					
Eu		248										
Ra			234	122								
Th			680	—	—	—						

Values in [ ] *are extrapolated; those in* ( ) *are uncertain.*

Table VIIc

Total Ionization Energy/Equivalent $= \frac{1}{n} \Sigma_n I_i$ *(in kcal)*

Li	Be	B	C	N	O	F
124	317	548	852	1231	1661	2163
Na	Mg	Al	Si	P	S	Cl
118	261	409	595	817	1061	1349
K	Ca	Sc	Ti	V	Cr	Mn
100	207	341	526	737	[1036]	[1334]
Rb	Sr	Yt	Zr	Cb		
96	192	304	455	613		
Cs	Ba	La				
90	175	278				
	Ra					
	178					
Cu	Zn	Ga	Ge	As	Se	Br
178	315	440	599	787	[990]	[1217]
Ag	Cd	In	Sn	Sb	Te	J
175	298	405	538	700	889	[1057]
Au	Hg	Tl	Pb	Bi		
213	318	433	556	[701]		

in chemical reactions of the metallic elements either all the *p* electrons can be removed, in which case the valency is $n - 2$, or all electrons can be removed, and the valency is equal to *n*, the total number of electrons in the outer shell. If, in an element in the second part of the long periods, all *n* electrons of the outer shell are removed, the outer shell of the ion is the 18-electron shell, $s^2 . p^6 . d^{10}$, with much higher ionization energies, from which, in a very few cases, only one or two electrons can be removed. This happens, as remarked earlier, in the copper-gold group, where one finds valencies of two for copper and silver, as well as the normal valency, one; and for gold, that it can be a univalent or tervalent metal. It is seen from the table that for the elements of the copper group, the second and third ionization energies are relatively low as compared with the first. *Table VIIIa* summarizes all the fluorides and oxides of the elements at the ends of the long periods and shows the occurrence of the two valencies *n* and $n - 2$ as well as the irregular higher valencies in the copper group. It will be explained later, why, in

Table VIIIa

Fluoride and Oxide Valencies

—	CuF_2	ZnF_2	—	GaF_3	GeF_2	GeF_4	AsF_3	AsF_5	SeF_4	SeF_6
Au_2O	CuO	ZnO	—	Ga_2O_3	GeO	GeO_2	As_2O_3	As_2O_5	SeO_2	SeO_3
AgF	AgF_2	CdF_2	—	InF_3	SnF_2	SnF_4	SbF_3	SbF_5	TeF_4	TeF_6
Ag_2O	AgO	CdO	In_2O	In_2O_3	SnO	SnO_2	Sb_2O_3	Sb_2O_5	TeO_2	Te_3O
AuF	AuF_3	HgF_2	TlF	TlF_3	PbF_2	PbF_4	BiF_3	BiF_5	—	—
—	Au_2O_3	HgO	Tl_2O	Tl_2O_3	PbO	PbO_2	Bi_2O_3	—	—	—

some cases, the lower compounds, GaF, Ga_2O, etc., are missing, and why, in others, e.g. Bi_2O_5, the compounds of higher valency cannot be prepared.

The elements in the beginning of the periods have different configurations. Since all elements of the first group (alkali metals) have one *s* electron in the outer shell, with a very low ionization energy, their normal valency is one; the next group, with two *s* electrons has a constant valency of two (alkaline-earth metals), but in the third group the electrons are of two kinds, *s* and *p*. In aluminium a very low value for the first ionization energy is found, and a valency of one for aluminium therefore seems possible. Compounds of univalent aluminium, in fact, have been observed: they are not stable in the solid state, but when the metal is heated in the vapour of the trichloride, gaseous monochloride is formed

$$2Al(s) + AlCl_3 \rightarrow 3AlCl(g)$$

In this reaction there is a considerable increase in the entropy, three mols of a gaseous compound, $3AlCl(g)$, being formed from one, ($AlCl_3$). In the reactions at low temperature, when all the compounds are solid, there is no increase in the entropy if AlCl is formed, and the compound is unstable.

In the following groups some of the valency electrons are *d* electrons. In chemical processes the *s* and *p* electrons of the outer shell will be removed first, but the *d* electrons can also be removed. The maximum valency is reached when all electrons in the outer shell plus the *d* electrons are given off, an ion with rare-gas configuration being formed. In addition to this highest valency, all kinds of lower valencies are possible: for titanium and vanadium the chlorides are

$$TiCl_2 \quad TiCl_3 \quad TiCl_4$$
$$VCl_2 \quad VCl_3 \quad VCl_4$$

Manganese, in its oxides, can have all valencies from two (MnO) to the maximal value, seven (Mn_2O_7).

A stable electron configuration is not only found in the groups s^2 (helium), s^2p^6 (rare gases) and $s^2p^6d^{10}$ (18-electron configuration in subgroup ions) but also in groups that have half-filled *d* or *f* groups. The ions Mn^{2+} and Fe^{3+} have such half-filled groups. They contain five electrons more than the preceding rare gas; because of the stable d^5 groups, the first ionization energies are relatively low, and the heat of formation of Mn^{2+} compounds is somewhat greater than that of divalent compounds of the neighbour elements; in the same way, iron forms stable compounds in which the metal is tervalent ($FeCl_3$), whereas the neighbour elements Mn, Co and Ni do not.

The half-filled f^7 group is still more important than the half-filled d^5 group, which causes a greater stability of Mn^{2+} and Fe^{3+} compounds only. The f^{14} group is completed in the rare earth or lanthanide group, the first element lanthanum of this group having the configuration

$$\underset{K}{1s^2} \quad \underset{L}{2s^22p^6} \quad \underset{M}{3s^23p^63d^{10}} \quad \underset{N}{4s^24p^64d^{10}} \quad \underset{O}{5s^25p^65d^1} \quad \underset{P}{6s^2}$$

and the last, lutecium, a complete *N* or $4s^24p^64d^{10}4f^{14}$ group. All fifteen elements have three electrons outside the complete $5s^25p^6$ group, and can form an ion with the same outer configuration as the preceding rare-gas atom by giving off these three electrons; the normal valency of all lanthanides, therefore, is three. The second element of the group, cerium, as a tervalent ion still has an isolated $4f$ electron in the *N* shell: this electron can be removed relatively easily, and cerium, therefore, also shows a valency of four, as, for example, in CeO_2 and CeF_4.

In the next element the $4f$ electrons still can be given off in chemical reactions; praseodymium still forms an oxide PrO_2 (that may be a combination of Pr_2O_3 and Pr_2O_5), but when more *f* electrons are present they are not given off as easily, and all the following elements form divalent ions only, until the seventh element in the group, europium. One would expect the atom of this element to have the configuration

$$K \,.\, L \,.\, M \,.\, 4s^24p^64d^{10}4f^6 \,.\, 5s^25p^65d \,.\, 6s^2$$

Since the half-filled $4f^7$ group has a special stability, one of the valency electrons, $5d$, can be used in europium to complete the $4f^7$ group: the element then has only two electrons in the *P* group, and becomes divalent, as, for example, in the compounds $EuCl_2$,

EuI_2 and EuS. The eighth element, gadolinium, is tervalent only, but the next element, terbium, has three valency electrons in the *P* shell and one isolated *f* electron, not forming part of the half-filled f^7 shell: this electron can easily be withdrawn, and terbium, therefore, shows a valency of four (in TbO_2) as well as its normal valency, three. The following elements all have only the normal valency, three, until the fourteenth element in the group. In the configuration

$$K . L . M . 4s^2 4p^6 4d^{10} 4f^{13} . 5s^2 5p^6 5d . 6s^2$$

one valency electron (5*d*) can be used to complete the $4f^{14}$ group, in which case a divalent ion will be formed. Valencies in the rare-earth group are given in *Table VIIIb*.

Table VIIIb

Valencies in the Rare-Earth Group

	La	Ce	Pr	Nd	Pro	Sm	Eu	Gd	Tb	Dy	Ho	Er	Tu	Yb	Lu
number of f electrons	0	1	2	3	4	5	6	<u>7</u>	8	9	10	11	12	13	<u>41</u>
valency						(2)	2							2	
	3	3	3	3	3	3	3	3	3	3	3	3	3	3	3
		4	4						4						

In the seventh period, after actinium, a group similar to the lanthanides is to be expected, in which the $5f^{10}$ group is formed. This group, the actinide group, is somewhat different from that of the lanthanides, because the 5*f* electrons have lower ionization energies than 4*f* electrons, and therefore the valencies in the first part of the group are higher (*see Table VIIIc*) than in the lanthanides, reaching six in the fourth element, uranium, in compounds UO_3, UF_6 and UCl_6. After this element the maximal valency decreases, and curium (Cm) has a valency of only three. Then a valency of two is to be expected for the seventh element, americium (corresponding to europium in the lanthanides), and a valency of four for the ninth, berkelium (corresponding to terbium in the lanthanides).

Table VIIIc

Valencies in the Actinide Elements

	Ac	Th	Pa	U	Np	Pu	Am	Cm	Bk	Cal	—
5 f electrons	0	1	2	3	4	5	6	7	8	9	10
		2					2(?)				
	3	3	3	3	3	3	3	3	3	3	
valencies		4	4	4	4	4			4		
			5	5	5	5					
				6	6						

From the ionization energies, by considering the stable electronic configurations, many more important conclusions can be drawn concerning the valencies that may be observed for a certain element. If one wishes to know whether a certain valency is realized in a specified compound, e.g. a fluoride or a chloride or an oxide, the influence of the other magnitudes that occur in the expression for the heat of formation have to be considered as well.

The determination of electron affinity is much more difficult than that of ionization energy, for it is not revealed by spectral data. For the halogens, the electron affinity can be determined from the change of equilibrium with temperature in reactions of the type (where e stands for an electron)

$$I + e \rightleftharpoons I^-$$

as was explained in Section 5, but this method cannot be used for the endothermic reaction

$$O + 2e \rightarrow O^{2-}$$

Now as the ionic radii in the series F^-, Cl^-, Br^-, I^- increase, the decrease of the electron affinity in this order is not unexpected. Hydrogen, also, has a positive electron affinity, and, as an element occurring before the gas helium, it should be regarded as a halogen. Hydrogen has a lower electron-affinity value than that of the other halogens, which is understandable when one considers that after taking up one electron the nucleus, with a charge of one, now has two electrons associated with it, so that in the H^- ion the negative charge of the atom is doubled while for the F^- ion it is only increased by one-ninth. According to recent investigations the electron affinity of fluorine seems to be considerably less than the value given in the table. In Section 16 it will be shown that this fact does not affect the general conclusions of the next chapters.

In order to form negative ions with higher valencies, more than one electron must be added to the atom. The second and third electrons are repelled by those already there and, in consequence, energy must be expended to attach them. The total energy necessary for the formation of the ions O^{2-} and S^{2-} is given in *Table IX*. The

Table IX

Electron Affinities in kcal

H^-	16	O^{2-}	−150
F^-	92	S^{2-}	−80
Cl^-	88		
Br^-	85		
I^-	73		

expression 'electron affinity' is actually superfluous since in place of the expression 'electron affinity of the chlorine atom' one could equally well use the nomenclature 'ionization energy of the Cl^- ion' with the opposite sign; in fact, the energy which is given out when an electron is added to a Cl atom is equal to the energy which is required to remove an electron from a Cl^- ion. When a H^+ ion takes up an electron, the energy which is released can be called the electron affinity of the H^+ ion; the process, however, is never described in this manner and we refer, instead, to the 'ionization energy of the H atom being released'.

Chapter IV

PROPERTIES OF IONIC COMPOUNDS

11. STRUCTURE OF MOLECULES

LET us suppose that fluorine reacts with a number of elements, for example those in the third period, Na, Mg, Al, Si, P and S, thereby forming the molecules NaF, MgF_2, AlF_3, SiF_4, PF_5 and SF_6. In MgF_2 there are two F ions, both of which are attracted by the Mg ion, but which repel each other, so that they will take up positions in which their potential energy is as small as possible. This will occur when they are as far as possible from each other; they will therefore lie on either side of the Mg^{2+} ion. The resulting structure of the molecule MgF_2 is shown in *Figure 3a.* Similarly, the three F ions

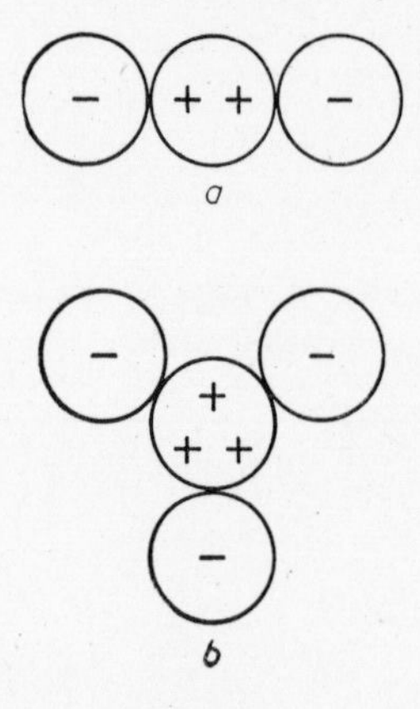

Figure 3

in the molecule AlF_3 will arrange themselves at the corners of an equilateral triangle (*see Figure 3b*). In the SiF_4 molecule, the four F ions will again take up positions in which they are as far from one another as is geometrically possible. For this to occur they will not be at the corners of a square, but arranged in space at the corners of a regular tetrahedron with the silicon ion in the centre. If r is the sum of the radii of F^- and Si^{4+}, then the distance between the two fluorine ions in a square would be $\sqrt{2}r = 1{\cdot}41r$, while in a tetrahedron it is $2\sqrt{6}r/3 = 1{\cdot}63r$. It is interesting to find that the idea that inorganic molecules are built up of ions should lead to the conclusion that in a molecule XY_4 the four Y^- ions are arranged in the form of a regular tetrahedron, which was first pointed out by VAN 'T HOFF as a structural feature of organic chemistry.

Let us now consider how the negative ions will be arranged in a molecule of the type XY_5, for example PF_5, so that they are again as far away from one another as possible. The structure will be a three-sided bipyramid with the P ion in the middle, while in the molecule XY_6, e.g. SF_6, the structure will be a regular octahedron. The structure of a molecule of the type XY_7, which seldom occurs, is not known. Theoretically, the eight negative ions in a molecule of the type XY_8, as OsF_8, should not occupy the corners of a cube. The actual structure is found by rotating one face of the cube through 45° about its mid-point, which results in the negative ions being somewhat farther apart. The figure obtained in this way is the so-called Archimedes antiprism. From electron-diffraction studies it appears fairly certain that OsF_8 has this structure.

In molecules with divalent negative ions other types of X_2O_3, for example B_2O_3 or Al_2O_3, can occur. In these, the molecule must have a shape such that the positive ions are as close as possible to the negative ions, and the negative ions as far as possible from each other. This occurs in a trigonal bipyramid in which the three O^{2-} ions lie in an equilateral triangle in the plane of the meridian and the two Al^{3+} ions lie at the apices of the bipyramid.

It is apparent that only the shapes of the simpler molecules can be ascertained by this method. For a molecule such as Cl_2O_7, a number of different structures can be postulated, of which one will have the smallest potential energy. This can be found by calculations for the different forms. As an example of such a calculation we will take a molecule of the type XY_3, say $AlCl_3$. If $x + y = r$ is the distance between the ions X and Y, then the distance between the two Y ions is $\sqrt{3}r$. By introduction of the first ion, the amount of energy released is $3e \,.\, e/r$. When the second Y ion approaches, it is repelled by the first, and, since it comes to within a distance $\sqrt{3}r$ of the latter, the energy required is $e \,.\, e/\sqrt{3}r$, so that the total gain in energy by bringing up the second Y ion is $3e^2/r - e^2/\sqrt{3}r$.

By the introduction of the third ion, which is repelled by both Y ions, the total energy released in the process is $3e^2/r - 2e^2/\sqrt{3}r$. Therefore the total energy which is released in the formation of the molecule from the ions is $9e^2/r - 3e^2/\sqrt{3}r$, in which the first term corresponds to the attraction of the three Y^- ions by the central ion, and the second term to the mutual repulsion of the three Y^- ions, the first term being the larger. For a molecule XY_3 the expression

$$\{9e^2/r - 3e^2/\sqrt{3}r\}$$

gives the amount by which the energy is reduced, if the ions are initially an infinite distance apart. If the energy corresponding to this state is E_∞ then the potential energy of the molecule is known in terms of E_∞. It was shown in Section 4 that this constant can be put equal to zero. Then the potential energy of the molecule becomes negative, and, per gram mol XY_3, is

$$-(9 - \sqrt{3})Ne^2/r$$

where N is Avogadro's number. As a second example, let us calculate the energy of a molecule XY_4 for the planar and tetrahedral models. The term due to attraction in both is equal to $4(4e\,.\,e)/r$. The term due to repulsion can be easily found in the following way. Between the four Y^- ions we can draw six lines joining them together, and there are therefore six repulsive terms corresponding to these. In the planar model four of these lines have a length $\sqrt{2}r$, two $2r$, while in the tetrahedral model all six lines have length $2\sqrt{6}r/3$. We therefore find per gram mol XY_4

$$E_{tetr} = -N\left(4\,\frac{4e\,.\,e}{r} - 6\,\frac{e\,.\,e}{\sqrt{6}r2/3}\right)$$

$$= -N\,\frac{e^2}{r}\,(16 - 3\sqrt{6}/2)$$

$$E_{plane} = -N\left(4\,\frac{4e\,.\,e}{r} - 4\,\frac{e\,.\,e}{\sqrt{2}r} - 2\,\frac{e\,.\,e}{2r}\right)$$

$$= -N\,\frac{e^2}{r}\,(16 - 2\sqrt{2} - 1)$$

$$E_{tetr} = -12{\cdot}39N\,\frac{e^2}{r}$$

$$E_{plane} = -12{\cdot}18N\,\frac{e^2}{r}$$

from which it follows that the tetrahedral model has the lowest energy content and is therefore the stable one.

Structures calculated in this manner have been confirmed by x-ray and electron-diffraction studies, and the compounds CO_2, CS_2, COS, $HgCl_2$ and $HgBr_2$ have been found to have linear structures. In BCl_3, BBr_3 and SO_3, the three negative ions lie in an equilateral triangle, while in CCl_4, CBr_4, SiF_4, $SiCl_4$, $SnBr_4$ and $TiCl_4$ they form tetrahedra. In PF_5 the five F^- ions form a trigonal bipyramid, while in SF_6, SeF_6 and TeF_6 the six F^- ions are arranged in an octahedron. There are, however, various molecules which have less symmetrical shapes. Thus none of the molecules H_2O, H_2S, Cl_2O, SO_2, ClO_2 and NO_2 is linear, while NH_3, PH_3, PF_3, PCl_3, AsF_3 and $AsCl_3$ have the shape of a trigonal pyramid, so that the positive ion is not in the same plane as the negative ion. We shall consider, at a later stage, some molecules in which the lower symmetry is partly caused by electrical-induction effects (*see* Section 44): in other molecules, however, such structures indicate that they are not true ionic compounds. A calculation of the energy of molecules, in which both the repulsive forces (*see* Section 6) and induction effects are taken into account, is given in Section 71.

12. VOLATILITY: SHIELDED AND NON-SHIELDED COMPOUNDS

If we compare two chlorides, NaCl and CCl_4*, we see that the properties of these compounds are so different that we are forced to the conclusion that they must have entirely different structures. NaCl is a solid, easily soluble in water in which it dissociates into ions, but insoluble in organic solvents. It is a good electrical conductor in aqueous solutions and in the molten state. It has a very low vapour pressure, with a boiling point above 1400°C, and it does not dissociate into its elements when heated. Carbon tetrachloride, on the other hand, is a volatile liquid boiling at 76°C, insoluble in water but soluble in a number of organic solvents. It is a non-conductor and at 1000°C decomposes into carbon and chlorine, and thus is, in all respects, the complete opposite of NaCl.

Are not these differences in conductivity evidence of a different kind of bond in the two molecules represented by NaCl and other salts, on the one hand, and carbon tetrachloride on the other, and do not the differences in volatility, chemical behaviour and, in fact, all their properties, point in the same direction?

We shall see later that the differences are not evidence against the correctness of the theory, but follow logically from the theory of the electrostatic bond. The reason why the molecules in molten NaCl dissociate into ions, but those in CCl_4 do not, is immediately apparent

* Carbon tetrachloride was cited earlier as an example of a homopolar compound; here, however, it is treated as a heteropolar compound to see how far the theory of the heteropolar bond can be applied. Only when difficulties are encountered need we look for another explanation.

when we consider what happens in dissociation. According to Kossel, the ions, which are bound in the molecule, must be separated from one another, which process requires a certain amount of energy. Now it can be easily understood that the energy required for the dissociation of CCl_4 will be much greater than that for NaCl, because in the latter the chlorine ion is removed from an ion with only a single charge, while in CCl_4 it must be removed from an ion with four times that charge. Therefore a measurable dissociation of CCl_4 into ions is to be expected only at high temperatures.

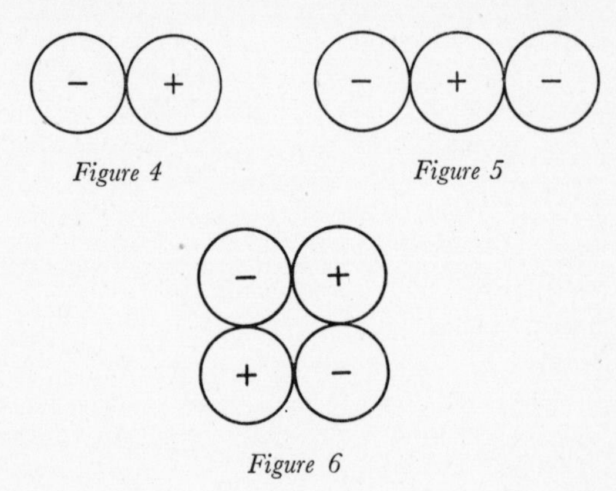

Figure 4 *Figure 5*

Figure 6

As regards volatility, there is an enormous difference between compounds, such as NaF, NaCl, CaO and Al_2O_3, in which the ratio of the numbers of anions and cations is not very different from one, and compounds such as CCl_4, SO_3, N_2O_5, WF_6 and OsF_8. We will consider the structure of a molecule from each of these groups, typified by NaCl and CCl_4, which will make the differences clear. The molecule of NaCl is shown schematically in *Figure 4*. It is electrically neutral, but if an electric charge is brought near the molecule it will nevertheless exert an electric force on it. A negative ion will be attracted by the positive charge of the sodium ion, but repelled by the negative charge of the chlorine ion. The negative ion will therefore attach itself to the sodium atom on the opposite side from the chlorine ion, because, in this position, the attraction is stronger than the repulsion (*see Figure 5*).

If a second molecule of NaCl is brought near the first, then the opposite charges in the molecules will attract each other and the two molecules will take up the position shown in *Figure 6*. Here the attraction of the oppositely-charged ions is greater than the repulsive action of the similarly-charged ions, because, in the double molecule, the ions with similar charges are farther apart from each other than the oppositely-charged ones. This coupling together of two molecules, with no free valencies, opens up quite new possibilities. In fact, in inorganic chemistry, there are many compounds known to be formed by combinations of different molecules in which all the valencies of the atoms are saturated. These compounds, KBF_4, K_2SiF_6, K_2HgI_4, etc., will hereafter be referred to as complexes. So, for NaCl, we must take note of the possibility that molecules may join together. *Figure 7* shows the way in which two double molecules

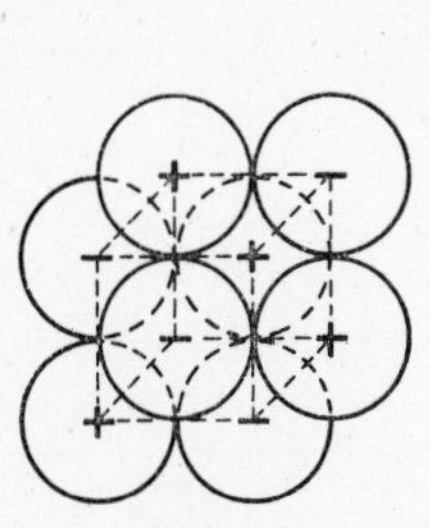

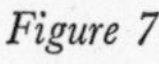

Figure 7

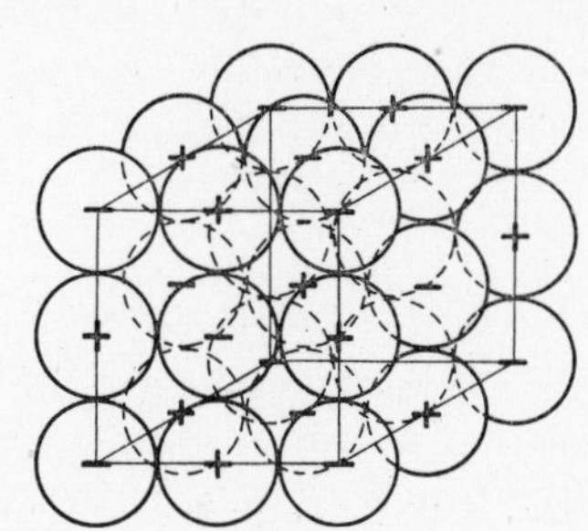

Figure 8

can do this. With a sufficient number of molecules, infinitely large aggregates will be formed, in which each Na ion is surrounded by six Cl ions and each Cl ion by six Na ions. A larger group built up in this manner is shown in *Figure 8*. The question now arises whether such molecules do occur. It can be proved that not only do they exist, but that NaCl at ordinary temperatures consists exclusively of this kind of molecule. In fact, a NaCl crystal is just such a giant molecule, the condensation of NaCl vapour to form solid salt representing the process by which the single molecules are added to the crystal. The correctness of this picture is shown by x-ray analysis of the crystal, the crystal structure of NaCl, and of many of the alkali halides, being exactly the same as that obtained by building up the molecules in the manner described.

It is to be remarked, that, in the crystal, the original molecules cannot be distinguished, each ion being symmetrically surrounded by six equivalent ions of opposite charge, and there is in the whole crystal no one pair of a Na^+ and a Cl^- ion that could be unambiguously distinguished from another pair and described as a molecule. A lattice of this type, in which separate molecules cannot be distinguished, every ion being symmetrically surrounded by a number of ions of the opposite charge, is called a (ionic) *coordination lattice*. Since the original molecues of NaCl in the crystal are held together by the attraction of oppositely-charged ions, strong bonds hold the crystal together and a large amount of energy is required to remove a molecule from the crystal. The separation of the crystal into constituent molecules, which occurs when a crystal evaporates, will therefore take place only at high temperatures, where the term $T\Delta S$ gives the required compensation for the increase in energy. At ordinary temperatures, the loosening of a molecule is rare and the vapour pressure of these compounds is low.

As the charge on each ion increases, the forces holding the crystal together become stronger and the vapour pressure correspondingly lower. For example, the oxides of divalent metals evaporate at higher temperatures than do the halides of the alkali metals, since the former are composed of double-charged ions, and x-ray analysis shows them to have the same crystal structure. The vapour pressure of crystals containing tervalent ions, such as LaN, is smaller still.

A crystal can be dissociated into molecules by means other than evaporation; it can be crushed or split, and the work required to overcome the electrostatic attraction between the ions is reflected in the hardness of the crystal. For crystals of similar structure, the harder ones will contain ions with higher charges, so that MgO is harder than NaF. Crystals of the XY_2 type can be built up from molecules in an analogous manner, and their properties will, in the main, be similar to those of compounds of the type XY.

What will be the state of affairs in compounds like CCl_4? The molecular model of this compound, still assuming that it is formed from ions (*see* Section 11), shows the carbon ion symmetrically surrounded by four negatively-charged Cl^- ions. The electric lines of force from the central ion will terminate on the outer ions, or, in other words, the field of the carbon ion will be largely shielded by the chlorine ions. The carbon ion will therefore exert little or no attraction on oppositely-charged ions of neighbouring molecules, and, further, a positive ion of one molecule can never be close to a negative ion of another molecule. As a result, the carbon tetrachloride molecule will show little tendency to combine with other molecules, but, there is of course, still a small residual attraction which will be effective in crystallization, although the molecules of such a crystal will be so loosely held together that they are easily separated from one another at low temperatures. The compound will therefore have a high vapour pressure, and its crystals will be much weaker, mechanically, than the crystals of the other types of compounds described.

In the lattice of CCl_4, the molecules still can be discerned, each carbon ion in the lattice being surrounded by the same number of chlorine ions as in the gaseous state. It is further evident that the chlorine ions are not surrounded by ions of the opposite charge only, but are in contact with only one carbon ion and a number of chlorine ions, depending on the way in which the CCl_4 molecules are arranged in the lattice. A lattice of this type, in which the molecules that form the vapour are still present, is called a *molecular lattice*.

The enormous difference in volatility between compounds like NaCl, CaO, AlN, CaF_2 and TiO_2 on the one hand, and such compounds as CCl_4, SiF_4, $SnCl_4$, WF_6, OsF_8, etc., on the other, is due to the fact that in the second group the central ion of the molecule is completely shielded by the surrounding negative ions so that the latter never will come near to a positive ion of another molecule.

From the differences in volatility, it cannot be concluded that there is an essential difference in the chemical bond between compounds of the two classes, the great differences in structure and properties being explained by the geometrical arrangement of the molecules that make the lattice when the crystal is formed by condensation from the gaseous state.

A question, which naturally arises, is how compounds such as aluminium fluoride, with three ions attached to its central ion, can fit into such a scheme. It would appear that these compounds have to be considered as belonging partly to the first group, with low volatility, and partly to the second group of compounds. Compounds will only belong to the second group if the central ion is completely shielded by surrounding ions, and this shielding effect will be greater, the smaller the central ion. Thus, if, in a compound XY_3, a small central ion is surrounded by large ones, it will be completely shielded and the compound will have properties corresponding to those of the class typified by CCl_4. If, however, a large central ion is surrounded by small ions then the shielding will be less complete, and the compound will have the properties of the first group, e.g. the low vapour pressure of the compounds forming a coordination lattice. AlF_3 and ScF_3 are good examples of this type.

Boron, which occurs in the second period of the periodic system as a tervalent ion, is naturally very small (*see Table V*), and, in the compounds which it forms with the halogens, the boron ion will be completely shielded by the three halogen ions, so that the boron halides are thus compounds with low boiling points. Of the halogen ions, iodine, which contains the most electrons, is the largest. In aluminium iodide the three iodine ions will shield the aluminium ion, as also do the somewhat smaller bromine or chlorine ions in their respective compounds. If, however, the halogen ion is sufficiently small, then a complete shielding will not be possible and compounds like aluminium fluoride, for example, will be in the less volatile group.

In *Table X* are a number of examples of halogen compounds in

Table X

Boiling Points of Halogen Compounds in °C

AlF_3	1261	SnF_4	705	SbF_3	319	TiF_4	284
$AlCl_3$	183	$SnCl_4$	116	$SbCl_3$	223	$TiCl_4$	136
$AlBr_3$	265	$SnBr_4$	203	$SbBr_3$	288	$TiBr_4$	230
AlI_3	381	SnI_4	346	SbI_3	401	TiI_4	360

which the boiling points of the fluorides, as a result of incomplete shielding of the central ion, can be seen to be higher than those of some of the other halides*. Shielding of the central ion by negative ions, which gives rise to volatility, occurs in the oxides as well as in the halides, but these compounds, as a group, are less volatile than the halides. The reason for this is readily apparent when it is remembered that shielding can take place only if the molecule contains at least three negative ions surrounding a positive one. While tervalent halides can thus be volatile, oxides, on the other hand, must have a hexavalent central ion surrounded by three oxygen ions. A valency of six or higher does not occur very often, which therefore accounts for the small number of volatile oxides. However, they do occur. In the series Na_2O, MgO, Al_2O_3, SiO_2, P_2O_5, SO_3 and Cl_2O_7, up to and including SiO_2 there is no shielding, so that these compounds all have high boiling points. SO_3 is apparently completely shielded, being a substance with the very low boiling point of 44·8°C, while P_2O_5, which sublimes at 347°C, represents the transition to the less volatile type. The boiling point rises with increasing size of the central ion because shielding is thereby decreased; this effect is seen in the boiling point of TeO_3, which is much higher than that of SO_3. Again, Ta_2O_5 has a much higher boiling point than P_2O_5, while SiO_2 has a boiling point greater than 2000°C and CO_2 at ordinary temperatures is a gas.

We can also expect to find volatile compounds among the sulphides, but the number of these compounds in which the positive

* The reason why boiling points of completely shielded compounds rise if the halogens are replaced by others with a higher atomic number will be dealt with later in Section 51.

ion has a charge of six or more is even smaller than in the oxides because, as shall be seen later, sulphides with highly-charged positive ions are less stable than the corresponding oxides. One example of a volatile sulphide is CS_2, boiling point 46·3°C. If the carbon ion is replaced by a larger one, say silicon, then the boiling point of the resulting compound, SiS_2, rises to 900°C. The boiling point of a shielded sulphide will be higher than that of the corresponding oxide, unless the latter is not completely shielded, in which case the sulphide can have a lower boiling point than the oxide as, for example, for silicon, where SiS_2 has a boiling point of about 900°C while that of SiO_2 is above 2000°C. This behaviour is exactly analogous to that of the compounds AlF_3 and $AlCl_3$, where the fluoride has a higher boiling point than the chloride (*see Table X*).

Following this line of reasoning, one should not expect to find volatile nitrides, because such compounds would contain three N^{3-} ions associated with a positive ion, which would then have a valency of nine. For shielded compounds, then, we have the following rules for volatility:

1. The volatility decreases if the negative ion is replaced by one of the same charge but containing a larger number of electrons, for example, in the two series

   F^-, Cl^-, Br^-, I^- and O^{2-}, S^{2-}, Se^{2-}

2. Such a substitution can increase the volatility if the replacement of a small negative ion by a larger positive ion causes more complete shielding, as in $AlF_3 \rightarrow AlCl_3$, etc.

When the central ion of a compound, such as $AlCl_3$, is already shielded, it does not become more completely shielded by replacement of chlorine by bromine and the boiling point will therefore not be lowered but will rise, as in every shielded compound when bromine replaces chlorine.

The situation is quite different with non-shielded compounds which are bound together by coulomb forces, the magnitude of which diminish as the radii of the ions increase. Here the rule that volatility increases if one of the two ions is increased in size will hold true. NaI, boiling point 1300°C, is more volatile than NaF, boiling point 1700°C, while CsCl, boiling point 1300°C, is more volatile than NaCl, boiling point 1400°C.

There are a few cases in which the rules for the volatility of compounds, derived from geometrical considerations, do not hold. The halides of lithium, for example, have somewhat lower boiling points than expected; it will be shown later that this discrepancy is due to the fact that the electrostatic theory of the chemical bond in its present form has to be refined by taking into consideration the induction effect. In other cases, however, the theory is not in agreement with experience, even after applying corrections for induction. It is already difficult to believe that the two oxygen ions in CO_2 are able to completely shield the C ion, and the fact that CO and NO are gaseous, completely contradicts the simple theory. If, in fact, NO and CO were true ionic compounds, then they should be solid substances like BeO and MgO, and the fact that they are not makes it appear that we are dealing here with compounds which have not ionic bonds but a bond similar to that found in such molecules as Cl_2 and O_2, which are built up from identical atoms.

It is once more apparent that not all compounds can be brought within the simple scheme of the ionic bond and it is difficult to say precisely where the division should be made. Carbon tetrachloride, for example, would be a volatile compound even if it were an ionic compound: that in actual fact it is volatile does not necessarily prove that it is ionic, because it is known that there are other volatile compounds which are definitely not ionic.

13. IONIC DISSOCIATION AND ELECTRICAL CONDUCTIVITY

Substances which are electrical conductors, either in the molten state or in solution in a suitable solvent, are called *electrolytes*, and it is assumed that these liquid conductors contain free ions. Such free ions must have been produced from molecules, and we have already calculated the energy required for dissociation of free molecules in Section 11. We found that, for a molecule in which the charge of the positive ions is n and the shortest distance between positive and negative ions is r, the most important energy term is $N(n^2e^2)/r$ per gram mol. From this term must be subtracted the energy corresponding to the mutual repulsion of negative ions; the latter is smaller than the attractive term, and therefore the energy required for the dissociation into ions decreases as the charge of the ions becomes less and their radii increase. All substances that contain large positive ions of low charge will show a tendency to dissociation. Since, for these compounds, the anion : cation ratio is not large, at normal temperature they will form coordination lattices, and there appears to be a connection between crystal structure and electrical conductivity, the compounds forming coordination lattices with ions of low charge forming conducting solutions. To determine the energy required to split one gram mol of solid NaCl into ions, one must calculate not the dissociation energy of N NaCl molecules, but the energy required to dissociate one mole of solid crystal into ions.

In Section 11 the dissociation energy of a gram mol of free molecules was found to be $N\,e^2/r$. In the following section it will be seen that the energy required to dissociate such a crystal aggregate is somewhat greater, viz. NAe^2/r, in which A, as will be shown in Section 14, is a quantity dependent on the structure of the crystal. For NaCl, A has the value 1·75, to which a correction of about ten per cent must be made if the ions cannot be considered as rigid spheres. If, in this formula, we now substitute the values $N = 0{\cdot}602 \times 10^{-24}$, $e = 4{\cdot}80 \times 10^{-10}$ e.s.u., and $r = 2{\cdot}814 \times 10^{-8}$ cm, then, per mol of dissociation of NaCl, we obtain a value

$$E = 7{\cdot}89 \times 10^{12} \text{ erg} = 188 \text{ kcal}$$

The magnitude of this energy can be appreciated from the fact that one gram mol of NaCl dissolved in one litre of water produces a solution that would cool to −188°C, assuming that the specific heat of water at low temperatures is unity. Actually, if NaCl is dissolved in water, the cooling effect is much smaller, so that, in some way or other, energy must be released as the NaCl goes into solution; this is demonstrated by other substances, such as NaOH, $CaCl_2$ and HCl, which actually give out heat on solution. It will be seen later that energy is released because the ions join with the water molecules, so that the solution of NaCl in water is, in fact, a much more complicated process than a simple dissociation into ions.

In every solution in which there are ions, i.e. in every electrolyte, the ions are combined with molecules of the solvent, producing 'solvate ions'. Since the dissociation into solvated ions is usually an endothermic process, the formation of ions, free or solvated, is only possible if the process is associated with an increase in entropy. In actual fact, a diluted solution always has a considerable entropy, because the ions are distributed over a large volume of the solvent. It will be clear that dissociation into ions, at a given temperature and volume, will be more complete, the lower the total energy connected with the formation of the ions.

If a compound, on fusion, forms a conducting liquid phase, the process is not one of simple dissociation because the ions are not completely free, but are either in contact with ions of opposite charge or combined with undissociated molecules. It is to be expected, however, that the number of free ions formed at a given temperature will be greater, the smaller the energy required for the dissociation process, and therefore that fused compounds will be better conductors, the smaller the charge and the greater the radius of the ions.

Table XI

Equivalent Conductivities in rec. ohm cm of Chlorides at their Melting Points

HCl 10^{-6}			
LiCl 166	$BeCl_2$ 0·086	BCl_3 0	CCl_4 0
NaCl 133·5	$MgCl_2$ 28·8	$AlCl_3$ $15\cdot10^{-6}$	$SiCl_4$ 0
KCl 103·5	$CaCl_2$ 51·9	$ScCl_3$ 15	$TiCl_4$ 0
RbCl 78·2	$SrCl_2$ 55·7	YCl_3 9·5	$ZrCl_4$?
CsCl 66·7	$BaCl_2$ 64·6	$LaCl_3$ 29·0	$HfCl_4$?
			$ThCl_4$ 16

There are very few data on the electrolytic dissociation of molten substances, and only the chlorides have been systematically investigated. *Table XI*, taken from a publication by BILTZ and KLEMM, gives the conductivity of a number of chlorides in the liquid state, from which it can be seen that the dividing line between conducting and non-conducting compounds runs diagonally through the periodic system. In the lower left-hand side of the system are found the conducting chlorides, where the positive ions have the smaller charges and larger radii.

There is little known concerning the conductivity of oxides: lithium oxide, at its melting point, has nearly the same conductivity as KCl; the dissociation energy is higher for Li_2O, but this is compensated by the higher temperature. Molten MgO, CaO, BaO, ZrO_2 and ThO_2 are also good conductors, partly due to the very high temperature. Compounds with screened molecules, e.g. SO_3 and N_2O_5, are, like CCl_4, insulators. MoO_3, which can be compared with $AlCl_3$, is an intermediate case.

14. CALCULATION OF CRYSTAL ENERGIES

In the preceding section consideration was given to the energy required to split one gram mol of solid NaCl into ions, which is, of course, the same as the energy gained when one gram mol is formed from free ions. This energy is called *crystal energy* or *lattice energy* and determines not only the dissociation of a substance into ions, but also occurs in a number of other energy calculations. We shall consider the calculation of the crystal energy of NaCl as an example. The structure of solid NaCl has alternate Cl^- ions and Na^+ ions (*see Figure 9*), and this structure can be built up by adding the ions one

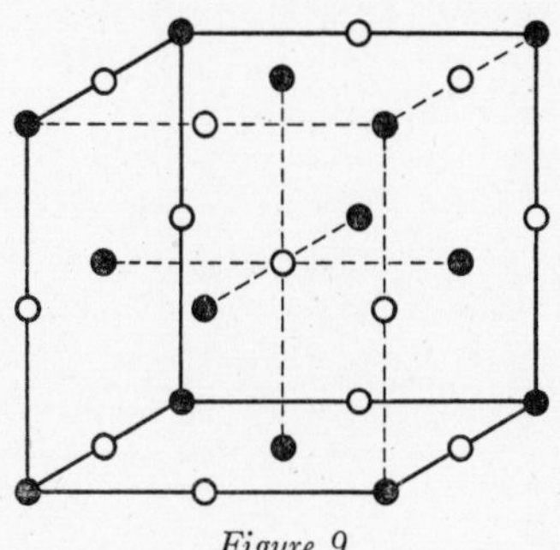

Figure 9

by one. Let us begin with a Cl ion. Around this must be placed six Na^+ ions at a distance r, which is equal to the sum of the ionic radii. Each of these ions will have a potential energy $-e^2/r$ due to the attraction of the Cl^- ion. From *Figure 9* it will be seen that after the first six Na^+ ions have been brought into their final positions, the twelve Cl^- ions, added at a distance $\sqrt{2}r$, will be repelled by the first Cl ion, opposite which they will each have a potential energy $e^2/\sqrt{2}r$. Subsequently, eight Na ions are placed at a distance $\sqrt{3}r$, etc. The potential energy of the original Cl^- ion opposite all the other ions in the crystal will then be $-6e^2/r + 12e^2/\sqrt{2}r - 8e^2/\sqrt{3}r. \ldots$, etc., in which the series must be summed over the whole of the crystal structure. The series can also be written

$$-e^2/r\{6 - 12/\sqrt{2} + 8/\sqrt{3} - \ldots.\}$$

Summation of the series gives a value 1·747 and is called Madelung's constant A. The expression Ae^2/r is the energy which is obtained when one ion is surrounded by all the others, or, equally well, the energy necessary to remove one ion from the crystal. In order to remove $2N$ ions in a gram mol of the crystal, in other words to dissociate it into ions, it would be expected that $2N$ times as much energy will be required. This, however, is not correct, because, having calculated the potential energy of each ion in respect to every other ion, the energy of a single ion, in relationship to all the others, would thus have been added twice. The expression must, therefore, be divided by two, obtaining $2NAe^2/2r = NAe^2/r$. This division by two is evident if one remembers that the energy required to separate two ions from each other is e^2/r, although two ions are obtained in this process.

The expression NAe^2/r then gives the energy which is released when one gram mol of ions, with charges e and $-e$ and radii r_+ and r_-, combine to form a crystal of the type NaCl, in which the shortest distance between the ions is equal to the sum of the radii $r = r_+ + r_-$. This expression is still not quite correct because, in the first place, the atoms were assumed to combine in fixed positions, whereas at ordinary temperatures the atoms in a crystal actually vibrate, and therefore the distances—even though the ions are regarded as rigid spheres—are not exactly equal to the sum of the radii but are somewhat greater. In addition, the assumption that the ions can be considered as completely rigid spheres is itself not completely true and it would be more correct to consider them as hard rubber spheres, which are somewhat deformed under the influence of their mutual attraction. The correction factor (*see* Section 71) due to the compressibility of the ions is $(n - 1)/n$, in which n has different values for different ions, usually having a value of about ten. Therefore the factor is generally 9/10, and the remaining necessary corrections are smaller still.

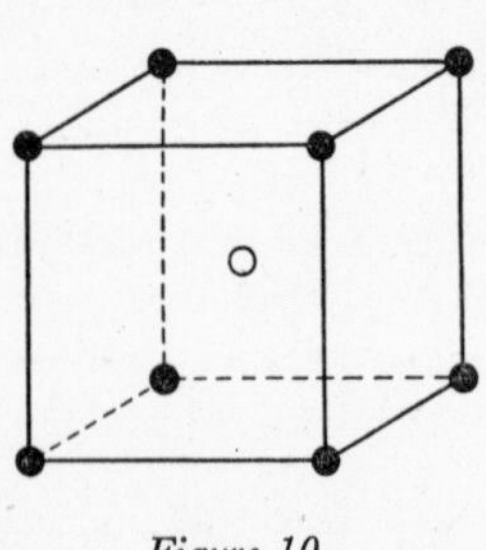

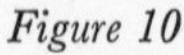

Figure 10

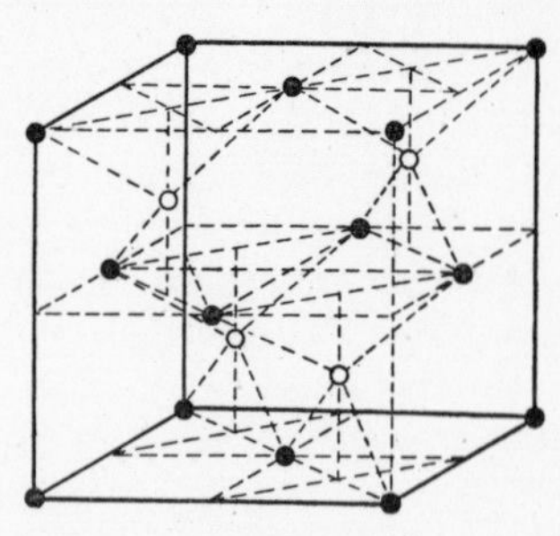

Figure 11

Not all ionic compounds crystallize in the same way as rock salt. *Figure 10* shows the lattice of CsCl in which each positive ion is not surrounded by six, but by eight Cl^- ions. The smallest unit, or unit cell of the crystal, is a cube in which the Cs^+ ions occupy the corners, with a Cl^- ion in the centre. The same configuration results if the Cs^+ ion is taken as centre, the Cl^- ions arranging themselves at the corners, because the crystal is built up of an enormous number of such units and it is therefore immaterial whether one starts with a Cl^- or a Cs^+ ion. There are other structures in which one ion is surrounded by four other ions, e.g. ZnS. Here, two slightly different structures occur, in both of which each positive ion is surrounded by four negative ones arranged at the corners of a regular tetrahedron, and each negative ion is surrounded by four positive ones. As a mineral, the cubic form is known as zinc blende, or *sphalerite*, and the hexagonal form as *wurtzite*. One of these structures is shown in *Figure 11*. If we now wish to calculate how much energy is released when Cs^+ ions and Cl^- ions combine to form one gram mol of solid CsCl, then the calculation will be exactly the same as that for NaCl, with the exception that the series will be somewhat different, giving a different value for Madelung's constant. For CsCl, $A = 1{\cdot}763$, while for the two crystal forms of ZnS it has the values 1·638 and 1·641. From this it follows that the greatest quantity of energy is released when the ions combine to give a CsCl structure, and we must now see why it is that Na^+ and Cl^- ions do not form crystals of the CsCl structure, which would be thought to have the lowest energy.

15. INFLUENCE OF IONIC RADII ON CRYSTAL STRUCTURE

According to GOLDSCHMIDT, the shape of the crystal lattice depends on the ratio of the ionic radii. If the crystal energy were the only determining factor, then all compounds of type XY would crystallize with the CsCl structure, because it corresponds to the lowest energy. This structure has, in fact, only been observed when the ions do not differ greatly in size. From the ionic sizes in *Table V*, Section 9, it appears that there are very few pairs of ions of equal and opposite charges and of equal size. CsCl and CsBr do, however, satisfy these conditions and consequently they have a ClCs structure. As long as the ions are of equal size in the CsCl structure, the positive ions can touch the negative ones without there being any mutual contact between pairs of positive ions or between pairs of negative ions. Positive and negative ions can therefore be as close together as is consistent with the sizes of the ions, and the value $r_+ + r_-$ can be used in the expression for the crystal energy. *Figure 12*, which shows a section of the diagonal plane of the CsCl crystal, makes this clear. Now if the positive ion, radius r_+, becomes smaller, then the whole figure contracts until r_+ is so small that the negative ions can touch one another. Further reduction of the size of the positive ion will result in positive and negative ions that are no longer touching. From *Figure 12* it will be seen that this occurs if $2r_- > 2\sqrt{3}(r_+ + r_-)/3$ and therefore if the ratio of the radii of positive to negative ions is smaller than 0·73/1. From this point onward, further reduction of the radius of the positive ions causes a reduction in the crystal energy of the CsCl structure to a value smaller than would be expected from the sum of the radii of the two ions, because in the expression for the crystal energy the distance r is no longer equal to the sum of the radii, but has a larger value.

Investigation of what would be the crystal energy for the NaCl, or rock-salt, structure, in which the ratio of ionic radii is smaller than 0·73/1, reveals that, where six negative ions surround the positive ion, these negative ions still can make contact with the positive ion.

Now the expression for the crystal energy of the CsCl structure contains a term in the denominator greater than the sum of the radii of the two ions, while in the expression for the compound in the NaCl structure this term is equal to the sum of the radii. The NaCl type of lattice therefore will have a larger negative value for the crystal energy, notwithstanding the fact that the value of A for this structure is somewhat smaller. The compound will therefore be stable in the rock-salt arrangement. If the ratio of the ionic radii further increases, then the rock-salt type is no longer possible and passes over to the zinc-blende type as soon as the larger ions (r_-) start to make contact. The condition for contact in the NaCl lattice is

$$2r_- = (r_+ + r_-)\sqrt{2}$$

and the NaCl lattice will become unstable if

$$2r_- > (r_+ + r_-)\sqrt{2}$$

or

$$r_+ < (\sqrt{2} - 1)r_-$$

or

$$r_+/r_- < (\sqrt{2} - 1)$$

or

$$r_+/r_- < 0{\cdot}41$$

The larger ions, however, will not make contact for the same ratio of ionic radii in the zinc-blende structure, with the result that the crystal energy is a minimum for this structure, which is, therefore, the stable one.

Although the caesium chloride arrangement always occurs when the ratio of radii is approximately unity, the crystal structure observed is not always the one that is expected, and the other alkali halides all have the rock-salt structure. In compounds with divalent ions, occurrence of the CsCl structure would not be expected, because the largest divalent positive ions are generally smaller than the smallest negative ions. We do find, however, several examples of the zinc-blende or wurtzite structures. *Table XII* shows how compounds of type XY are distributed over the various crystal structures.

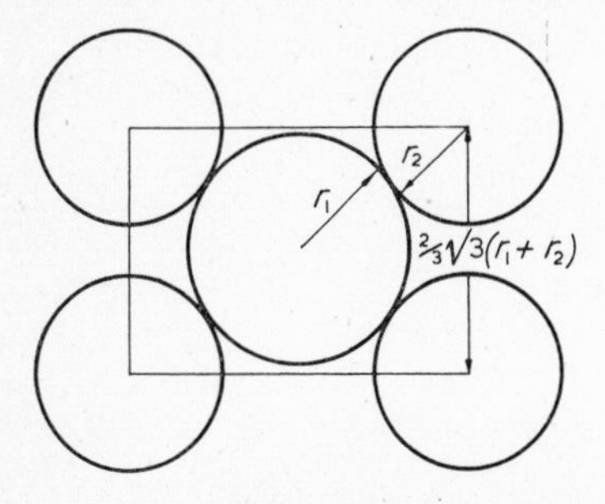

Figure 12

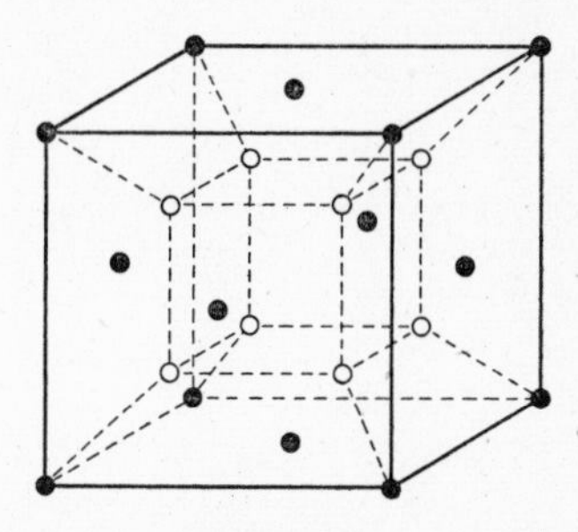

Figure 13

Compounds of XY_2 also have various crystal structures, the occurrence of which are connected with the ratio of the ionic radii. When the difference between the radii is small, the calcium fluoride, or fluorite, structure shown in *Figure 13* is obtained in which each divalent ion is surrounded by eight univalent ions, and each univalent ion by four divalent ones—a very common structure. The divalent ion can be negative as well as positive, as in the compounds Li_2O, Li_2S, CaF_2 and BaF_2, and the same structure also appears in compounds like ThO_2 and UO_2, which contain relatively large, tetravalent, positive ions and small, divalent, negative ones. When the ratio of the radii increases, then a new type of crystal structure occurs, in which each divalent ion is surrounded by six univalent ions, and each univalent by three divalent ones. This arrangement, shown in *Figure 14*, is called the *rutile* type, named after the mineral TiO_2. While CaF_2 still has the structure with 8 : 4 coordination, the rutile structure is observed in MgF_2 because of the smaller radius of the Mg^{2+} ion. After the rutile type there is a further reduction of the coordination to 4 : 2; this type of structure occurs in BeF_2 and SiO_2: in the different modifications of silica, each silicon ion is surrounded by 4 O^{2-} ions, and each O^{2-} ion is between two Si^{4+} ions. The ionic ratio r_+/r_- can also be decreased if,

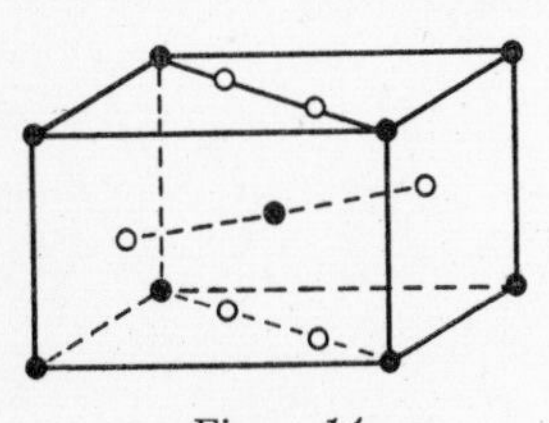

Figure 14

in a fluoride, the fluorine ions are substituted by the larger chlorine ions; thus the rutile lattice is also observed in some chlorides and bromides with the formulae ACl_2 and ABr_2. In compounds of this

Table XII

Crystal Types of Various Compounds AB

	F	Cl	Br	I
Li	6	6	6	6
Na	6	6	6	6
K	6	6	6	6
Rb	6	6	6	6
Cs	6	8	8	8
Cu	—	4*Z*	4*Z*	4*Z and* 4*W*
Ag	6	6	6	4*Z*
Tl	**	8	8	8

	O	S	Se	Te
Be	4*W*	4*Z*	4*Z*	4*Z*
Mg	6	6	6	4*W*
Ca	6	6	6	6
Sr	6	6	6	6
Ba	6	6	6	6
Zn	4*W*	4*Z and* 4*W*	4*Z and* 4*W*	4*Z*
Cd	6	4*Z and* 4*W*	4*Z and* 4*W*	4*Z*
Pb	*	6	6	6

8 *caesium chloride type.* 4*Z zinc-blende type.*
6 *rock-salt type.* 4*W wurtzite type.*
* PbO *is tetragonal or rhombic.* ** TlF *is rhombic*

group, the influence of induction becomes so important that often the lattice is deformed by this effect, and completely different structures appear (*see* Section 42).

Table XIII features a number of halides and metal oxides containing ions with eighteen electrons in the outer shell. Compounds containing such ions are exceptional in many of their properties, and we shall come across numerous examples of them. In general, it can be said that these ions behave as if their attraction by negative charges is greater than that expected of ions of their size. This is apparent from the fact that the value of the crystal energy, calculated according to a cyclic process, is considerably greater than the theoretical value (discussed in Section 16).

Table XIII

Heats of Dissociation of Molecules in kcal per Atom

H_2				O_2	S_8	Se_8
51·9				59	64	57
F_2	Cl_2	Br_2	I_2	N_2		
32	29	23	18	85		

This extra attraction leads to a contraction, in the sense that the shortest distance is now somewhat smaller than $r_+ + r_-$, which is apparently responsible for the compounds of ions belonging to the subseries having the curious property of low coordination numbers. We have already found this to occur in the halides of Cu and Ag, and in the sulphides of Zn and Cd. The compounds of GeO_2, SnO_2 and PbO_2 also show this property of low coordination number and have a rutile, rather than a CaF_2, structure. We will not go any further at this stage into the influence of ionic size on crystal structure. Goldschmidt's theory does not fit all the experimental observations, being only a rough approximation—and, as was seen in the calculation of crystal energy, the fact that the ions cannot be regarded as rigid spheres must be taken into account.

16. CALCULATION OF HEAT OF FORMATION

In Section 13 it was shown that a large amount of energy is required to split a compound into ions. Such a dissociation would be expected to occur at high temperatures, unless another kind of dissociation requiring smaller energy, e.g. dissociation into elements, occurs. Thus a sodium chloride molecule would not break up into the ions Na^+ and Cl^- at very high temperatures, but into the atoms Na and Cl, instead. The formation of atoms from the ions Na^+ and Cl^- corresponds to an energy change $I_{Na} - E_{Cl}$, which, according to the data in Section 10, is a positive quantity. A further decrease of energy occurs by the combination of the Cl atoms in the formation of molecules.

Dissociation into elements is the reverse process of compound formation, in which the energy released in the process is the heat of formation; the less the heat, the lower the temperature at which dissociation into elements occurs. The stability of a compound is therefore dependent, to a large extent, on its heat of formation, which we will now proceed to calculate.

In Section 8 a preliminary calculation was carried out starting with the free atoms Na and Cl and ending with the free molecule, NaCl. Now, if sodium and chlorine are brought into reaction at normal temperatures, the sodium atoms are not free but combined in the solid sodium, the chlorine atoms are combined to form molecules Cl_2, and the NaCl finally obtained is a crystal. These initial and final states, therefore, must be taken into account in the calculation. This is carried out by the so-called cyclic process of BORN and HABER. Here the NaCl is imagined to be formed in two ways: first by direct combination of solid sodium with gaseous chlorine, corresponding to a heat of formation ΔH; and second, by transforming solid sodium and gaseous chlorine into free atoms, which are then ionized. These subsequently combine to form solid salt

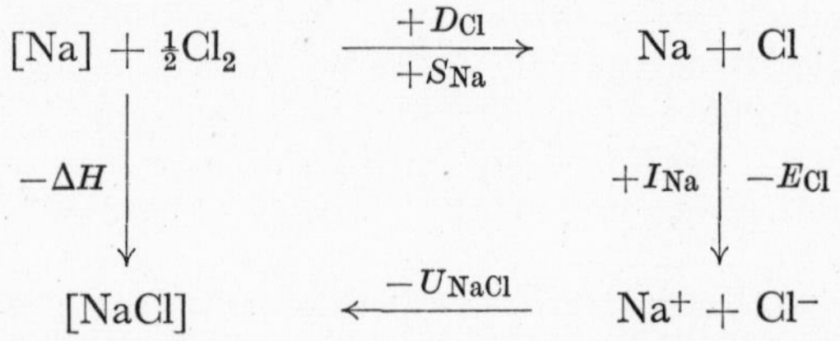

$$\begin{array}{ccc} [\mathrm{Na}] + \frac{1}{2}\mathrm{Cl}_2 & \xrightarrow[+S_{\mathrm{Na}}]{+D_{\mathrm{Cl}}} & \mathrm{Na} + \mathrm{Cl} \\ \Big\downarrow -\Delta H & & +I_{\mathrm{Na}} \Big\downarrow -E_{\mathrm{Cl}} \\ [\mathrm{NaCl}] & \xleftarrow{-U_{\mathrm{NaCl}}} & \mathrm{Na}^+ + \mathrm{Cl}^- \end{array}$$

From the law of conservation of energy, the energy changes in both processes must be the same because the initial and final states are the same. The heat required to dissociate sodium into free atoms is the heat of sublimation S_{Na}. To dissociate half a gram mol of Cl_2 into atoms requires the dissociation energy D_{Cl}. To transform the sodium atoms into ions will require the ionization energy I_{Na}, while heat, corresponding to the electron affinity of chlorine, E_{Cl}, will be released during the combination of Cl atoms and electrons. Finally, the combination of ions to give solid salt will release the crystal energy U_{NaCl}. Taking the cycle as a whole, we have

$$\Delta H = -S_{Na} - D_{Cl} - I_{Na} + E_{Cl} + U_{NaCl}$$

This expression, therefore, gives the correct value of the heat of formation. The heats of sublimation of elements can usually be determined directly, but are mostly derived from the change of vapour pressure of the solid with the change of temperature, making use of the Clapeyron equation which relates these quantities.

Determination of D is somewhat difficult. The higher its value, the higher the temperature at which marked dissociation occurs. A relation between D and the change of degree of dissociation with changing temperature would therefore be expected, and D can be calculated when the dissociation equilibrium $Cl_2 \rightleftharpoons 2Cl$ can be measured as a function of temperature. The dissociation energies of F_2, Cl_2, Br_2 and I_2 are well known, but those of O_2, N_2, S_8 and P_4 are less accurately known.

The heats of formation of halides can now be calculated because all the necessary data are available, and the agreement between observed and calculated values is very good for the alkali halides, as *Table XIV* shows. In all these calculations the corrections to the crystal energy, mentioned in Section 14, have been applied.

Table XIV

Heats of Formation of the Alkali Halides in kcal

	Li	Na	K	Rb	Cs
F	145 143	137 136	134 134	133 131	131 129
Cl	97 94	98 99	105 105	105 105	107 103
Br	84 80	86 87	94 95	96 96	97 94
I	65 65	69 69	79 80	81 81	84 80

It has been shown that the values of electron affinities, given in Section 10, are not very reliable, but they can be calculated as follows

$$\Delta H = -S - D - I + E + U$$

from which it follows that

$$E = S + D + I - U - \Delta H$$

In this last expression all quantities are known and, if the theory *is* correct, all the fluorides should give the same value of E_F, as they do to within a few kilocalories. Thus

$$E_F = 98, \qquad E_{Cl} = 92, \qquad E_{Br} = 87, \qquad E_I = 79$$

all the values being somewhat higher than those given in Section 10. The calculated heat of formation is in error by about 4·5 kcal if the directly determined electron affinities are used in the calculation, but even this agreement is most satisfactory, in spite of the accumulation of small errors in the five quantities in the equation. It was remarked before, in Section 10, that the electron affinity of fluorine probably is lower than that given in the table. This will not affect the calculations, because D for fluorine will probably not only be lower, as well, but lower by the same amount.

17. CONDITIONS GOVERNING HEATS OF FORMATION

We have just seen that the calculated heats of formation of the alkali halides agree most satisfactorily with experimental values, but the agreement is not as good for other compounds. These discrepancies are in part due to inaccurate data for the heats of sublimation, ionization energies, dissociation energies and electron affinities of the elements concerned. In addition, the simplifying assumptions introduce large errors into calculations for compounds containing highly-charged ions. To recapitulate, these assumptions were:

1. The assumption of the idea of completely rigid, spherical ions. In fact, the distance between the ions is markedly influenced by the magnitude of the electric attraction between the ions, so that the F ion behaves as a smaller ion when linked to a hexavalent S^{6+} ion, than when it is bound to a Na^+ ion (*see* Section 71).
2. All forces between the ions, other than those due to the electric charges, were neglected.

In any exact calculation, corrections must be applied for the van der Waals forces (Section 51), and for induction effects (Section 41). Both corrections can be partially applied, but the calculation then becomes considerably more complicated. They will not be considered further here, but, neglecting the fact that agreement between calculated and observed heats of formation is not exact, we will try to obtain a general picture of the change of heat of formation when an ion in a compound is replaced by another with different radius, charge and, eventually, different electronic structure.

The heat of formation of compounds is usually given in kcal per mol of the compound formed from elements at 20°C, and from gaseous elements, at a pressure of one atmosphere. Evidently, this heat of formation per mol is not the most adequate quantity if one compares, the heats of formation of, say, a series of oxides, i.e. K_2O, CaO, Sc_2O_3, TiO_2, V_2O_5, because these compounds do not contain the same amount of oxygen. In comparing the heat of formation of a group of compounds containing the same positive ion, i.e. LiF, Li_2O, Li_3N, it is evident that it would be better to compare amounts containing the same number of Li^+ ions. Both requirements are fulfilled if the heats of formation of equivalent amounts of both ions are compared.

If we look in the literature at the values for heats of formation, then we will see immediately that this quantity depends on the size, charge and structure of the ions, and the following rules are found to hold true:

1. The heat of formation per equivalent increases when a positive ion, with a noble-gas structure, is replaced in a compound by another ion of equal charge, but greater radius.
2. The heat of formation decreases if the charge of the positive ion, with a noble-gas structure, is increased, the radius remaining the same.
3. The heat of formation decreases if the radius of the negative ion increases.
4. The heat of formation decreases if the charge of the negative ion is increased.
5. Substitution of a noble-gas ion by one with an 18-electron structure leads to a decrease in the heat of formation, provided the charge and the radius remain the same.

Table XV demonstrates the decrease of the heat of formation per equivalent, with increasing charge of the positive ion. It is evident that the heats of formation per mol would not show a constant decrease, but a maximum for $AlCl_3$. Similarly, the decrease with

Table XV

Some Heats of Formation in kcal per Equivalent

positive ions	NaCl	$MgCl_2$	$AlCl_3$	$SiCl_4$	PCl_5
	98	76·5	56	37	26
negative ions	LiF	Li_2O	Li_3N		
	145·5	71	15		

increasing charge of the negative ions of the heat of formation per equivalent is not observed when the heats of formation per mol are compared. When not explicitly stated otherwise, heats of formation are always given per equivalent.

In the following section it will be shown how well these empirical rules for the heat of formation can be reconciled with the idea of the ionic bond, or can be derived from it.

18. RELATION BETWEEN HEAT OF FORMATION AND RADIUS OF POSITIVE ION

Table XVI shows the effect of the increase of the radius of the positive ion on the heat of formation.

Table XVI

Heats of Formation in kcal per Equivalent

CO_2	SiO_2	TiO_2	ZrO_2	HfO_2	ThO_2
23·5	49·5	54	64	68	83
	SO_3	CrO_3	MoO_3	WO_3	UO_3
	17	25	29	32	49
BCl_3	$AlCl_3$	$ScCl_3$	YCl_3	$LaCl_3$	
31	55	—	—	89	
N_2O_5	P_2O_5	V_2O_5	Cb_2O_5	Ta_2O_5	
1·4	36·5	44	—	49	
BeS	MgS	CaS	SrS	BaS	
—	40	56	56	55·5	
BeI_2	MgI_2	CaI_2	SrI_2	BaI_2	
44·5	43	64	68	72·5	
CCl_4	$SiCl_4$	$TiCl_4$	$ZrCl_4$	$ThCl_4$	
6	35	46	58	84	
BeO	MgO	CaO			
72·5	73	76			

In order to explain the change of the heat of formation with the change of the radius of the positive ion, the following facts must be taken into consideration. Two of the quantities occurring in the formula for the heat of formation, namely ionization energy and heat of sublimation, are related to the positive ions. Two more, dissociation energy and electron affinity, are related to the negative ion only, while the crystal energy is dependent on both. If, therefore, the heats of formation of a series of compounds, all of which have the same negative ion, are compared, the electron affinity and dissociation energy cancel out. The value for the heat of sublimation per equivalent usually does not change very much with increasing radius of the positive ion, and so the heat of formation will only be influenced by it to a minor extent. We can begin, therefore, by assuming constant heat of sublimation.

The heat of formation per mol for a compound AX_n, where X is a halogen ion, is

$$V_m = -S - n(D - E) - \sum_n I_i + U$$

and that per equivalent is

$$V_e = -S/n - (D - E) - \frac{1}{n}\sum_n I_i + U/n$$

If the heats of formation for a series of halides with the same negative ion are compared, the factor $(D - E)$ is the same for all compounds, and thus does not appear in the difference between the terms in the series.

The change in heat of formation, as a result of a change of the positive ion, will be primarily dependent on the values of I and U. In Section 2 it was shown that increasing the radius of the ions decreases the ionization energy, since in the larger ions, the coulomb energy of the outer electrons is smaller. This energy should be equal to e^2/a, if the electron were at rest at a distance a from the nucleus, and if all the other electrons could be considered to be concentrated in the nucleus. The radius would then be approximately equal to the radius of the atom. Since, however, the electron is not really stationary, and the other electrons are not localized in the nucleus, this expression cannot be exactly correct; but one can expect that such an expression will give an approximate relationship between ionization energy and atomic radius.

It may also be assumed that there will be a relationship between the size of the atom and that of the resulting positive ion, such that the ionization energy I will be approximately equal to ke^2/r, in which the factor k is introduced as a correction factor, its value being about one-half. If, in a compound such as $CaCl_2$ the Ca^{2+} ion is replaced by the larger Ba ion, then I is inversely proportional to the ratio of the radii of the Ca^{2+} and Ba^{2+} ions. As a result of the lower ionization energy, the heat of formation increases, but the crystal energy decreases at the same time, because the replacement of the positive ion by a larger one increases the value of $r_+ + r_-$ in the denominator (*see* Section 14). The influence of the positive ion, however, is smaller here because a given change in r leads to a smaller change of $r_+ + r_-$, particularly if the positive ion is small in comparison with the negative ion. Therefore, as a result of changing the positive ion, the crystal energy will decrease less than the ionization energy and, since the latter occurs with a negative sign in the expression for heat of formation, increasing the radius of the positive ion will lead to an increase in the heat of formation of the compound.

Highly-charged positive ions always have smaller radii than those of the negative ions, with the result that compounds having positive ions with a charge greater than two obey the rule without exception as long as the positive ions have the same electronic configuration.

When the charge of the positive ion is low, as in the alkali metals, the ionic radius will be large. If these large positive ions are then combined with small negative ions, the positive ions may be even larger than the negative ones, and there is no guarantee that the effect of increasing size of the positive ion will be much smaller on the lattice energy than on the heat of formation. In that case, the heat of formation may *decrease* with increasing radius of the positive ion, as for instance in the series

LiF	NaF	KF	RbF	CsF	
146	136	134	133	132	kcal/equivalent

where the calculation, with the aid of the correct formula, gives values that agree exactly with the observed ones (*see* p. 70). The same increase with increasing radius of the positive ion is observed and only observed, in combinations of the large alkali- and alkaline-earth ions with the four small negative ions H^-, F^-, O^{2-} and N^{3-}. Lithium nitride has a very low heat of formation, 15·5 kcal/equivalent, and that of Na_3N evidently is so low that the compound is unstable at room temperature and, so far, has not been prepared in the pure state.

Table XVII

Heats of Formation of Alkali Compounds in kcal per Equivalent

LiH	NaH	KH	RbH	CsH
21·6	14	10	12(?)	12(?)
Li_2O	Na_2O	K_2O	Rb_2O	Cs_2O
71	50	43	41·5	41
		CaO	SrO	BaO
		76	70·5	66·5

19. HEAT OF FORMATION AS A FUNCTION OF THE CHARGE OF THE POSITIVE ION

From *Table XVIII* it may be seen that when a positive noble-gas ion is replaced by one with the same structure but having a larger charge, the heat of formation decreases. The decrease of heat of formation with the charge of the positive ion also follows from the general

Table XVIII

Heats of Formation in kcal per Equivalent

Li_2O	BeO	B_2O_3	CO_2	N_2O_5			
71·5	72·5	47	23·5	1·4			
Na_2O	MgO	Al_2O_3	SiO_2	P_2O_5	SO_3	Cl_2O_7	
50	73	63	51	37	17	1	
$NaCl$	$MgCl_2$	$AlCl_3$	$SiCl_4$	PCl_5			
98	76·5	56	37	26			
Na_2S	MgS	Al_2S_3	SiS_2	P_2S_5			
45	41	21	3·5	(?)			
Cs_2O	BaO	La_2O_3	HfO_2	Ta_2O_5	WO_3	Re_2O_7	OsO_4
41	66	76	68	49	32	21	12

formula for heat of formation. It was noted earlier that the ionization energy increases for each subsequent electron as a result of the larger coulomb energy required to remove an electron from a highly-charged ion. On the basis of ionization energy, therefore, compounds containing divalent positive ions would be expected to have a lower heat of formation than those containing univalent ones, and increasing charge would be expected to further decrease the heat of formation, although this effect is compensated to a large extent by the increase of crystal energy due to the higher charge of the ions, even though this increase, depending on the denominator $r_+ + r_-$, is less than that of the ionization energy. The charge would, therefore, have a fairly small effect, were it not for the fact that by loss of more electrons the radii of the ions decrease; and it is this decrease of the radius of the positive ion, according to the first rule, which gives rise to the lower heat of formation. The rule, that the heat of formation decreases with increasing charge of the positive ion, is valid only if the positive ion is much smaller than the negative ion, as occurs in highly-charged ions but not always in those with a low charge, e.g. compare Na_2O and MgO with Li_2O and BeO. However, still another effect must be considered.

A compound A^+B^- has a larger Madelung constant per equivalent than a compound $A^{2+}B_2^-$. Therefore, while, for equal ionic radii, a halide A^+X^- has a larger equivalent crystal energy than a compound $A^{2+}X_2^-$,which favours a decrease of heat of formation with increasing charge, a calcide $A_2^+Y^{2-}$, on the other hand, has a lower crystal energy than one with the formula $A^{2+}Y^{2-}$, which in itself would cause an increase of heat of formation with increasing charge and consequently give rise to a maximum in the heats of formation in the second group. (A calcide is a compound formed from a metal and an element of the oxygen group, a calcogen.) The decrease of the Madelung constant with increasing anion : cation ratio is a consequence of the mutual repulsion of the A ions, of which there is a greater number in a compound $A_2^+Y^{2-}$ than in a compound $A^{2+}Y^{2-}$, which has only one-half the number of positive ions. This effect is still more clearly seen in the nitrides. The compound $Al^{3+}N^{3-}$ has a large crystal energy; the maximum heat of formation occurs in the third group, where again are found the compounds of the type AN. The heat of formation of AlN, 26·7 kcal/equivalent, is considerably larger than that of Li_3N, 15·5 kcal.

The rule discussed here is particularly important, since we now know why increase of valency is limited. Extrapolation to compounds with higher charge would lead to negative values of the heats of formation and there would be no compound formation, because endothermic compounds cannot be stable.

The previous discussion has been limited to ions with noble-gas structure; the same phenomena occur in the highly-charged elements of the subgroups, as can be seen from the values of the heats of formation of some of the oxides, *Table XIX*, where again the

Table XIX

Heats of Formation of Subgroup Compounds in kcal per Equivalent

Cu_2O	ZnO	Ga_2O_3	GeO_2	As_2O_5	SeO_3	(Br_2O_7)
20·5	41·5	43	32	22		
Ag_2O	CdO	In_2O_3	SnO_2	Sb_2O_5	TeO_3	(I_2O_7)
3·5	30·5	37	34	23	14	
Au_2O	HgO	Tl_2O_3	PbO_2	(Bi_2O_5)		
—	10·5	20	16			

compounds with highly-charged positive ions either do not exist or cannot be prepared in the pure state.

20. INFLUENCE OF SIZE AND CHARGE OF NEGATIVE IONS ON HEAT OF FORMATION

If the halogen ion in a halide is replaced by a larger one, the heat of formation decreases, as can be seen from the examples given in *Table XX*. This fact can be deduced easily from the formula for heat of formation. Since the positive ion is unchanged, S and I remain constant and we are only concerned with the quantities D, E and U. Experiment shows that the values of both E and D decrease from F_2 to I_2, in such a way that the difference $D - E$ does not change appreciably. The change in heat of formation, caused by substitution of one halogen by another, influences only the crystal energy, and, since this quantity decreases when the radius of the negative ion increases, the fluorides have larger heats of formation than the chlorides, which again have larger values than those of the bromides, and so on (*see Table XX*).

Table XX

Heats of Formation of Halides in kcal per Equivalent

LiF	LiCl	LiBr	LiI
145·5	97·5	84	65
BaF_2	$BaCl_2$	$BaBr_2$	BaI_2
144	103	90	72·5
AlF_3	$AlCl_3$	$AlBr_3$	AlI_3
110	55·5	42	24
SiF_4	$SiCl_4$	$SiBr_4$	SiI_4
40·5	36	23	7

The replacement of a divalent negative ion by a larger one is far less simple; here the electron affinity is always negative, while the absolute value of that of the larger ion will be smaller. Thus, if a smaller ion O^{2-} is replaced by a larger one S^{2-}, this has the effect of increasing the heat of formation, but the increase will be compensated by the decrease of crystal energy. Let us compare some oxides with the corresponding sulphides. The heat of formation of the latter per equivalent will be greater by $E_O - E_S + D_O - D_S$ than those of the sulphides. The sulphur compounds will, however, have a smaller crystal energy, and the difference in the crystal energy will be all the greater the smaller the radius and the higher the charge of the positive ion. For highly-charged ions with a large crystal energy, and therefore a large value of U(oxide) minus U(sulphide), the heat of formation of sulphides will be smaller than that of oxides. Only in compounds containing very large positive ions, K^+, Rb^+ or Cs^+, of low charge, is the crystal energy, and thus the difference U(oxide) minus U(sulphide), so small that this difference cannot compensate for the difference in D and E (*see Table XXI*). The heat of formation of selenides and tellurides is lower than that of the sulphides.

Table XXI

Heats of Formation in kcal per Equivalent

	Cs	Rb	K	Na	Ca	Mg	Al
oxides	41	41·5	43·1	49·7	75·8	73·0	63·3
sulphides	43·5	44·0	44·0	44·9	57·7	41·1	23·4

Chalcides

	H	Ca	Zn	Tl
oxides	H_2O 34	CaO 76	ZnO 42	Tl_2O 21
sulphides	H_2S 4	CaS 57	ZnS 23	Tl_2S 11
selenides	H_2Se −7	CaSe 44	ZnSe 17	Tl_2Se 6
tellurides	H_2Te −17	CaTe —	ZnTe 16·5	Tl_2Te 3·5

The difference in heat of formation is even more marked between the nitrides and phosphides. By the same reasoning as for the oxides and sulphides, the alkali phosphides (where r_+ is large) should have higher heats of formation than nitrides; while the nitrides, with the exception of Li_3N, cannot be prepared, the phosphides and arsenides of the alkali metals are fairly stable compounds.

We will now investigate the way in which the heat of formation is influenced by the change in charge of the negative ion, the radius being constant. The radii of the ions F^-, O^{2-} and N^{3-} do not greatly differ, so that in the compounds LiF, Li_2O and Li_3N, the heat of formation will depend mainly on the charge of the negative ion. The effect of this charge is to be found in the change of the electron affinity E and the crystal energy U. The same difficulty is encountered here as when considering the influence of the radius of the negative ion, namely, lack of data on electron affinities. It is plausible, however, to assume that the influence of the electron affinity will be preponderant in any compounds with large positive ions of low charge where the influence of the crystal energy is relatively small so that, with increasing charge of the negative ion, the heat of formation decreases; but this rule cannot be absolutely proved. The fact that so few nitrides exist, compared with oxides and fluorides, and so few phosphides, compared with sulphides and chlorides, shows that we can accept this rule, however. The few heats of formation which are available do support its validity (*see Table XXII*).

Table XXII

Heats of Formation in kcal per Equivalent

LiF	Li_2O	Li_3N
145·5	71	15
NaF	Na_2O	Na_3N
136	49·5	~0
BaF_2	BaO	Ba_3N_2
144	65·5	30
$CaCl_2$	CaS	Ca_3P_2
95·5	57	20·0
AlF_3	Al_2O_3	AlN
110	63	27·5

The Madelung constant also plays an important part in the heat of formation. In the series

$$\begin{array}{lccc} & \text{LiF,} & \text{Li}_2\text{O,} & \text{Li}_3\text{N} \\ V = & 146 & 35{\cdot}5 & 15{\cdot}5 \ \text{kcal/equivalent} \end{array}$$

where the Madelung constant is very unfavourable for the nitride, and high for the fluoride, the decrease in the heat of formation from the fluoride to the nitride is much greater than in

	AlF_3,	Al_2O_3,	AlN	
$V =$	110	63	26·7	kcal/equivalent

where the nitride has the higher Madelung constant.

21. HEAT OF FORMATION AND ELECTRON CONFIGURATION

In a compound in which the positive ion with a rare-gas configuration is replaced by one of equal size and charge, but with an 18-electron configuration, there is considerable decrease in the heat of formation, which is caused by the greater ionization energy of the subgroup ion. On calculating, from the experimental heat of formation, the lattice energy of a compound in which the positive ion has an 18-electron configuration, it is found that this value is considerably lower than that calculated by the formula $U = (n - 1)/n \,.\, Ae^2/r$. It can be shown that this difference is directly related to the greater ionization energy of the 18-electron ion. If the ionization energy of an Ag^+ ion is greater than that of a K^+ ion, although the size of both ions is nearly equal, it follows that the Ag^+ ion exerts a greater attraction than the K^+ ion on the electron that is being removed during the ionization process. This greater attraction of an electron by the Ag^+ ion will still be active when the electron forms part of a negative ion, and it follows that, if the Ag atom has a higher ionization energy than the K atom, the Ag ion will attract negative ions more strongly than the K ion. There will, therefore, be a difference in the heat of formation of two compounds KX and AgX, the decrease of the heat of formation, due to the higher ionization energy of silver, being counteracted by the higher lattice energy of the silver compound. Since the first effect will always be greater than the second, the heat of formation of a compound will be reduced if the positive ion is replaced by one with a higher ionization energy but of equal size and charge.

A silver ion can be imagined to be formed from a potassium ion by adding ten positive units to the nucleus and surrounding the ion by ten more *d* electrons. If it is found by this process that the attraction of a negative charge at a distance r is increased, it follows that the effect of the positive charge, which is added to the nucleus, is not completely annihilated by the ten electrons; or, in other words, the ten *f* electrons do not completely screen the ten positive units added to the nucleus. Since there is no appreciable change when eight positive units of nuclear charge and eight electrons ($s^2 + p^6$) are added to a sodium ion to form a potassium ion, it follows that the s^2p^6 shell has a better screening effect than the ten d electrons. This imperfect screening effect of the d^{10} electrons, as compared with that of a shell of s and p electrons, is associated with the differing forms of the orbitals, as expressed in the older quantum theory, and with varying distributions of the electrons, according to modern quantum mechanics. It is to be expected that the screening by a shell of electrons will decrease as the series $s, p, d, f, \ldots$ progresses and is very poor for incomplete shells.

If this assumption is made, many more details of the heat of formation as a function of electron configuration can be readily explained. All examples will be taken from the group of the chlorides (*see Table XXIII*), for which many data on heats of formation are known. However, the statements can be verified in other cases as well. The $3d^{10}$ shell is completed in the fourth period from Sc to Ni. In this group the heats of formation of many dichlorides have been measured.

Table XXIII

	$CaCl_2$	$TiCl_2$	VCl_2	$CrCl_2$	$MnCl_2$	$FeCl_2$	$CoCl_2$	$NiCl_2$	$CuCl_2$	$ZnCl_2$
heat of formation (kcal/equivalent)	95	57		48	56	41	37	36·5	27	50
number of d electrons	0	2	3	4	5	6	7	8	9	10

Comparing the heats of formation with that of $CaCl_2$, in which compound the positive ion has a rare-gas structure, there is a steady decrease with increasing number of d electrons, until, in Mn^{2+}, the d group is half-filled. The higher heat of formation of $MnCl_2$ demonstrates the greater stability of the half-filled d^5 group. After $MnCl_2$, the decrease of the heat of formation continues. The increase at the end of the period is due to the completion of the $3d^{10}$ group in the Zn^{2+} ion.

There are only few data on the trichlorides, but here again the same decrease is observed, and again there is the higher value for $FeCl_3$, because of the half-filling of the $3d^{10}$ shell. A similar behaviour is found in the fourth group, where the $4d^{10}$ shell is completed, and in the lanthanide group (*see Table XXIV*), where the $4f^{14}$ shell is formed, the heats of formation decreasing with increasing numbers of these electrons.

Table XXIV

Heats of Formation in kcal per Equivalent

	La	Ce	Pr	Nd	Pm
	87·9	86·6	85·9	84·8	—
lanthanide chlorides	Sm	Eu	Gd	Tb	Dy
	—	—	817	—	79·2
	Ho	Er	Tm	Yb	Lu
	77·6	77·3	76·5	—	75·9
fifth period (after silver)	AgCl	$CdCl_2$	$InCl_3$	$SnCl_4$	
	49	82	43	32	
sixth period (after gold)	AuCl	$HgCl_2$	$TlCl_3$	$PbCl_4$	
	8	27	20	~20	
pentoxides of the nitrogen group	N_2O_5	P_2O_5	As_2O_5	Sb_2O_5	Bi_2O_5
	1·3	36	22	23	15
lower chlorides of the 4th and 5th subgroups	NCl_3	PCl_3	$AsCl_3$	$SbCl_3$	$BiCl_3$
	−18	26	24	30	30
			$GeCl_2$	$SnCl_2$	$PbCl_2$
			—	40	43

In the subgroups, too, a remarkable influence of the electron configuration on the heat of formation is observed. In the fifth group, nitrogen, arsenicum and bismuth form trichlorides only, phosphorus and antimony, however, form pentachlorides. Let us assume for a moment that the non-existence of the pentachlorides of the three other elements is caused by a lower heat of formation, so that $V(NCl_5) < V(PCl_5)$, $V(PCl_5) > V(AsCl_5)$, $V(AsCl_5) < V(SbCl_5)$ and $V(SbCl_5) > V(BiCl_5)$. The increase from NCl_5 and PCl_5 can be attributed to the greater radius of the P^{5+} ion. The decrease then, from PCl_5 to $AsCl_5$, is due to the change of the electronic configuration from $3s^2 . 3p^6$ to $4s^2 . 4p^6 . 4d^{10}$ (18-electron configuration) in $AsCl_5$. The configuration remains the same in $SbCl_5$, and, because of the greater radius of the Sb^{5+} ion, there is a slight increase of the heat of formation. The lower value for $BiCl_5$ has still to be explained.

The heats of formation of all compounds in the sixth period (after gold) are all much lower than those in the fifth (after silver), as is seen in *Table XXIV*. In the former compounds, the screening of the 18-electron shell seems to be particularly incomplete, probably as a result of the underlying thirty-two shell ($s^2\ p^6\ d^{10} f^{14}$) that has been completed in the same period, in the lanthanide group. The alternation of the heats of formation in the chlorides of the subgroups is observed in other compounds, too: the oxides of the nitrogen group afford a good example. The alternation is not observed in compounds of lower valency in the subgroups, where the ions still have their two s electrons. This s^2 group giving perfect screening, the imperfect screening of the underlying groups is almost annihilated in the halides. In the trichlorides of the fifth subgroup (*Table XXIV*), the decrease with increasing radius of the positive ion has disappeared. In the trioxides, where the lattice energy is more important, there remains a decrease from $V(Sb_2O_3) = 28$ to $V(Bi_2O_3) = 23$ kcal per equivalent.

22. STABILITY OF COMPOUNDS

The relation between heat of formation and stability is not a simple one. A compound will be unstable at low temperatures if its heat of formation is negative; if the compound is formed from one element that is solid at room temperature and a second element that is gaseous, the pressure of the latter will be higher than one atmosphere if the heat of formation per mol gas formed is lower than $T\Delta S$, or 300×35 cal $= \sim 10$ kcal. A halide, therefore, will be unstable at room temperature for it will decompose into its compounds when V (heat of formation per equivalent) is smaller than $\frac{1}{2} \times 10$ kcal, because two equivalents must decompose to form one mol of halogen (for an oxide this limit is $\frac{1}{4} \times 10$ kcal and for a nitride $\frac{1}{6} \times 10$ kcal). Thus, in spite of a heat of formation as low as 2 kcal per equivalent, a nitride will be perfectly stable at room temperature.

It is due to the decrease of the heat of formation that, at the end of the periods, the highest halides, oxides, sulphides and nitrides become unstable. In the second period no normal halides are formed after carbon. In the third period the fluorides extend to SF_6, in the fifth group to IF_7. The normal oxides, too, extend to higher valencies in the third period, where are SO_3 and Cl_2O_7, than in the second, where N_2O_5 is the highest oxide.

Compounds like carbides and silicides, that on decomposition do not form a gaseous phase, may be stable up to very high temperatures, although their heat of formation is very low; CSi, with a heat of formation of 27 per mol, or 6·7 kcal per equivalent, decomposes only at ~2000°C, when the silicon becomes volatile. On the other hand, compounds may be very unstable, although their heat of formation is considerable, if they can decompose in any reaction other than that of decomposition into their components.

The heat of formation of $SbCl_5$ is 105 kcal per equivalent; it would therefore require 42 kcal per mol Cl_2 to decompose the compound into antimony and chlorine. This reaction can occur only at high temperatures, i.e. above 1000°K, and thus, if only the decomposition reaction is considered, the compound can be said to be very stable. There is, however, another reaction that requires much less energy, viz. the decomposition into a compound of lower valency. The reaction

$$SbCl_5 \rightarrow SbCl_3 + Cl_2 - Q$$

in which Q is equal to the difference in heat of formation (per mol) of $SbCl_5$ and $SbCl_3$, requires only 13 kcal per mol Cl_2. This reaction, therefore, will occur at a much lower temperature than the total decomposition. If $SbCl_5$ is heated, it will dissociate into $SbCl_3$ and Cl_2 at a relatively low temperature, but further dissociation of $SbCl_3$ will require a much higher temperature. Another example of a compound that easily decomposes into compounds of lower valency, but where total decomposition requires a much higher temperature, is chromium tetrachloride

$$2CrCl_4 \rightarrow 2CrCl_3 + Cl_2 + 24 \text{ kcal}$$
$$2CrCl_3 \rightarrow 2CrCl_2 + Cl_2 - 70 \text{ kcal}$$
$$CrCl_2 \rightarrow Cr + Cl_2 - 97 \text{ kcal}$$

The compound $CrCl_4$ is unstable at room temperature, while $CrCl_3$ is very stable and decomposes into Cl_2, and the next lower chloride $CrCl_2$ only at very high temperature. This dichloride again is so stable that the actual decomposition into its components cannot be observed. Other examples are

$$4CrO_3 \rightarrow 2Cr_2O_3 + 3O_2 - 16 \text{ kcal}$$
$$2Cr_2O_3 \rightarrow Cr + 3O_2 - 540 \text{ kcal}$$
$$UCl_6 \rightarrow UCl_4 + Cl_2 - 12 \text{ kcal}$$
$$UCl_4 \rightarrow U + 2Cl_2 - 125 \text{ kcal}$$
$$2MnO_2 \rightarrow 2MnO + O_2 - 64 \text{ kcal}$$
$$2MnO \rightarrow Mn + O_2 - 184 \text{ kcal}$$

The existence of stable lower compounds often provides the explanation of the unexpected instability of higher compounds.

According to the rule for the heat of formation as a function of the radius of the positive ion, $V(VCl_5)$ should be larger than $V(PCl_5)$, $V(CrF_6)$ larger than $V(SF_6)$ and $V(UCl_6)$ larger than $V(WCl_6)$. In actual fact, VCl_5 and CrF_6 are not known to exist, and UCl_6 is certainly less stable than WCl_6. In the same way, the heat of formation of UO_3 is larger than WO_3, although, again, WO_3 is much more stable than UO_3. In all cases, the reason for the instability is a very high heat of formation of the lower compound. Because $V(WCl_4)$ is lower than $V(UCl_4)$, less energy is required for the decomposition

$$UCl_6 \rightarrow UCl_4 + Cl_2 - 12 \text{ kcal}$$

than for the corresponding reaction of WCl_6. This is further demonstrated by the following examples

$$2UO_3 \rightarrow 2UO_2 + O_2 - 72 \text{ kcal}$$
$$2WO_3 \rightarrow 2WO_2 + O_2 - 130 \text{ kcal}$$

The reason for the great heat of formation of the lower compound is either a particularly stable electron configuration or the fact that the first-ionization energies are low.

For vanadium and chromium the first ionization energies are much lower than the first ionization energies of phosphorus and sulphur, respectively. This explains the high heats of formation of VCl_3 and $CrCl_3$. In uranium, the tetravalent state is more stable than that in tungsten because uranium as an actinide has a different electron configuration.

Instability of a compound may also be caused by a *disproportionation.* This term is used for reactions in which a compound decomposes into a higher compound and an element or a compound of lower valency. For example

$$2CuF \rightarrow Cu + CuF_2$$

The compound CuF cannot be prepared. From the rule that the heat of formation always increases when a halogen ion is replaced by a smaller one, it follows that CuF has a greater heat of formation than CuCl. Therefore, if the former compound does not exist, the reason for this non-existence cannot be a low heat of formation, and the instability is thus due to the fact that the heat of formation per equivalent is higher for the compound of higher valency.

It has been found that, in the halide group, the lower fluorides often have a tendency to disproportionation, whereas the iodides tend to decompose into lower compounds. Both reactions are determined not by the absolute magnitude of the heat of formation, but by the differences in the heat of formation of the successive compounds, as can be easily shown from the form of the curve that is obtained when the heat of formation (per mol in this case) of a group of compounds, e.g. halides AX, AX_2, AX_3, AX_4, is plotted against valency.

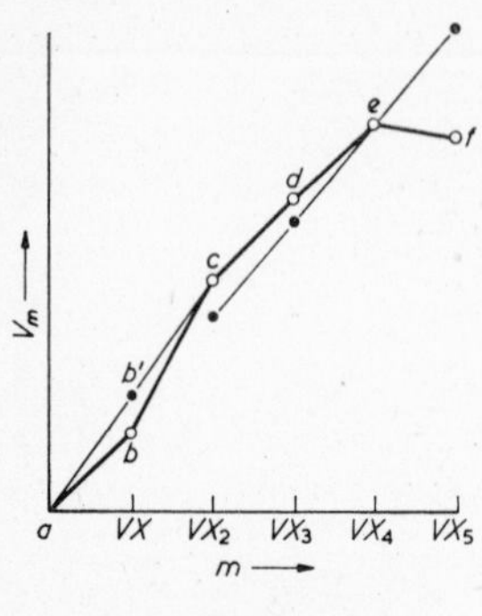

Figure 15

Let us assume that this is done for an element of valency 5. The heats of formation of the compounds (*see Figure 15*) VX, VX_2, VX_3, VX_4 and VX_5 that are determined by the quantities S, $(D - E)$, $\sum I_i$ and U are represented by dots. It is evident that the compound VX_5 is unstable, for since

$$V_m(AX_5) < V_m(AX_4)$$

the reaction

$$2AX_4 + X_2(g) \rightarrow 2AX_5$$

has a negative heat effect. Since there is not an increase in entropy, assuming AX_4 and AX_5 to be solids, this reaction can never occur. Even if we try to prepare the compound by another method, it will always tend to decompose into AX_4 and X_2, unless the speed of this reaction happens to be very slow. AX_4, however, is a stable compound because its heat of formation is higher than that of any of the lower compounds.

The compound VX would not be stable, either. By drawing the line *ac* we find a point b' that represents one-half of the heat of formation of a mixture of one mol A and one mol AX_2. Since this is greater than the heat of formation of one mol of AX, the heat effect of the reaction

$$2AX \rightarrow A + AX_2$$

is positive. Thus AX cannot exist, unless the speed of the disproportionation reaction is very low. The other compounds, AX_2 and AX_3, can both exist, since the line that connects *a* with *d* passes below *c*, and the line that connects *c* with *e* passes below *d*.

Four lower chlorides of platinum, PtCl, $PtCl_2$, $PtCl_3$ and $PtCl_4$, have been described, and the heats of formation per equivalent are almost equal. The heats of formation per mol, plotted against valency, therefore lie almost on a straight line (*see Figure 16*). Now if the successive chlorides ACl, ACl_2, ACl_3, ... lie on a straight line, it can be shown that all fluorides, except that with the highest valency, are unstable, because they all will disproportionate into the metal and the highest fluoride. From the curve of the chlorides, that of the fluorides can be obtained by adding the difference in the heats of formation, which, according to Section 20, is equal to the difference of the lattice energies. Since the lattice energy of both chlorides and fluorides is a quadratic function of the valency *m*, the

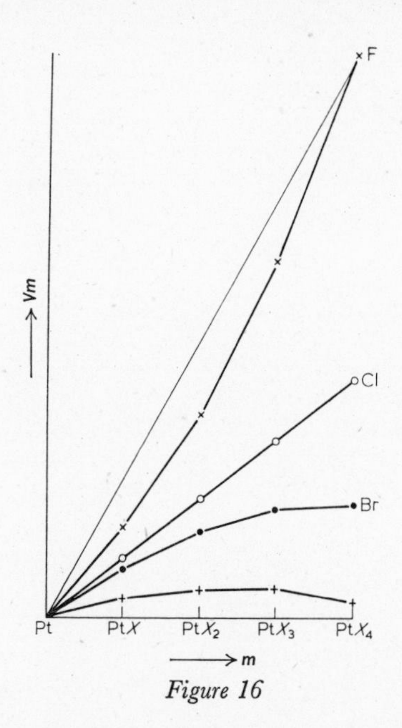

Figure 16

difference will be almost a quadratic function, too, that, when added to the linear curve of the chlorides, will give a fluoride curve that is convex towards the V_m axis. It thus follows that all the lower fluorides will be unstable, the disproportionation reactions having a positive heat effect. It is easily seen, by applying the same reasoning to the bromide curve, that the latter is concave to the V_m axis and all the bromides will be stable, but the concavity of the iodide curve may be so strong that a maximum appears, in which case one or two of the higher iodides will become unstable.

The chloride curve usually is not a straight line: the stability diagram then is more complicated than for the platinum halides, but it always shows, as typical features, the non-existence of the lower fluorides and the instability, or non-existence, of the highest iodides. Some typical examples are given in *Table XXV*. There are a few cases in which there are deviations from this rule, e.g. in the rhenium halides (*see Table XXV*), where the fluorides are ReF_4 and ReF_6 and the chlorides are $ReCl_3$ and $ReCl_5$. No explanation of this situation can be given: the whole set of rhenium halides would become normal if the recent observation, that ReF_4 does not exist, turned out to be correct. Between oxides XO_m and sulphides XS_m

Table XXV

Compound Stability

	vanadium halides					*copper halides*	
fluorides	—	—	VF_3	VF_4	VF_5	—	CuF_2
chlorides	—	VCl_2	VCl_3	VCl_4		CuCl	$CuCl_2$
bromides	—	VBr_2	VBr_3			CuBr	$CuBr_2$
iodides	—	VI_2				CuI	

	rhenium halides					
fluorides	—	—	—	(RhF_4)	—	RhF_6
chlorides	—	—	$RhCl_3$	—	$RhCl_5$	
bromides	—	—	$RhBr_3$			
iodides	—	—	RhI_3			

	iron calcides		
oxides	—	Fe_3O_4	Fe_2O_3
sulphides	FeS	—	—

there is a difference similar to that between fluorides and chlorides, but in the first set there is a complication. In the difference V(oxide) — V(sulphide), the difference $\Delta(D - E)$ cannot be neglected. This, however, will not lead to an essentially different situation, the V_m versus V curve being steeper for the oxide than for the sulphide. Accordingly, it is found that EuS is a stable compound, but EuO cannot be prepared, and FeO is not stable (*see Table XXV*), whereas there is no higher sulphide.

By considering the rules for the heat of formation and stability it is possible, in the case of the halides, to explain in detail the existence or non-existence of a certain compound. Only in a very few cases are there any discrepancies between theory and experience, and these discrepancies are observed mainly in the group of halides formed from non-metallic elements. In this group the rules derived for ionic compounds often do not apply because another type of chemical binding replaces the ionic form. In the oxides, as well, the existence or non-existence of compounds can be explained with the aid of the theory of the ionic bond, but there are, here again, some deviations. In the sulphide group, the deviations become more important, and it can be concluded that in the sequence halides → oxides → sulphides → nitrides, the influence of non-ionic binding becomes more important.

23. HYDROGEN COMPOUNDS

The first element in the periodic system has such characteristic properties that it requires separate discussion. Hydrogen occupies a place in the periodic system immediately before the noble gas helium, from which we conclude that hydrogen, like other elements immediately preceding a noble gas, should be capable of taking up one electron and forming a univalent negative ion in the same manner as a halogen. In the formation of molecules, hydrogen is, indeed, analogous to halogens, fitting into the series H_2, F_2, Cl_2, Br_2, I_2. The tendency of hydrogen to form negative ions is most marked when it reacts with elements which can easily give up electrons. In fact, when alkali- or alkaline-earth metals are heated in hydrogen, hydrides are formed which are comparable with the halides. For example, the alkali hydrides have the same crystal structure as the halides, and the fact that the electrolysis of molten LiH and CaH_2 produces hydrogen at the positive electrode shows that the H ion occurs as a negative ion in the hydrides.

The radius of the negative H^- ion can be calculated from the interionic distance of Li^+ and H^-, and is found to be as large as that of the F^- ion. (PAULING calculated a somewhat larger value for the H^- ion.) Applying the stability rules, therefore, we could conclude that the hydrides should be approximately as stable as the fluorides. If this conclusion were correct, more hydrides would be known and they would be less easily dissociated into metal and hydrogen. In point of fact, the crystal energies of the hydrides are of the same order as those of the corresponding fluorides, but the other quantities, D and E, which occur in the formula, are very different from those of the halogens.

The dissociation energy of the hydrogen molecule is considerably greater than that of fluorine, while its electron affinity, on the other hand, is considerably smaller; the reason for this small value was discussed previously. The hydrides, as a group, obey the general stability rules very well, the most stable being those of the alkali metals. If the charge increases, the stability decreases, mostly for elements with small ionic radii, with the result that there are no hydrides of Be and Mg in the second group of the periodic system. In the third group there are hydrides of lanthanum and the other rare earths, but none of B and Al, nor probably of Sc. These hydrides, however, contain less hydrogen than corresponds to the

Table XXVI

Heats of Formation of Hydrogen Compounds in kcal per Equivalent

HF	HCl	HBr	HI
95	22	8·5	−6
H_2O	H_2S	H_2Se	H_2Te
34	2·5	−8	−17
H_3N	H_3P	H_3As	H_3Sb
5	+2	−14	−11·5

formula XH_3*. In the fourth group there are no normal hydrides of the type XH_4, but there are some compounds known, however, that have a lower hydrogen content.

While hydrogen can be compared with the halogens, it is also, in some respects, analogous to the alkali metals. In common with these it possesses one isolated valency electron, and therefore can form univalent positive ions and compounds in which the existence of positive hydrogen ions can be assumed. In *Table XXVI* are given the heats of formation of twelve hydrogen compounds. Probably the heat of formation of H_3Sb does not fit into the scheme, because the heats of formation of this compound and of H_3As are not accurately known.

When we now compare these compounds with the corresponding sodium ones, we find very large differences between them; the most striking being that, whereas the sodium compounds are all solid substances of low volatility, those of hydrogen are, without exception, very volatile. Water has the highest boiling point of them all, but

* The composition of lanthanum hydride is $LaH_{2\cdot8}$. This is a striking example of a chemical compound, the composition of which changes with changing pressure and temperature. Such a compound probably ought to be regarded as a mixed crystal of the hydride with the metal, in the sense that a number of H ions are replaced in the lattice by electrons. In the last ten years a number of such compounds have become known, especially among the oxides (*see* Section 24).

even that is only 100°C. From the discussion in Section 12, we should hardly expect these particular compounds to be so volatile. The reason, however, is the unique structure of the H^+ ion. When a hydrogen atom becomes a positive ion, it loses its one electron, the H^+ ion being simply a hydrogen nucleus, or proton. H^+ is therefore an ion without an electron cloud, and is the only known example of such an ion*. All other ions, because of their electron clouds, repel

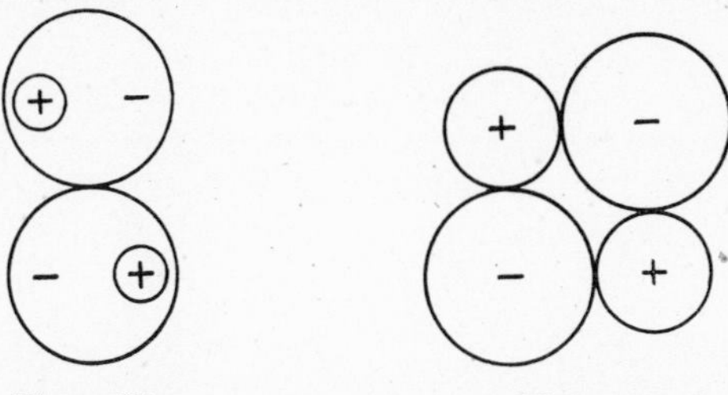

Figure 17 *Figure 18*

one another as soon as they come to within a certain distance of each other. Hydrogen, however, has nothing to prevent its approach to, and actual penetration of, the electron cloud of a negative ion, its final position being determined by the repulsion of the nucleus of the negative ion.

In a molecule such as HCl, the molecule is, as it were, itself an electron cloud in which there are two nuclei, one belonging to the Cl^- ion and the other to the H^+ ion. As can be seen from a diagram of two such molecules (*Figure 17*), there will be a much smaller attraction between them than between two molecules of NaCl, shown in *Figure 18*. The HCl molecules obviously cannot form a lattice of the same type as NaCl unless the hydrogen nuclei are brought to the periphery of the Cl^- ion, which would require a large amount of energy. Thus, for HCl, a molecular lattice will be formed rather than a coordinated one. This will be accompanied by a small release of energy, resulting in a much smaller heat of sublimation than for NaCl, which explains the high volatility of hydrogen compounds.

The influence of the penetration by the hydrogen ion on the volatility of compounds can be appreciated in another way. As long as the H ion is on the periphery of the Cl^- ion, the molecule will, in many respects, resemble that of NaCl, possessing analogous properties, but if the positive H^+ ion could penetrate the molecule so that it

* Ions, such as He^{2+}, Li^{3+}, etc., have no existence in chemical compounds, for in contact with other atoms they would immediately take up electrons as a result of their high ionization energies.

eventually coincided with the nucleus of the Cl^- ion, we would then have, substantially, an argon atom. Such a fictitious process would increase the nuclear charge of the Cl^- ion by one; the actual HCl molecule therefore has properties intermediate between those of NaCl and an argon atom, and resembles the latter in its high volatility. The penetration of the electron cloud by the hydrogen ion will naturally alter the electronic configuration of the negative ion, so that there is actually little point in considering the HCl molecule as a combination of two ions.

Penetration by the hydrogen ion certainly alters the character of an ionic compound, and there is much to be said for considering the altered compound as a homopolar compound, which will be dealt with in greater detail later, but treating HCl as a true homopolar compound unfortunately does not enable us to predict any of its properties. It is, therefore, instructive to consider it as a distorted ionic structure, and to attempt to predict its properties in a qualitative manner. HCl always behaves as a normal ionic compound in its reactions with oxides, which will be referred to again in Section 27.

Hydrogen compounds containing a positive H^+ ion provide one of the best examples of the use of the stability rules which have been derived for ionic compounds. *Table XXVI* gives the heats of formation, which decrease continuously as the size of the ion and its charge increase, HF having the largest value and H_3Sb the smallest. Even without knowing the heats of formation, it can be shown that the stability rules hold. Thus HF is a very stable compound, while HI is much less stable and dissociates into H_2 and I_2 at 400°C and 1 atmosphere. Again, water is a fairly stable compound and dissociates at 2000°C into H_2 and O_2. The dissociation of water cannot be compared directly with that of HF because there are no data on the dissociation of the latter at high temperatures, but it can be compared with ammonia which would be expected to show marked dissociation at much lower temperatures.

In the manufacture of ammonia the temperature is not taken above 600°C because the equilibrium is then displaced towards the side of nitrogen and hydrogen. H_2S is less stable than H_2O because of the larger radius of its negative ion, while H_2Se and H_2Te are less stable still. PH_3 is less stable than NH_3, and AsH_3 and SbH_3 decompose so easily that it is very difficult to prepare them in the pure state. The hydrogen compounds therefore obey the stability rules of the heteropolar compounds.

As regards ionic dissociation, this will occur more easily the smaller the charge and the larger the radius, so that HI will split most easily into ions, while NH_3 will be the most difficult. Ionic dissociation is a process requiring a large quantity of energy; it is never observed in a pure substance, but is only detected when the pure substance is dissolved in a suitable solvent in which the ions formed combine with the molecules of the solvent, thus compensating for a part of the ionization energy required. Easy dissociation of this group of compounds in water means that they behave as strong acids, and we come therefore to the conclusion, in complete agreement with experience, that HI is the strongest acid of the whole group. HF, because of the smaller radius of the negative F^- ion, should therefore be a weaker acid, which in fact it is. This is not always understood, for it is often assumed that because HF attacks glass and metals strongly, it is therefore a strong acid. Of the compounds in the second column, H_2S is known to be a weak acid, yet it dissociates more easily into ions than H_2O. The dissociation constants for the four calcides are given in *Table XXVII.* By comparison, the dissociation constant of acetic acid is $K = 1{\cdot}9 \times 10^{-5}$.

Table XXVII

Dissociation Constants of the Calcides

substance	H_2O	H_2S	H_2Se	H_2Te
dissociation constant K	$1{\cdot}2 \times 10^{-16}$	$9{\cdot}1 \times 10^{-8}$	2×10^{-4}	2×10^{-3}

The influence of the charge is clearly seen from the fact that H_2S is a weak acid as compared with HCl. The weakest acid is NH_3; that is, it has such a low tendency to split off H^+ ions that the opposite phenomenon nearly always occurs, and it takes up H^+ ions to form the NH_4^+ ion. It will be seen later that this behaviour must be ascribed to the very strong attraction exerted by the tervalent negative nitrogen ion.

A very good picture of some of the properties of hydrogen compounds can be obtained with the aid of an electrostatic model, but we must be careful not to conclude that all the hydrogen compounds are therefore ionic in character. In addition to NH_3, there are two other nitrogen compounds, hydrazine H_2NNH_2 and hydroxylamine NH_2OH, which have properties not fundamentally dissimilar to those of ammonia. It is not possible to devise a plausible electrostatic model for these compounds because of the bond between like atoms. In addition to water there is also the compound hydrogen peroxide, H_2O_2, and a number of sulphur compounds with the composition H_2S_n, in which n can be as high as 5. There is also the compound H_2PPH_2, which is analogous to H_2NNH_2.

Finally, there are the hydrogen compounds of the fourth group, CH_4, SiH_4 and GeH_4, for which no satisfactory picture is possible on the basis of either positive or negative hydrogen ions; in this group there are also many hydrogen compounds in which bonds between like atoms occur. There are, as well, several remarkable hydrogen compounds of boron, for which no electrostatic models are possible.

24. COMPOUNDS OF VARIABLE COMPOSITION

When an element like titanium is heated in an excess of fluorine, chlorine, bromine, oxygen or sulphur, all electrons outside the rare-gas shell are removed from the atom, and the 'normal' compounds TiF_4, $TiCl_4$, TiO_2 and TiS_2 are formed, in which the titanium ions have a 'normal' rare-gas configuration. Compounds of higher valency cannot be formed, but from the compounds with maximum valency, compounds of lower valency can be obtained by reduction. It will be assumed that this reduction is effected by using metallic titanium as the reducing agent: all stable compounds of the lower valency AX_p can always be obtained from the normal compound AX_n by reduction with the metal A. This method has the advantage that no products other than the lower compounds can be formed. Thus if $TiCl_4$ is heated with titanium in a closed vessel, the final product will depend on the Ti : $TiCl_4$ ratio. If the ratio is exactly 1 : 1, the final product will be pure $TiCl_2$

$$Ti + TiCl_4 \rightarrow 2TiCl_2$$

If the ratio is 1 : 3, the final product will be $TiCl_3$

$$Ti + 3TiCl_4 \rightarrow 4TiCl_3$$

If the ratio falls between these two ratios, a mixture of $TiCl_2$ and $TiCl_3$ will be formed, and microscopic examination or x-ray diffraction will show the product to consist of two kinds of crystals, one of $TiCl_2$, the other of $TiCl_3$.

A different result will be observed when the oxide TiO_2 is reduced with titanium. Ti and TiO_2, in the ratios 1 : 1 and 1 : 3, will yield TiO and Ti_2O_3, respectively, but intermediate ratios will not always yield a mixture of the two substances. In other words, one single kind of crystal, with an intermediate composition, will be formed, instead of two kinds of crystals with the compositions TiO and Ti_2O_3.

Whereas the crystals of the dichloride have the constant composition $TiCl_2$, the crystals of the corresponding oxide TiO can be prepared either with titanium or with oxygen in excess, the composition ranging from $Ti_{1-x}O$ to TiO_{1+y}, where x and y are variables. Titanium oxide is not an exception: the greater part of all oxides derived from polyvalent metallic elements have a variable composition. The limiting values for x and y are markedly different for different oxides; in some cases they are so low that the oxide has practically a constant composition, in other cases the limits are very wide, as, for example, in the oxides of cerium where there is a continuous range of composition between Ce_2O_3 and CeO_2.

Since cerium ions have only the charges three and four, and intermediate values are excluded, and since the oxygen ions always have a charge of minus two, a cerium oxide with a composition between Ce_2O_3 and CeO_2, e.g. Ce_4O_7 or $CeO_{1\cdot75}$, must contain Ce^{3+} and Ce^{4+} ions in the proportion 1 : 1, and the product, forming one single phase, can be described as a *solid solution* of the two oxides, not a mixture of the two. A mixture of the two oxides would consist of two phases, viz. separate CeO_2 and Ce_2O_3 particles or crystals.

Solid solutions, or mixed crystals, may be formed between two compounds that contain similar molecules or similar ions. If CBr_4 crystallizes from a solution that contains CCl_4 molecules as well as CBr_4 molecules, some of the CCl_4 molecules are taken in by the growing CBr_4 crystals, and the product formed can be described as a crystal of CBr_4, in which part of the CBr_4 crystals are replaced by CCl_4 molecules, which are not very different from CBr_4 molecules, either in form or size. The molecules C_2Cl_6 or C_2Cl_4 will not form solid solutions with CBr_4: these molecules are too different in shape, and therefore do not fit easily into the CBr_4 lattice.

Ionic crystals can form solid solutions, too. KBr, in the presence of KCl, will form crystals, in which some of the Br ions are substituted by Cl ions. If KCl is in excess, a KCl crystal is formed with some of the chlorine ions replaced by bromine ions. Smaller ions, like F^-, or larger, like I^-, do not replace Br^- ions in KBr in considerable quantities; KF and KBr do not form solid solutions, unless at high temperature or between very narrow limits. In chloride: bromide systems the composition of the solid solution may range from pure chloride to pure bromide.

Substitution of Cl^- for Br^- in a bromide will always cause a deformation of the lattice, because Cl^- and Br^- are not exactly equal. Thus the energy of the solid solution will be always higher than that of its two components, and if it were not for the greater entropy of the solid solution, these solid solutions would not be formed at all.

If the solid solution contains one mol of the compound A and

$(1 - \alpha)$ mol of B, the energy change can often be represented by $-\alpha(1 - \alpha)M$ (*see* Section 52), where M is a constant dependent on the two compounds, being smaller the more similar the compounds. The change in entropy is $R\{\alpha \ln \alpha + (1 - \alpha) \ln (1 - \alpha)\}$ per mol mixture. From these data the saturation concentration, as a function of temperature, can be calculated. There is not an essential difference between the behaviour of liquid and solid solutions. The mutual solubility decreases with decreasing temperature, becoming zero at $T = 0°K$.

Two chlorides of the same element, such as $TiCl_2$ and $TiCl_4$, usually will not form solutions because the molecules are too different in form. In actual fact, $TiCl_4$ will have a molecular lattice consisting of separate molecules, whereas $TiCl_2$ has a so-called layer lattice (*see* Section 42), in which, as in a coordination lattice, no separate molecules can be distinguished. Thus, substitution of $TiCl_2$ by $TiCl_4$, or vice versa, to any considerable extent is impossible because of the different structure of their crystal lattices.

For the oxides, the situation is quite different. Whether a compound AB_n will form a coordination lattice or a molecular lattice, or one of intermediate type, depends mainly on the cation: anion ratio. If this ratio is higher than 1 : 3, the molecules will usually be completely screened and form a molecular lattice: if it is below 1 : 3, the lattice will be a coordination lattice. The three titanium oxides, TiO, Ti_2O_3 and TiO_2, in actual fact have coordination lattices, TiO forming a NaCl lattice and TiO_2 a rutile lattice (*see* Section 15). In a coordination lattice, e.g. in TiO, some of the positive ions can be substituted by ions of a higher charge. It is in this way that three Ti^{2+} ions can be substituted by two Ti^{3+} ions. By this process the electrical neutrality is maintained, and it can be shown that this process will not be connected with a very great change in energy. However, this substitution will cause some of the positions of the positive ions to be unoccupied. If 30 per cent of the Ti^{2+} ions are substituted by 20 per cent of Ti^{3+} ions, 10 per cent of the Ti^{2+} positions will be unoccupied. It can be shown that both by the introduction of the 20 per cent Ti^{3+} ions as well as by the formation of the 10 per cent gaps, the entropy is increased. The product of the formula $Ti^{2+}_{0\cdot70}\, Ti^{3+}_{0\cdot20}O^{2-}$ has not only a higher energy, but a higher entropy as well: it will therefore be stable at a sufficiently high temperature, but not at low temperatures, where it decomposes into two phases, one containing a preponderance of Ti^{2+} ions and one a preponderance of Ti^{3+} ions. In equilibrium, at very low temperature, it would form the two pure oxides, TiO and Ti_2O_3.

The compounds with variable composition become very interesting if the pure compound does not exist. An example of this behaviour is found among the oxides of iron. Since iron in many compounds is divalent, an oxide FeO is to be expected. However, a compound of this composition cannot be prepared, because this oxide disproportionates into iron and the higher oxide (Section 22)

$$4FeO \rightarrow Fe + Fe_3O_4$$

this reaction being slightly exothermic. The oxide Fe_3O_4 will be discussed later in the section on complex oxides. At room temperature there is no ferrous oxide. If, however, a mixture of iron and Fe_3O_4 (or Fe_2O_3), in the right proportion, is heated to a temperature of 570°C, an oxide phase with a composition $FeO_{1\cdot07}$ or $Fe_{0\cdot93}O$ appears. X-ray analysis of this compound has shown that this phase, as is to be expected for FeO, has the NaCl structure in so far as the oxygen ions are concerned, but the Fe^{2+} ions are partially replaced by Fe^{3+}, which process involves the formation of a certain number of gaps in the Fe positions. On one mol of oxygen there are Fe^{2+} ions, Fe^{3+} ions and gaps in such numbers that electric neutrality is maintained, and the formula of the compound can be written

$$Fe^{2+}_{0\cdot79}\ Fe^{3+}_{0\cdot14}\ \square_{0\cdot07}\ O_{1\cdot00}$$

Although the energy of this compound is higher than that of FeO, it is stabilized at higher temperature because it has a greater entropy, the Fe^{2+} ions being partially replaced by Fe^{3+} ions and gaps. The formula for the entropy would be

$$R(0\cdot79 \ln 0\cdot79 + 0\cdot14 \ln 0\cdot14 + 0\cdot07 \ln 0\cdot07)$$

The phase $Fe_{0\cdot93}O$ can be described as a solid solution of 0·79 mol FeO and 0·07 mol Fe_2O_3. At higher temperature, phases with other compositions become stable, but the composition never reaches that of the pure compound FeO. The pure compound FeO does not exist: it only occurs when stabilized by some admixture of Fe_2O_3. In the stabilized form, the Fe^{2+} and Fe^{3+} ions and the gaps are distributed at random over the cation positons in the NaCl lattice.

It will depend on the special form of the lattice and the possible valencies what kind of solid solution, with cation and anion gaps, is formed. In some cases, both processes can take place simultaneously: it has been found that the compound CbO has a NaCl lattice, with 25 per cent gaps in both the Cb^{2+} and O^{2-} positions.

Compounds with non-stoichiometric, or variable, compositions are very common, not only in oxides, but in sulphides, selenides, nitrides, phosphides and carbides as well. They cannot be formed if the metal from which they are derived has only one valency. CaO, BaO, etc. therefore have a strictly stoichiometric composition, except at very high temperature, where they lose oxygen and the metal dissolves in the oxide.

If, in a compound, gaps in either the anion or the cation lattice are formed, the effect will be an increase in the entropy. In spite of the fact that the energy of NaCl will be greatly increased if gaps in the lattice are formed, at high temperature there will be a (small) number of holes, both in the Na^+ and the Cl^- positions. The deficiencies of the lattice have a very important influence on the physical properties. If there are gaps in the lattice, ions of both kinds can easily move into adjacent positions, with the result that the solid compound becomes an electrolytic conductor; this is what occurs in NaCl near the melting point.

If a compound contains two ions of different valency it may become an electronic conductor. NiO is not an electronic conductor, because, if electrons move from one Ni^{2+} ion to another, a pair $Ni^{2+} + Ni^{2+}$ is changed into a pair $Ni^{3+} + Ni^+$, in which both ions have unusual, unstable valencies. Now suppose that part of the Ni^{2+} ions are substituted by Ni^{3+} ions. Then an electron can travel from a Ni^{2+} ion to a Ni^{3+} ion, forming a Ni^{3+} ion from the first and changing the second into a Ni^{2+} ion

$$Ni^{2+} + Ni^{3+} \underset{\textit{electron}}{\rightarrow} Ni^{3+} + Ni^{2+}$$

Now the number of Ni^{2+} and Ni^{3+} ions is not changed, the electron jump is not connected with a change in energy, and this electron jump can be repeated in the same way with the next ion. Compounds containing two kinds of ions of the same metal are often very good electronic or metallic conductors.

Compounds with variable composition are not really stable at low temperature. Even at room temperature the entropy is insufficient for stabilization. At room temperature, however, the speed of the reaction, in which the two pure oxides are formed, e.g.

$$TiO_{1\cdot02} = Ti_{0\cdot98}O_{1\cdot00} \rightarrow 0\cdot94TiO + 0\cdot02Ti_2O_3$$

is so slow, that it cannot be observed; if a compound with non-stoichiometric composition is formed, it is impossible, at low temperature, to split it into its two component oxides.

In the compounds so far discussed, the oxygen lattice is intact, and two kinds of ions occupy the positions of one kind, leaving a certain number of positions unoccupied. The opposite type, with gaps in the oxygen positions, has been observed as well. A good example is the system Ce_2O_3 : CeO_2. CeO_2 has a CaF_2 structure, Ce^{4+} ions and O^{2-} ions taking the position of Ca^{2+} and F^-, respectively. Now if a sample of CeO_2 is reduced, which can be effectuated by heating the oxide *in vacuo*, part of the Ce^{4+} ions go over into Ce^{3+} ions. In order to maintain electric neutrality, oxygen ions must leave the lattice. This process goes on until all Ce^{4+} ions have become Ce^{3+} ions. Writing the ceric oxide as Ce_2O_4, it is seen that, in the end, one-fourth of the oxygen ions have disappeared. The lattice is still essentially that of CeO_2, but of the eight oxygen ions that surround one Ce^{4+} ion in CeO_2, only six, surrounding a Ce^{3+} ion, remain.

FeO and Ce_2O_3 are oxidized in a completely different way: FeO, in which there are no gaps in the oxygen position, loses iron; Ce_2O_3, in which there are unoccupied O^{2-} positions, takes in oxygen.

Chapter V

CHEMICAL REACTIONS

25. REACTIONS BETWEEN ELEMENTS AND COMPOUNDS: SUBSTITUTION BY NEGATIVE IONS

WE have already seen that the heat of formation of a halide is greater, the smaller the negative ion in the compound. It is obvious that if the heat of formation of a fluoride is greater than that of a chloride then between fluorine and potassium chloride the following reaction will occur

$$2KCl + F_2 \rightarrow 2KF + Cl_2$$

The fluorine can be said to displace the chlorine from the compound, in the same way that chlorine displaces bromine or iodine

$$2KI + Cl_2 \rightarrow 2KCl + I_2$$

We have therefore deduced from the formula for the heat of formation of ionic compounds the important rule that the halogens replace one another in the order F_2, Cl_2, Br_2, I_2. There are no known exceptions to this rule. Fluorine displaces chlorine, bromine and iodine from all chlorides, bromides and iodides, while chlorine and bromine displace iodine from all iodides. It is to be expected that the same substitution reactions can take place with the chalcogens O_2, S, Se and Te, and, since the heat of formation of the oxides is, as a rule, greater than that of the sulphides, the reactions of the type

$$2ZnS + O_2 \rightarrow 2ZnO + 2S$$

are rare. One example is the slow oxidation of a solution of H_2S, according to the equation

$$2H_2S + O_2 \rightarrow 2H_2O + 2S$$

In all reactions between sulphides and oxygen occurring at high temperatures, the sulphur produced is oxidized by an excess of oxygen, so that actually a different reaction is observed in the oxidation of zinc sulphide

$$2ZnS + 3O_2 \rightarrow 2ZnO + 2SO_2$$

Whether sulphur, as such, is really formed in this reaction when there is no excess of oxygen has not been thoroughly investigated, nor is it known whether selenium and tellurium are formed when sulphur reacts with selenides and tellurides.

Up to now we have only considered substitution of an element by another element belonging to the same group, as, for example, I^- by Cl^-, Cl^- by F^-, S^{2-} by O^{2-} and P^{3-} by N^{3-}. We will now discuss more generally the reaction of an electronegative element with a compound. The stability of a compound decreases with increasing charge of the negative ion, so that a fluoride is usually more stable than the corresponding oxide, and the oxide more stable than the nitride. Further, it is to be expected and is, in fact, observed, that chlorine will displace sulphur from sulphides, while phosphides should react with sulphur to give sulphides and phosphorus, but too few examples of the latter reaction are known to warrant drawing general conclusions.

We can construct a diagram in which the arrow indicates that an element will replace the following one, whose positive ion has a high charge and a large radius.

$$\begin{array}{ccccc} N & \leftarrow & O & \leftarrow & F \\ \downarrow & & \downarrow & & \downarrow \\ P & \leftarrow & S & \leftarrow & Cl \\ \downarrow & & \downarrow & & \downarrow \\ As & \leftarrow & Se & \leftarrow & Br \\ \downarrow & & \downarrow & & \downarrow \\ Sb & \leftarrow & Te & \leftarrow & I \end{array}$$

In the diagram the elements displace the elements in the compounds to their left because the former have a lower charge, and an element displaces the one below it because it has a smaller radius. If we now proceed further and inquire what reaction occurs between chlorine and an oxide, and vice versa, we cannot say exactly what will happen. Chlorine has the advantage of a smaller ionic charge while the oxygen has the smaller radius. In the reaction between oxygen and hydrochloric acid

$$O_2 + 4HCl \rightleftarrows 2H_2O + 2Cl_2$$

a process actually used technically for the industrial manufacture of chlorine, the reaction is not complete and an equilibrium is established. The reactions between chlorine and oxides must be considered on the basis of the differences in heats of formation, as were the reactions between sulphides and oxides in Section 20. The chlorides have the higher heat of formation per equivalent because of the greater electron affinity of the chlorine. As against this difference, which is constant for each pair of compounds per equivalent, the difference in crystal energies is large if the positive ion is small or highly charged, and small if the positive ion is large or carries a low charge.

Now the heats of formation of the alkali chlorides are larger than those of the oxides, but WO_3 has a much larger heat of formation than WCl_6. The difference between the two groups is clearly shown by the fact that alkali oxides (with the exception of Li_2O) yield chlorides in a strongly exothermic reaction so that the oxide burns in chlorine, while WCl_6 when it reacts with O_2 gives WO_3, also with the development of heat.

If chlorine is replaced by bromine, the equilibrium will be displaced toward $A_2O + Br_2$, because the bromide has a lower heat of formation than the chloride. The oxidation of a bromide by oxygen is therefore a more common event than that of the corresponding chloride. Oxidation is commoner, still, with iodides where, in general, iodine is very easily replaced by oxygen; AlI_3, for example, reacts so easily with air or oxygen that the vapour can explode during the reaction

$$4AlI_3 + 3O_2 \rightarrow 2Al_2O_3 + 6I_2$$

Since nitrides have lower heats of formation than oxides, the reaction between chlorine and nitrides will be more complete than between chlorine and oxides. Nitrides react with chlorine to give chlorides and nitrogen. Chlorine, in fact, can displace all negative elements from their compounds, with the exceptions of oxygen and fluorine only.

Recapitulating, oxygen displaces all elements with the exception of fluorine and chlorine, while fluorine displaces all negative elements from their compounds. The reactions between halogens and chalcides, or between chalcogens and halides, are not simple displacements since the element which is set free combines with an excess of the displacing element, as with oxygen and zinc sulphide. When fluorine reacts with a sulphide, a metal fluoride and a fluoride of sulphur are produced, and chlorine with a sulphide gives sulphur chloride and a metal chloride. The reaction can be complicated by the formation of a complex between the two compounds which are formed (*see* Section 28). Under these conditions it is no longer possible to determine whether or not a substitution reaction is taking place, as when BaS is heated to give $BaSO_4$

$$2BaS + O_2 \rightarrow 2BaO + 2S$$
$$2S + 3O_2 \rightarrow 2SO_3$$
$$2BaO + 2SO_3 \rightarrow 2BaSO_4$$

the final reaction being

$$BaS + 2O_2 \rightarrow BaSO_4$$

The formation of complexes can alter the heat effects to such an extent that a change of sign will occur. Thus sulphur can react with oxides as in the following reaction

$$4BaO + 4S \rightarrow BaSO_4 + 3BaS + 151 \text{ kcal}$$

which is endothermic because of the formation of $BaSO_4$.

We know still very little about the reactions of elements of the nitrogen group with their compounds, e.g. nitrides and phosphides. Usually the heat of formation of the nitrides will be higher than that of the phosphides, but just as in the oxide-sulphide group, the alkali phosphides may have a higher heat of formation than the nitrides, because for the former compounds $(D - E)$ is greater. In actual fact, the alkali phosphides are known to exist, but the nitrides, except Li_3N, have not been prepared. The main reason for the instability of the nitrides may be in their lower heat of formation; however, the change in entropy also has its influence, the change being very small in phosphides, where the vapour consists of molecules P_4.

26. REACTIONS BETWEEN ELEMENTS AND COMPOUNDS: SUBSTITUTION BY POSITIVE IONS

In the previous section substitution by negative ions was considered, but similar phenomena also occur with positive ions. By the action of sodium on iron chloride, sodium chloride and iron are obtained; and the following is a reaction of the same type

$$H_2 + CuO \rightarrow Cu + H_2O$$

These reactions are two examples of a process used for obtaining metals from oxides, in which the metal is said to be 'reduced'. Since technical processes are concerned only with the production of the metal they are called reduction processes, overlooking the fact that hydrogen is oxidized during the reaction. Actually, these reactions consist of the substitution of one positive ion in an oxide by another. From the stability rules it is possible to predict which metal will displace a positive ion in any given compound. In general, one must choose a reducing metal which has larger ions, or ions with a lower charge, than the positive ion that is to be reduced. There are, however, some exceptions; the alkali metals do not reduce the oxides of Mg, Ca, Sr and Ba, the latter group having larger heats of formation than those of the alkali oxides.

The difference in charge plays the biggest part, so that the alkali- and alkaline-earth metals are the most powerful agents in reducing all high valency metal compounds to their metals. Of the alkali metals, sodium is frequently used to produce the metals V, Ta, Ti, Zr, Th, etc, from their chlorides. Hydrogen is less powerful for this purpose, because the ionic radius of the element is small, the dissociation energy of the H_2 molecule large and its electron affinity very small, indeed. Hydrogen, therefore, will reduce the less stable compounds containing highly-charged ions, such as WO_3 and WCl_6, or those which do not contain a noble-gas ion, such as the compounds containing elements of the subgroups*.

The compounds of elements of the first three columns of the periodic system are not reduced by hydrogen, and those in the subsequent columns only partly so. At high temperatures $TiCl_4$ is easily reduced to $TiCl_3$, but the reaction proceeds no farther because the charge of the titanum ion is reduced. Further complications can occur in the reaction of a metal with a compound if the two metals can, themselves, combine to give a compound. In such instances the reaction will proceed in quite a different way from that expected from the stability rules. Because of the different heats of formation of halides and chalcides it can happen that a given element, for example Na, can reduce a chloride but not an oxide.

$$CaO + 2K \rightarrow Ca + K_2O - 66 \text{ kcal}$$

$$CaCl_2 + 2K \rightarrow Ca + 2KCl + 17 \text{ kcal}$$

It is surprising that a non-metallic element can sometimes act as a reducing agent; iodine has a relatively large affinity for fluorine and chlorine. When iodine reacts with a chloride that can give up a part of its chlorine easily, for example VCl_4, a chloride of lower valency, ICl, is formed, as follows

$$2VCl_4 + I_2 \rightarrow 2VCl_3 + 2ICl$$

* Exceptions to the general reduction scheme given above do sometimes occur; thus sodium results from the heating of sodium carbonate with iron powder. The basic reaction is $Na_2O + Fe \rightarrow FeO + 2Na$ which takes place because sodium, in this reaction, escapes as a vapour, with the result that the equilibrium is displaced to the right of the equation. Whenever reactions take place with the formation of gaseous products, the change of entropy may act against the energy change.

27. DOUBLE DECOMPOSITIONS

The stability rules can also provide information as to what will happen when two compounds react together. As a first example we will take the type of reaction in which both reacting compounds consist of ions, all of which have the same charge.

If two compounds, AB and CD, react with one another, there are four different ions to consider and the question arises which combination, $AB + CD$ or $AD + CB$, will have the lowest energy, the energies concerned naturally depending on the ionic radii. Let us call the radii of the two positive ions a and c, and those of the negative ions b and d. The energy of the combination $AB + CD$ is equal to the negative value of the heat of formation of AB plus that of CD, and the energy of the system $AD + CB$ is similarly equal to the negative value of the heat of formation of AD plus that of CB. The reaction

$$AB + CD \rightarrow AD + CB$$

will therefore proceed in the direction indicated, if the energy of the first pair is greater than that of the second. Since S, D, E and I all disappear from the equation, the necessary condition for the reaction is

$$-\left(\frac{NAe^2}{a+b} + \frac{NAe^2}{c+d}\right) > -\left(\frac{NAe^2}{a+d} + \frac{NAe^2}{c+b}\right)$$

If all the compounds have the same crystal structure, then the Madelung constants are equal, and

$$\frac{1}{(a+b)(c+d)} < \frac{1}{(a+d)(c+b)}$$

or

$$(a+b)(c+d) > (a+d)(c+b)$$

or

$$ad + bc > ab + dc$$

or

$$(a-c)(d-b) > 0$$

The condition is therefore $\begin{cases} a > c \\ d > b \end{cases}$ or $\begin{cases} a < c \\ d < b \end{cases}$

The reaction will therefore proceed in such a way that the smallest ions combine to form one compound, and the largest to form another. These double decompositions have been fully investigated for the alkali halides and it is found that the reaction always proceeds so that the smallest ions combine. For example

$$\mathrm{LiI + NaCl \rightarrow LiCl + NaI}$$

Another reaction of this type that we would expect is

$$\mathrm{MgTe + BaO \rightarrow MgO + BaTe}$$

but such reactions have not as yet been investigated to any great extent.

In reactions in which compounds of the subgroup elements take part, such a simple treatment is no longer applicable. AgF and KCl react to give AgCl and KF. Here the smaller positive ion combines with the larger negative one. The crystal energy of AgF and AgCl is affected by the extra field of the Ag^+ ions, and simple rules for the way in which the reaction proceeds cannot be found.

In most reactions between compounds the charges of the ions will not be equal and a much more complicated situation presents itself, because we have now to deal with the influence of the radii, as well as that of the charges. As a first example, let us take the reaction

$$\mathrm{PCl_5 + 5KF \rightarrow PF_5 + 5KCl}$$

in which only the negative ions differ in size. The general form is

$$pAB_n + nCD_p \rightarrow pAD_n + nCB_p$$

Now if n is much greater than p, or the charge of the first positive ion is much greater than that of the second, then $a < c$, in which a is the radius of the ion A and c that of the C ion. The energy terms which determine the crystal energy are

$$-\frac{pE_n}{a+b}, \quad -\frac{nE_p}{a+d}, \quad -\frac{pE_n}{c+d}, \quad -\frac{nE_p}{c+b}$$

in which $E_n = NA_n e^2 n^2$. It is here assumed that the compounds AB_n and AD_n, as well as CD_p and CB_p, have the same crystal structures. Now if $n > p$, then $-pE_n < -nE_p$ because E_n has the order of magnitude n^2E. If now we put $nE_p/pE_n = \alpha$, then α is always <1. The necessary condition for the reaction to proceed in the direction given is

$$-\frac{1}{a+b} - \frac{\alpha}{c+d} > -\frac{1}{a+d} - \frac{\alpha}{c+b}$$

which is satisfied if

$$\frac{1}{a+d} - \frac{1}{a+b} > \alpha\left(\frac{1}{c+d} - \frac{1}{c+b}\right)$$

or

$$\frac{b-d}{(a+d)(a+b)} > \alpha\frac{b-d}{(c+d)(c+b)}$$

or, since d is smaller than b in the example chosen

$$\frac{1}{(a+d)(a+b)} > \alpha\frac{1}{(c+d)(c+b)}$$

which is correct since

$$(c+d)(c+b) > \alpha(a+d)(a+b)$$

because

$$c > a \qquad \text{and} \qquad \alpha < 1$$

Only if the difference in charges becomes smaller can c be greater than a, and α nearly unity, so that the reaction will proceed in the reverse direction. This means that the difference in radii of the positive ions overcomes the effect of their charge, a state of affairs which occurs infrequently.

In reactions in which both positive ions have high charges, exceptions occur, as for example

$$3CCl_4 + 4AlI_3 \rightarrow 3CI_4 + 4AlCl_3$$

where, although Al^{3+} has a lower charge and a larger ionic radius than C^{4+}, it combines with the smaller Cl^- ion. This can occur if the α of this type of reaction is greater than unity, that is, if the energy of the carbon compounds is abnormally low, which is conceivable in the above instance if the Cl^- ions no longer touch the small C^{4+} atom. It is worthy of note that here the heat of formation of the purely ionic carbon compounds would be so small that they would be incapable of existence. We come therefore to the inevitable conclusion that some of the compounds taking part in the reaction are not ionic; in this reaction the non-ionic compounds are those of carbon. The differences between chlorides and bromides or iodides in non-ionic compounds are much smaller than in ionic ones, and, in fact, may be neglected in a first approximation. In the reaction

$$3CCl_4 + 4AlI_3 \rightarrow 3CI_4 + 4AlCl_3$$

the heat effect is practically determined by the ionic aluminium compounds. The reaction proceeds in the direction to form a compound ($AlCl_3$) with the highest heat of formation.

In what has been said above it was assumed that the charges of the positive ions were different. An example of a reaction in which the negative ions have different charges is the following

$$K_2S + 2LiCl \rightarrow Li_2S + 2KCl$$

which we might surmise would take place in the direction indicated. Such a reaction comes within the same general scheme, except that now *A* and *C* are negative ions. Here the difference in radii is not large, and the smaller positive ion combines with the negative ion having the greater charge.

Lastly, we must consider the reaction in which the charges of both kinds of ions are different. The reaction

$$2PCl_5 + 5H_2O \rightarrow P_2O_5 + 10HCl$$

is a good example and there are many other reactions of the same kind. If PCl_5 and H_2O react, the highly-charged phosphorus ions must combine with the highly-charged negative ions to yield an oxide and HCl. If a chloride, such as NaCl, reacts with water there is no reason whatever why the oxygen ions should prefer the sodium to the hydrogen ion; and, in fact, since the H ion is the smaller, this will certainly combine with the highly-charged negative oxygen. If Na_2O is added to HCl, the highly-charged negative ion will combine with the smaller positive ion and the following reaction will take place

$$Na_2O + 2HCl \rightarrow 2NaCl + H_2O$$

Now let us consider MgO instead of Na_2O. In MgO the oxygen ion has the choice of combining with the very small H^+ ion with a single charge, or with the Mg^{2+} ion with double that charge. This reaction proceeds thus

$$MgO + 2HCl \rightarrow MgCl_2 + H_2O$$

but not to completion; and it can easily proceed in the reverse direction. In other words, $MgCl_2$ is partly hydrolysed by an excess of water. If the charge of the positive ion is even greater, the oxygen will tend to combine with it. The reaction

$$Al_2O_3 + 6HCl \rightarrow 2AlCl_3 + 3H_2O$$

also does not proceed to completion; if $AlCl_3$ is brought into contact with water it is strongly hydrolysed. If now the charge of the positive ion is raised still further, then the following reaction proceeds almost to completion

$$SiCl_4 + 2H_2O \rightarrow SiO_2 + 4HCl$$

These reactions can be collected together in the following scheme

$$Na_2O + 2HCl \longrightarrow 2NaCl + H_2O$$
$$MgO + 2HCl \underset{\longrightarrow}{\leftarrow} MgCl_2 + H_2O$$
$$Al_2O_3 + 6HCl \underset{\longrightarrow}{\leftarrow} 2AlCl_3 + 3H_2O$$
$$SiO_2 + 4HCl \longleftarrow SiCl_4 + 2H_2O$$

The way in which such reactions proceed is not usually attributed to the effect of the charge or to the radii of the ions, but instead it is said that, in this case, $SiCl_4$ is hydrolysed by the water because it is a chloride of a non-metallic element. The fact that $SnCl_4$ is a chloride of a metallic element and is hydrolysed easily is because the Sn^{4+} ion, like the Si^{4+} ion, has a high charge. In addition to $SnCl_4$, the following chlorides: $CbCl_5$, $TaCl_5$, $MoCl_5$, WCl_5 and $SbCl_5$, as well as the corresponding fluorides and bromides of these elements, in so far as they are known, react strongly with water and form oxides or hydroxides, although they are all halides of metals.

The following reaction

$$Na_2O + 2HCl \rightarrow 2NaCl + H_2O$$

is said to take place because HCl is an acid and Na_2O is a basic oxide, while SiO_2 plus HCl does not yield $SiCl_4$ because SiO_2 is not a base-forming oxide. Following this line of argument further, it must then be explained why Na_2O is a base-forming oxide and SiO_2 is not. In fact, there is really no need to introduce the conception of acids and bases The phenomena can be comprehended on the basis of the charge and radius of each ion. Later we shall return to this question of acids and bases and see that acid- and base-forming behaviour is, to a large extent, dependent on these two factors. It would amount to the same thing if the reaction between HCl and an oxide were explained either by saying that Na_2O is base-forming, or that Na^+ is a large ion of low charge.

When NaF reacts with gaseous HCl, NaCl and HF are produced. Using the normal terminology, it can be said that the strong acid, HCl, drives HF from its salts, but such a description of the process is unnecessary, because, in the reaction between NaF and HCl, the smallest ions combine, giving HF and NaCl. In the old terminology, the answer to the question of why HCl is a stronger acid than HF becomes

$$r_{Cl} > r_F$$

It is frequently found that a stronger acid does not replace a weaker one in its salts, as in the reaction

$$5HF + PCl_5 \rightarrow PF_5 + 5HCl$$

Here the smaller negative ion, the F^- ion, has the choice of combining with the H^+ ion or with the highly-charged P^{5+} ion. The charge of the latter outweighs the influence of the small radius of the H^+ ion, and therefore, in the reaction of HF on a chloride containing highly-charged positive ions, the corresponding fluoride is formed and the weaker HF replaces the stronger HCl. Thus it is evident that the well-known rule, that a stronger acid replaces a weaker one, is not valid at all. It may be argued that this rule should not be applied to the reaction

$$PCl_5 + 5HF \rightarrow PF_5 + 5HCl$$

since PCl_5, being a chloride of a non-metallic element, is not a salt. However, $ThCl_4$, which really is a chloride of a metal, reacts with KF in exactly the same way.

The rule about the exchange between salts and acids is valid only for salts of metals of low valency, and should be replaced by the rule that compounds react in such a way that the ions which combine are those possessing the strongest electric fields; this rule also embraces the older one on salt-acid exchange.

The rules that we have derived apply to most of the reactions in inorganic chemistry, but complications can, and do, occur. In the first place, it must be remembered that the heat of reaction is often small, causing a reverse reaction at high temperatures and therefore resulting in an equilibrium. Theoretically, every reaction in which phases with variable compositions occur can be considered as an equilibrium reaction. That is, the concentration of none of the components can ever be zero. If one of the components is in excess, then the reaction can always proceed in the reverse direction. We would expect LiCl and water to be formed from Li_2O and HCl, but if LiCl is heated in a stream of steam, then a trace of HCl will occur in the vapour phase at equilibrium. When, however, the HCl is continuously removed by the steam, there will be some dissociation of LiCl into Li_2O. The theory, of exchange based on ionic charges and radii, is strictly valid only for solids at low temperatures where the course of the reaction is not affected by changes in the entropies, where none of the components is present in great excess.

Double-decomposition reactions are more important in preparative chemistry than are substitution reactions. If one element displaces another from a compound, then the resulting compound will naturally be more stable. Chlorides are not often prepared from iodides, nor oxides from sulphides, because the chlorides and the oxides can be made more readily than iodides or sulphides. When, however, the sulphide occurs as a mineral, the replacement of sulphur by oxygen is used extensively in the so-called 'roasting' of sulphides. The replacement of one metal by another is of the greatest importance in the technical preparation of metals, but the compounds obtained in such processes are mainly the oxide or chloride of hydrogen, or of the alkali- or alkaline-earth metals. Double-decomposition reactions, however, may give compounds which cannot be prepared in any other way. A number of reactions which proceed abnormally are important in this respect. The halides of the platinum group, as will be shown later, can scarcely be considered as ionic compounds. If, therefore, $PtCl_4$ is added to KI in solution, then the heat of reaction will be determined by the difference in the heats of formation between KCl and KI. KCl is formed as well as the iodide of platinum. The iodides of those elements which cannot be prepared by the direct action of iodine on the metal can thus be produced in this way because the iodides are almost insoluble in water. As by far the greatest number of double decompositions are carried out in aqueous solutions, the rules we have considered in this section need corrections because of the effect of hydration of the ions (*see* Section 44).

It is interesting to note that qualitative analysis depends very largely on such double-decomposition reactions. By the addition of HCl in the first and H_2S in the second group, chlorides and sulphides of the subgroup elements are precipitated. Sulphur and chlorine apparently have a tendency to combine with ions of the 18-electron configuration, or with ions having abnormal valencies, e.g. PbS. The reason for this behaviour must be attributed, in the first place, to the extra field of the subgroup ions (Section 21), but, in addition, it must be remembered that there are strong polarization effects produced when subgroup ions combine with strong polarizable negative ions such as Cl^-, Br^-, I^-, S^{2-}, Se^{2-} and Te^{2-} (*see* Section 42).

28. REACTIONS WITH CHANGE OF VALENCY: OXIDATION AND REDUCTION

In the double decompositions just considered, the valencies of the reacting atoms remained unchanged. This is not always so, and a reaction can lead to the formation of an unstable compound which decomposes with a valency change to a lower value. If KI is added to $CuCl_2$, the reaction is

$$2KI + CuCl_2 \rightleftharpoons 2KCl + CuI_2*$$

However, CuI_2 is unstable and decomposes into CuI and iodine, the complete reaction therefore being

$$4KI + 2CuCl_2 \rightarrow 4KCl + 2CuI + I_2$$

If the reaction takes place in aqueous solution, then it can be written as an ionic one in which the K^+, Cl^- and some of the I^- ions remain unchanged, so that the ionic reaction is

$$2Cu^{2+} + 2I^- \rightarrow 2Cu^+ + I_2$$

in which an electron is transferred from the iodine to the copper ion. Reactions of this type, involving such an electron transfer, are very common, and are to be expected if positive ions which can accept electrons easily come into contact with negative ions which can lose them easily.

Positive ions can take up electrons easily if the ionization energy is very high. This will occur for highly-charged, or small, positive ions and for those which have a high ionization energy as a result of a particular structure. Iodine is among the negative ions which easily give up loose electrons, but negative divalent and tervalent ions will do so with even more facility. In the same way, the S^{2-} gives up electrons in a number of reactions, and changes into sulphur. If H_2S is led into a solution of $FeCl_3$, the reaction

$$3K_2S + 2FeCl_2 \rightarrow Fe_2S_3 + 6KCl$$

does not take place, but, instead, FeS, KCl and S are obtained as a result of the transfer of an electron from the S^{2-} to the Fe^{3+} ion, as follows

$$2Fe^{3+} + S^{2-} \rightarrow 2Fe^{2+} + S$$

This electron transfer is even more general with highly-charged positive ions; thus, if CrO_3, containing a hexavalent Cr ion, reacts with H_2S, sulphur and a lower oxide of chromium are formed according to the equation

$$2CrO_3 + 3H_2S \rightarrow Cr_2O_3 + 3H_2O + 3S$$

in which the following electron transfer takes place

$$2Cr^{6+} + 3S^{2-} \rightarrow 2Cr^{3+} + 3S$$

It will be obvious that the energy change in such a reaction is not completely determined by the electron transfer, but will also be

* This ionic reaction is an abnormal one because the Cu^{2+} ion does not possess a noble-gas structure.

dependent on the energy of each of the reaction products, determined by the charge and radii of the ions. Since solid sulphur is formed in the reaction, the energy which is released in its formation from the atoms must be taken into account, and, further, in aqueous solutions, the hydration energy must be included. Iodine ions, and also bromine and chlorine ions, can lose their charge to a Cr^{6+} ion. Thus

$$2CrO_3 + 12HCl \rightarrow 2CrCl_3 + 6H_2O + 3Cl_2$$

$$2Cr^{6+} + 6Cl^- \rightarrow 2Cr^{3+} + 3Cl_2$$

The negative ions of the nitrogen group lose their charge so easily that even monovalent Ag^+ ions will discharge them, as a result of their 18-electron configuration. If AsH_3 is added to a silver salt, a black precipitate of a mixture of silver and arsenic is obtained, the electron-discharge reaction being

$$3Ag^+ + As^{3-} \rightarrow 3Ag + As$$

while the total reaction can be represented by

$$3AgNO_3 + AsH_3 \rightarrow 3HNO_3 + 3Ag + As$$

As Ag and As are formed in this reaction in the proportions in which they occur in the compound Ag_3As, the precipitate often was mistaken for a compound and the question of compound formation remained unresolved until the development of x-ray analysis. In those instances where a mixture is still formed it is possible, however, to consider that the compound is first formed, and subsequently decomposes, as

$$Ag_3^+As^{3-} \rightarrow 3Ag + As$$

This representation is not essentially different from the earlier one; if we say that Ag_3As is so unstable that it decomposes into its elements, then this is really the same as saying Ag^+ ions accept electrons from the As^{3-} ions. The number of such reactions can easily be extended further. We will consider one exceptional example wherein two ions of the same element react together with mutual loss of charge. Thus

$$SO_2 + 2H_2S \rightarrow 2H_2O + 3S$$

corresponds with the electron transfer

$$S^{4+} + 2S^{2-} \rightarrow 3S$$

The last reaction almost certainly is not purely ionic in character, since SO_2, and H_2S, are certainly not purely ionic compounds. In the reaction

$$H_2S + 2FeCl_3 \rightarrow 2HCl + 2FeCl_2 + S$$

H_2S undergoes the same change as it does when reacting with oxygen. This reaction

$$2H_2S + O_2 \rightarrow 2H_2O + 2S$$

is usually described as an oxidation of H_2S to S. As a matter of fact, the earlier conception of oxidation has now been very considerably broadened, the removal of hydrogen now considered similar to the addition of oxygen. Since oxygen, which oxidizes iron to Fe_2O_3, has the opposite effect from hydrogen, which reduces oxide to metal, it has become customary to call withdrawal of oxygen reduction and withdrawal of hydrogen oxidation. This is the sense in which the expression oxidation is frequently used in organic chemistry, an example being the production of an aldehyde from an alcohol, in which two hydrogen atoms are withdrawn from the alcohol. Every substance with which this process can be carried out is called an oxidizing agent, and chlorine must be included in this category. This leads to the description of the reaction of a metal with chlorine as an oxidation. To what extent is this broadening of the oxidation idea reasonable? If we regard the reaction of calcium with oxygen as involving an electron transfer, the metal changes to an ionic state and two electrons are given up by each atom of the metal. The same reaction occurs by the action of chlorine, fluorine, bromine, iodine, sulphur, etc. It is, therefore, reasonable to regard the removal of electrons as the basis of an oxidation process, and to call all such processes oxidations, and, further, to regard those processes in which electrons are taken up as reductions. Thus in the reaction

$$Ca + Cl_2 \rightarrow CaCl_2$$

calcium is oxidized by chlorine, which itself is reduced, since the calcium loses electrons which the chlorine accepts. In this way all processes involving change of valency would come within an oxidation-reduction reaction scheme. Thus, in the reaction

$$2FeCl_3 + H_2S \rightarrow 2FeCl_2 + S + 2HCl$$

the Fe^{3+} ion is reduced to the Fe^{2+} ion, and the S^{2-} ion is oxidized to sulphur. Many other reactions can be included under this definition of oxidation and reduction. The solution of a metal in a dilute acid can be represented simply as follows

$$2M + 2H^+ \rightarrow 2M^+ + H_2$$

Here the metal gives off two electrons to the hydrogen ions, and the fact that these ions are not present as free protons but combine with water to produce H_3O^+ ions does not alter the picture. The metal is thus oxidized to ions and the hydrogen ions are reduced to free hydrogen. Again it must be borne in mind that in these processes the energy is not determined by the electron transfer alone. The heat of reaction of

$$2Na + 2HCl \rightarrow 2NaCl + H_2$$

is not equivalent to the ionization energy of the sodium less that of the hydrogen, and the corrent value for the heat of reaction ΔH per equivalent must be obtained from

$$\Delta H = -S_{Na} + \tfrac{1}{2}D_{H_2} - I_{Na} + I_H + H_{Na^+} - H_{H^+}$$

$$\begin{array}{ccc} [Na] + (H^+) & \xrightarrow[H_{H^+}]{S_{Na}} & Na + H^+ \\ \Big\downarrow -\Delta H & & \Big\downarrow I_{Na} \; -I_H \\ (Na^+) + \tfrac{1}{2}H_2 & \xleftarrow[-\frac{1}{2}D_{H_2}]{-H_{Na^+}} & Na^+ + H \end{array}$$

In this cycle H is the hydration energy, S the heat of sublimation, I the ionization energy and D the dissociation energy; the square brackets indicate that the metal is present in the solid state, and the round brackets that the ion is hydrated.

From the fact that silver does not dissolve in dilute acid we must conclude that the electron cannot be taken up by the hydrogen ion because of the high ionization energy of the silver. Gold is naturally less soluble in dilute acids, but it does dissolve in chlorine water, because chlorine, with its large electron affinity, can extract electrons from noble metals since free chlorine has stronger oxidizing power than hydrogen ions.

Silver dissolves easily in dilute nitric acid in which the NO_3^- ion is the oxidizing agent. Assuming that in N_2O_5, from which this NO_3^- ion can be derived, there is a pentavalent nitrogen ion with three normal oxygen ions, corresponding to the structural formula $N^{5+}O_3^{2-}$, it is this pentavalent nitrogen ion that has the oxidizing properties and accepts an electron from the silver, thereby changing from NO_3^- ($N^{5+}O_3^{2-}$) into NO_3^{2-} ($N^{4+}O_3^{2-}$), which then dissociates into NO_2 and O^{2-}. The scheme of the reaction is therefore

$$\begin{array}{ll} Ag + NO_3^- & \rightarrow Ag^+ + NO_3^{2-} \\ NO_3^{2-} & \rightarrow O^{2-} + NO_2 \\ 2H^+ + O^{2-} & \rightarrow H_2O \\ \hline Ag + 2H^+ + NO_3^- & \rightarrow Ag^+ + H_2O + NO_2 \end{array}$$

It is to be noted that the oxidizing power of nitric acid is not due to its oxygen content, but to the presence of an unstable positive ion. In this connection it is quite well known that Ag_2O is a strong oxidizing agent while WO_3, with more oxygen in the molecule, is not. The power of an oxide as an oxidizing agent depends upon its stability. If this is great it does not change easily to an oxide with lower valency, and, consequently, has no oxidizing effect. An unstable oxide can decompose spontaneously, thereby causing the transfer of the electrons in the oxygen ions to the positive ion, and the resultant production of oxygen molecules. Thus

$$2Ag_2^+O^{2-} \rightarrow 4Ag + O_2$$

If, however, the oxide is in contact with particles which give up electrons more easily than the oxygen ions, then it will be these particles which lose the electrons. In this way N_2O_5 can take electrons from the S^{2-} ion to give either free sulphur or even to form S^{4+} or S^{6+} ions. H_2S, S and SO_2 are therefore oxidized by N_2O_5, but the oxygen ions play no important part in the process, the transfer occurring between the positive ions. The reaction can be shown as

$$N_2O_5 + SO_2 \rightarrow 2NO_2 + SO_3$$

but the essential reaction is

$$2N^{5+} + S^{4+} \rightarrow 2N^{4+} + S^{6+}$$

It is known that potassium permanganate reacts with H_2O_2 in acid solution. Thus

$$2KMnO_4 + 3H_2SO_4 + 5H_2O_2 \rightarrow 2MnSO_4 + K_2SO_4 + \\ + 5O_2 + 8H_2O$$

for which the basic reaction is

$$2MnO_4^- + 6H^+ + 5H_2O_2 \rightarrow 2Mn^{2+} + 5O_2 + 8H_2O$$

since the SO_2^{4-}, K^+ and some of the H^+ ions are unchanged in the process. In this particular reaction it is frequently assumed that an oxygen atom of the permanganate ion combines with an oxygen atom of H_2O_2 to give a molecule of oxygen so that half of the oxygen produced in the reaction comes from the H_2O_2. If we regard the process as an electron transfer, then obviously the oxygen would play no part in it. The Mn^{7+} ion takes electrons from the H_2O_2, which then decomposes into H^+ ions and O_2. In H_2O_2 we can assume the existence of O_2^{2-} ions and thus regard it as a weak acid, so that the whole process can be expressed by

$$2Mn^{7+} + 5O_2^{2-} \rightarrow 2Mn^{2+} + 5O_2$$

in which all the oxygen will come from the H_2O_2. It is possible to demonstrate the validity of this in the following manner. Let us suppose that instead of using H_2O_2 we use the same compound but with the oxygen atoms in the molecule replaced by those of a radioactive oxygen isotope with an atomic weight of eighteen. The oxygen produced in the reaction can then be analysed to find whether it contains all the radioactive or heavy oxygen, or only half of it. If, as does happen, it is found to consist entirely of the heavy oxygen, then the reaction, as shown above, is correct, and provides further proof that the newer conception of the oxidation process is to be preferred to the older ones, at least for ionic compounds. The description of oxidation as an electron-transfer process is very convenient for ionic compounds, but does lose its meaning for covalent compounds. Thus one cannot define the reaction

$$C_2H_2 + 2H_2 = C_2H_6$$

as oxidation or reduction. On the other hand, it is easy to see that in the reaction

$$2Li + H_2 = 2LiH$$

lithium is *oxidized* by hydrogen.

Chapter VI

COMPLEX COMPOUNDS

29. DEVELOPMENT OF THE IDEA OF COMPLEXES

IN Section 24 it was shown that, under favorable conditions, two oxides of the same metal, in different states of valency, may form solid solutions which have been described as compounds with variable composition. The stabilizing factor in this case is the increase in entropy, due to the random distribution of the two positive ions: these systems, strictly speaking, are stable only at elevated temperature. The conditions may be such that two oxides form a real compound, because this process is connected with a decrease in energy. The compounds formed in this way have a stoichiometric composition, with two kinds of positive ions in fixed positions, so arranged that the energy of the system is minimal. A good example of a compound of this type is Fe_3O_4.

A good example of a compound formed by two fluorides of the same metal is the newly discovered compound CsF_3, that is formed when CsCl is heated with fluorine. This CsF_3, or $CsF . CsF_5$ (or $Cs(CsF_6)$, probably has a structure similar to $CsSbF_6$, and seems to be a compound of two Cs fluorides, CsF and CsF_5. From structure analysis it is known that the compound $CsSbF_6$ contains ions SbF_6^-, that in the compound alternate with Cs^+ ions in essentially the same way as Na^+ and Cl^- alternate in the NaCl structure, the SbF_6^- group as a whole playing the same part as a Cl^- ion. Ions like SbF_6^-, that are composed of a number of other ions, are called complex ions, and compounds containing such complex ions are called complexes. The latter term will be used more freely, and will be applied to any compound formed from two halides, oxides, sulphides, etc., even if they do not contain isolated complex ions like SbF_6^-. The existence of real complex ions has been demonstrated by x-ray analysis in many cases, e.g. in KBF_4, K_2SiF_6 and K_2PtCl_6. It will be shown below that the groups SO_4^{2-}, PO_4^{3-} and NO_3^- have to be considered as complex ions, as well, and that sulphates, phosphates, nitrates, etc. are to be regarded as complex compounds, formed from two oxides. For example

$$BaO + SO_3 \rightarrow BaSO_4$$

$$CaO + N_2O_5 \rightarrow Ca(NO_3)_2$$

In this group, and in many others, e.g. KBF_4 and K_2PtCl_6, the existence of the complex ions in solutions was known long before their existence in the solid state was proved by x-ray analysis. The essential point in the process of complex formation

$$KF + BF_3 \rightarrow K^+ + BF_4^-$$

is a transfer of an ion from one compound (KF) to the other (BF_3), forming a negative complex ion out of the latter, and leaving the former as a positive ion. The change in energy in the process of complex formation will be discussed in more detail in the next section. It will, however, be already clear at this point that the transfer of the negative ion is due to the attraction of the highly-charged positive ion in the second compound (acceptor) and that this attraction will be enhanced if the positive ion in the first compound (donor) is large and has a low charge, its attraction for the negative ion not hindering that ion's transition to the second positive ion. The energy change in complex formation is, therefore, very considerable if the two positive ions are greatly different in radius and charge. That the compound $Cs^+CsF_6^-$ can be formed at all is probably due to the large heat of complex formation; it is this change in heat content that helps to overcome the high ionization energy required to ionize the Cs^+ ion to the pentavalent state in Cs^{5+}.

It is not customary to regard the oxygen compounds, such as sulphates, nitrates and phosphates, as complexes, but it can be shown that there are good reasons for not making a fundamental distinction between what were formerly regarded as complexes, e.g. KBF_4 and $KMgF_3$, and compounds like $BaSO_4$ and $CaTiO_3$. In the first place, the formation of the two kinds of compounds, the first from two fluorides and the other from two oxides, takes place according to the same reaction equations

$$BaO + SO_3 \rightarrow BaSO_4$$

$$KF + BF_3 \rightarrow KBF_4$$

and

$$CaO + TiO_2 \rightarrow CaTiO_3$$

$$KF + MgF_2 \rightarrow KMgF_3$$

The resemblance between the two sets is not merely a formal one: it has been shown by x-ray analysis that $BaSO_4$ and KBF_4 have exactly the same structure, K^+ ions in KBF_4 taking the place of the Ba^{2+} ions in $BaSO_4$, and both compounds containing a tetrahedral group of ions, a complex ion BF_4^- in KBF_4 and a similar ion SO_4^{2-} in $BaSO_4$.

The reasons for making a distinction between complexes like KBF_4 and 'non-complex' compounds like $BaSO_4$ will now be discussed. In most textbooks KBF_4 is called a complex, and $BaSO_4$ a normal compound or an oxygen salt, simply because a structural formula

```
     O     O
    / \   //
  Ba    S
    \ /   \\
     O     O
```

can be constructed for the latter compound. This is not possible for KBF_4, because fluorine is univalent and there is no means of coupling the potassium to the boron by way of the fluorine atoms. The question, however, arises as to how far structural formulae of this kind have any real significance, and whether there is any reason to make a sharp distinction between KBF_4 and $BaSO_4$.

In fact, such structural formulae have no meaning at all, for the reason that oxygen salts such as $BaSO_4$, $CaCO_3$, K_2SO_4, $Ca_3(PO_4)_2$, etc. are only known in the solid state or in solution. They mostly decompose rather than sublime and, even when they do exist as molecules in the vapour state, little or nothing is known regarding their size or shape. In solution they dissociate into ions, no molecules being formed. We have therefore to confine ourselves to consideration of the solid state, where it is known that oxygen salts form coordination structures in the same way as the simpler ionic compounds, such as CaO and K_2O, but are somewhat more complicated because of the larger number of atoms present in the lattice.

If the oxygen in CaO is replaced by the group CO_3^{2-}, then a lattice essentially similar to that of CaO is obtained. It is not exactly the same, as the shape of the CO_3^{2-} is different from that of the O^{2-} ion, but each CO_3^{2-} ion is still surrounded by six Ca^{2+} ions. Consequently, there is no basis whatever for employing the formula

```
     O
    / \
  Ca    C = O
    \ /
     O
```

in which each Ca is only connected to two oxygen ions. Molecules of $CaCO_3$, as such, can no more be distinguished in the structure than can molecules of CaO in calcium oxide. In fact, the lattice is built up of the ions Ca^{2+} and CO_3^{2-}.

The structures of complex compounds not containing oxygen are very similar to those of the oxygen salts. If the oxygen in K_2O is replaced by the group $PtCl_6$, the compound K_2PtCl_6 is obtained in which the $PtCl_6$ ion occurs as a separate entity surrounded by eight K^+ ions (*see Figure 19*). The analogy between oxygen salts and other

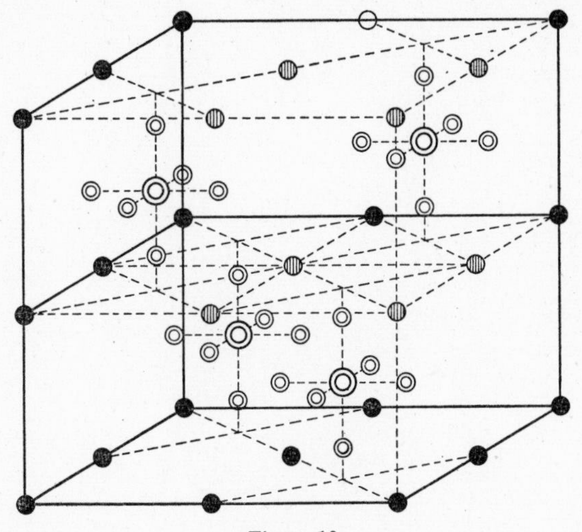

Figure 19

complex compounds is very well demonstrated by examples taken from both groups, which often have precisely the same structures. Thus, for example, $KClO_4$, containing the complex ion ClO_4^-, has the same structure as KBF_4, containing the BF_4^- complex ion. Many compounds of this kind often have very complicated structures. One of these groups is given in *Table XXVIII.* These compounds all crystallize in the rhombic system, and their structural similarity is apparent from the closeness of the crystallographic axial ratios. In *Table XXIX* are further examples of groups of compounds with the same crystal structure, in which complexes and 'normal' compounds both occur together. Here, again, the structural similarity is apparent from the values of the crystallographic ratios.

Table XXX(*a*) contains a number of compounds having the structure shown in *Figure 20*, which indicates their relationship to the true coordinated structure. In $CaTiO_3$ the Ti^{4+} ion occupies the centre position, surrounded by six negative oxygen ions, which are again surrounded by eight positive calcium ions. This group is named the perowskite group corresponding to the mineral $CaTiO_3$. In this group the central ion can be divalent (Mg, Ni, Zn), tervalent (Ga, Al, Mn), tetravalent (Sn, Zr, Ti) or pentavalent (Cb).

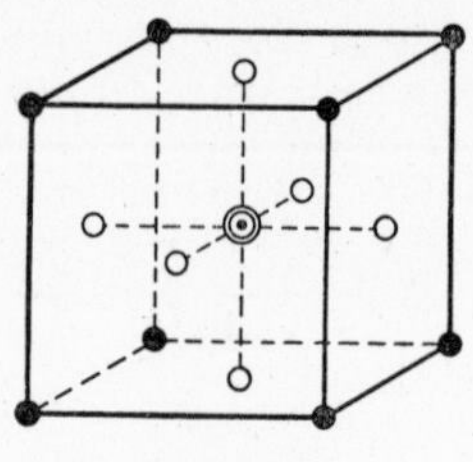

Figure 20

Table XXVIII

compound	*approximate axial ratios*
KBF_4	0·79 : 1 : 1·28
$BaSO_4$	0·81 : 1 : 1·31
$BaCrO_4$	0·82 : 1 : 1·32
$BaSeO_4$	0·81 : 1 : 1·31
$KClO_4$	0·78 : 3 : 1·28
$KMnO_4$	0·80 : 1 : 1·30
$(NH_4)MnO_4$	0·82 : 1 : 1·32

Table XXIX

compound	*axial ratios*
K_2BeF_4	0·57 : 1 : 0·74
K_2ZnCl_4	0·58 : 1 : 0·72
Cs_2HgBr_4	0·57 : 1 : 0·74
K_2SO_4	0·57 : 1 : 0·74
Rb_2SO_4	0·57 : 1 : 0·75
K_2CrO_4	0·57 : 1 : 0·73
K_2MnO_4	0·57 : 1 : 0·74
K_2MoS_4	0·57 : 1 : 0·76
$(NH_4)_2WS_4$	0·57 : 1 : 0·78
K_2WS_4	0·57 : 1 : 0·75

Table XXX

(a) Compounds of the Perowskite Type

$NaCbO_3$	$CaTiO_3$	$LaGaO_3$	$KMgF_3$
$KCbO_3$	$SrTiO_3$	$FeMnO_3$	$KNiF_3$
	$BaTiO_3$	$YAlO_3$	$KZnF_3$
	$CaZrO_3$	$LaAlO_3$	

(b) The Spinel Group

Li_2SO_4	Mg_2TiO_4	$K_2Zn(CN)_4$	Fe_2FeO_4	Fe_2FeS_4
Li_2MoO_4	Al_2MgO_4	$K_2Cd(CN)_4$	Co_2CoO_4	Co_2CoS_4
Ag_2WO_4	Al_2ZnO_4	$K_2Hg(CN)_4$		Ni_2NiS_4

Another important group contains the spinels, named after the mineral $MgAl_2O_4$ (*see Table XXX(b)*). The compounds of the fourth and fifth columns in *Table XXX(b)* are generally written with the formula Fe_3O_4, Co_3S_4, etc. All these examples show quite clearly that there is no essential distinction to be made between oxygen and sulphur salts, on the one hand, and halogen complexes, on the other.

30. COORDINATION NUMBERS OF COMPLEX IONS

At first sight there appears to be nothing systematic about the formation of complex ions. Some are formed by reaction with oxygen ions, as for example

$$SO_3 + O^{2-} \rightarrow SO_4^{2-}\text{*}$$
$$N_2O_5 + O^{2-} \rightarrow 2NO_3^-$$
$$Cl_2O_7 + O^{2-} \rightarrow 2ClO_4^-$$
$$P_2O_5 + 3O^{2-} \rightarrow 2PO_4^{3-}$$
$$TeO_3 + 3O^{2-} \rightarrow TeO_6^{6-}$$

while many complex ions are formed from fluorides, such as

$$BF_3 + F^- \rightarrow BF_4^-$$
$$SiF_4 + 2F^- \rightarrow SiF_6^{2-}$$
$$PF_5 + F^- \rightarrow PF_6^-$$

and others are formed from the other halogens

$$PtCl_4 + 2Cl^- \rightarrow PtCl_6^{2-}$$
$$SbCl_5 + Cl^- \rightarrow SbCl_6^-$$
$$SnBr_4 + 2Br^- \rightarrow SnBr_6^{2-}$$
$$HgI_2 + 2I^- \rightarrow HgI_4^{2-}$$

There are also complex ions of sulphur, such as

$$CS_2 + S^{2-} \rightarrow CS_3^{2-}$$
$$As_2S_5 + 3S^{2-} \rightarrow 2AsS_4^{3-}$$

which are analogous to the corresponding oxygen compounds. In certain instances complex ions can be formed by combination with

* In the formulae for complex ions the index at the top right-hand corner corresponds to the total charge of the ion, and not to the charge of the negative ion. If it is wished to express the charges of the individual ions, then the formulae would have to be written $S^{6+}O_4^{2-}$ or $N^{5+}O_3^{2-}$. From such formulae the total charge can be derived, but if it is necessary to express it, the ions can be written: $(S^{6+}O_4^{2-})^{2-}$, $(N^{5+}O_3^{2-})^{-}$, etc.

positive ions, the best known examples being the ammonium and phosphonium ions, thus

$$NH_3 + H^+ \rightarrow NH_4^+$$
$$PH_3 + H^+ \rightarrow PH_4^+$$

A third, the hydronium ion $OH_2 + H^+ \rightarrow OH_3^+$, will be discussed later. Complex formation is quite a general phenomenon, and even mixed complex ions such as $(PO_3F_3)^{2-}$ and $(PO_2F_2)^-$ can be formed; on the other hand, not every coupling of two fluorides or oxides will form a complex, and we will have to investigate what the conditions are for stability of a complex.

An important part of the energy change in complex formation is in the formation of the complex ion, e.g. the reaction

$$O^{2-} + SO_3 \rightarrow SO_4^{2-} + Q$$

In order to calculate the change in heat content in this process, the following cycle is used:

1. SO_3 is dissociated into the ions, the process requiring an amount of energy $-E_M$.
2. The SO_4^{3-} ion is formed from the ions obtained in the former process plus a fourth O^{2-} ion, releasing an energy $-E_C$.

The heat effect, connected with the formation of the complex ion from the molecule and a free ion, is therefore

$$Q = E_C - E_M$$

If E_{SO_4} is greater than E_{SO_3}, Q will be positive and the complex ion will be formed. The method of calculating the energy of a compound was given in Section 11. It is to be remembered that the oxygen ions form a triangle in SO_3, and a tetrahedron in SO_4^{2-}. The calculation gives the following results

$$E_{SO_3} = -(3 \,.\, 6e \,.\, 2e/r - 3 \,.\, 2e \,.\, 2e/\sqrt{3}r) = -29{\cdot}2e^2/r$$
$$E_{SO_4} = -(4 \,.\, 6e \,.\, 2e/r - 6 \,.\, 2e \,.\, 2e/\tfrac{2}{3}\sqrt{6}r) = -33{\cdot}3e^2/r$$

from which is obtained

$$Q = 4{\cdot}1e^2/r$$

It is assumed in these calculations that the interionic distances are always equal to the sum of the ionic radii. To complete the calculations we have to determine whether SO_3 can combine with more than one oxygen ion, and so for the energy of the SO_5^{4-} we find

$$E = -34{\cdot}2e^2/r$$

and in the same way for SO_6^{6-}

$$E = -32{\cdot}0e^2/r$$

These calculations show that the energy is at a minimum when the sulphur ion is surrounded by five oxygen ions. Similar calculations can be carried out to determine how many oxygen ions, and also univalent negative ions, correspond to a minimum value of the energy when the central ion has a charge of 1, 2, 3, etc. The numbers obtained in this way, given in *Table XXXI*, are called

Table XXXI

Coordination Numbers

charge of central ion	1	2	3	4	5	6	7
coordination numbers for univalent ions	2	4	5	6	8	8	8
coordination numbers for divalent ions	1	2	3	4	4	5	6

'coordination numbers for isolated ions'. If the compound, which combines with ions, is not gaseous then the formulae for the heat of complex formation must be corrected for heat of sublimation. If, for example, TeO_4^{2-} ions are formed from solid TeO_3, the latter compound must first be vaporized, which requires the heat of sublimation, the formula for Q then becoming

$$Q = -S_{TeO_3} + E_{TeO_4} - E_{TeO_3}$$

According to *Table XXXI*, hexavalent ions should combine with five divalent negative ions, whereas, in fact, the S^{6+} ion has a maximum of four ions. Similarly, a tervalent positive ion should combine with five negative univalent ions, whereas, from BF_3, BF_4^-, and not BF_5^{2-}, is produced as a complex ion. There are two reasons why the actual coordination number is very often lower than the calculated value. The first arises from the assumption that the molecules combine with free ions. Such an idea is fictitious, since ions are never free even in solution where, as was seen in Section 13, they are associated with the water molecules. If, for example, the chlorine ions of NaCl react with the compound $PtCl_4$, then a correction for the hydration energy must be introduced, the magnitude of which will be proportional to the number of ions combining to form the complex. The result will be that the energy minimum will correspond to a complex with a smaller number of ions, which means that the coordination number will have a lower value.

If the SO_4^{2-} ion is made by the reaction of solid BaO and SO_3, the O^{2-} ion has to be made from BaO, which requires the lattice energy of BaO, equal to Ae^2n^2/r or $4Ae^2/r_{Ba} + r_O$. In the formation of an SO_5^{4-} ion, the heat released would be $-(34{\cdot}2 - 33{\cdot}3)e^2/r$ greater than for an ion SO_4^{2-}, but in the latter case an amount $4Ae^2/(r_{Ba} + r_O)$ would be required, which is much greater than the difference $E(SO_5^{4-}) - E(SO_4^{2-})$. SO_5^{4-} would be formed only if in some way or other SO_3 molecules contained free O^{2-} ions.

The second reason is due to the volume of the ions. If the central ion is very small, fewer negative ions than the theoretical coordination number can be arranged in such a way that they all touch it. Therefore, since complex formation occurs mainly with small positive ions of high charge, it frequently happens that complexes of elements of the first period have less than the ideal coordination number, while those of the second and third conform to the theoretical value. Thus, instead of the ideal complex ions

$$BeO_2^{2-}, \quad BO_3^{3-}, \quad CO_4^{4-}, \quad NO_4^{3-}$$

the following are actually formed

$$BeO_2^{2-}, \quad BO_3^{3-}, \quad CO_3^{2-}, \quad NO_3^{-}$$

Normal ions are formed in the third period

$$SiO_4^{4-}, \quad PO_4^{3-}$$

It is therefore clear why a nitrate ion has the formula NO_3^- while the phosphate ion is of the form PO_4^{3-}.

The sulphate and perchlorate ions belonging to the third period still do not have normal coordination numbers and it is only when Te^{6+} and I^{7+} are reached, which are considerably larger than S^{6+} and Cl^{7+}, that orthotellurates, X_6TeO_6, and the orthoperiodates, X_5IO_6, are formed with higher coordination numbers. The tellurates X_2TeO_4 and periodates XIO_4 can, of course, be formed as well, and in solid X_6TeO_6 the coordination number is actually greater than the theoretical value.

Fluorine complexes behave in the same way. Boron, in the first period, still does not show the normal coordination number and only forms BF_4^-, while the larger aluminium ion forms Na_3AlF_6 with a higher coordination number. The carbon ion in CF_4 is, however, so small that the coordination number is limited to four and complex formation is completely absent. On the other hand, the larger Si^{4+} ion gives normal complexes such as K_2SiF_6, etc.

This factor of space limitation around the ion reduces the

coordination number to an even greater extent when the negative ions are large, and accounts for the fact that fewer complex sulphide, than oxygen, ions are known. Complexes of chlorine, bromine and iodine are fewer in number than those of fluorine. BCl_3 and $SiCl_4$ do not form complexes analogous to KBF_4 and K_2SiF_6. Nevertheless, the agreement between theoretical and experimentally determined values is surprisingly good when the corrections for hydration and ionic sizes are introduced. Attention has already been drawn to the fact that ions cannot be considered as free when in solution, but are always associated with water molecules.

31. THE COORDINATION IN CRYSTALS

There is still a further reason why in crystals the observed coordination number is not equal to that calculated for free complex ions formed from free ions and molecules, but is, in actual fact, often much higher than that calculated. A free molecule NaCl, according to the calculation, would combine with one Cl^- ion: in the lattice of solid NaCl, however, each sodium ion is connected with six chlorine ions, and in CsCl this number is even larger, eight chlorine ions surrounding each Cs^+ ion. In a free ion $NaCl_n^{-(n-1)}$, the nCl^- ions repel each other, and this repulsion limits the coordination number to two. In the solid state, however, each $NaCl_6$ group is symmetrically surrounded by a number of positive Na^+ ions, and the attractive forces between these Na^+ ions and the Cl^- ions of the $NaCl_6$ group counteracts the repulsion between the Cl^- ions. This effect is so important that, in crystals of ionic complexes, the actual coordination number is not determined by the charges of the constituent ions, as is the case with free complex ions, but is determined almost exclusively by the size of the ions, each ion being surrounded by as many ions of the central ion as possible without making too close a contact. For small central ions of high charge, the coordination number is small and approaches that calculated for free complex ions. If, however, the charge of the positive ion is only two, and the radius therefore is relatively large, as in $KMgF_3$, the coordination number (6) is much greater than that calculated for the free complex ion.

But even in complexes containing ions of higher charge the coordination number (c.n.) may exceed that of the ideal free ion, as, for example, in orthotellurates, with the composition A_6TeO_6, (c.n. for the free ion equalling four), or in the compound K_3ZrF_7, that according to x-ray analysis contains groups $(ZrF_7)^{3-}$, although the c.n. for the free ion would be six.

In the compound $KMgF_3$, the structure of which is shown in

Figure 20, each Mg^{2+} ion is surrounded by six F ions. Since, according to the formula, the Mg : F ratio is only three, each F^- ion must form part of two MgF_6 groups. These groups therefore are not isolated groups as are the SiF_6 groups in K_2SiF_6, and the structure of this complex is rather different from that of the other complexes so far described. Sometimes the two groups of complexes like KBF_4, $BaSO_4$ and K_2SiF_6, with isolated complex ions, are separated from those in which, as in $KMgF_3$ and $CaTiO_3$, these complex groups are interconnected by the negative ions. In this book the two groups will not be separated, the main reason being that there is really not a sharp difference between the two of them. The two groups, together with their transition forms, will be discussed later. In the next sections we will first derive some general rules for the stability of complexes that belong to the first class with isolated complex ions.

32. EFFECT OF NON-COMPLEX ION ON STABILITY OF COMPLEX ION

We have already shown that a complex ion cannot be considered as being formed from free ions and molecules, because free ions do not exist as such but only in association with water molecules. Instead of forming a complex by reacting $PtCl_4$ and NaCl in solution, let us suppose that it is formed from $PtCl_4$ and solid NaCl, yielding Na_2PtCl_6. In such a reaction the energy released cannot be put equal to $E_{PtCl_4} - E_{PtCl_6}$. The ions must first be formed from NaCl and this requires the crystal energy U_{NaCl}. The energy released when the chlorine ions combine with $PtCl_4$ to give $PtCl_6^{2-}$ is

$$Q = E_{PtCl_4} - E_{PtCl_6}$$

Finally, the ions Na^+ and $PtCl_6^{2-}$ have to be combined to form the solid, so that the energy of complex formation will be

$$-U_{NaCl} - E_{PtCl_4} + E_{PtCl_6} + U_{Na_2PtCl_6}*$$

$U_{Na_2PtCl_6}$* is the energy released when the solid salt is formed from the ions $2Na^+ + PtCl_6^{2-}$. Now, the crystal energies of complex salts will be less than those of the salts from which they are formed for the simple reason that the complex ion, $PtCl_6^{2-}$ in this case, has a larger volume than the chlorine ion. As a first approximation, the energy of the complex salt can be neglected in comparison with that of the other compounds, and the energy of formation of the complex reduces simply to $Q - U$, where Q has the meaning given earlier. A

* The total crystal energy corresponds to a building up of the crystal from the free ions $2Na^+$, Pt^{4+} and $6Cl^-$.

very general rule governing stability can be derived from this formula, which can be illustrated by comparing a number of complexes with the same complex ion, for example the carbonates, sulphates and platinum chlorides.

Since Q will have the same value in each group that contains the same complex ion, the stability will be determined solely by the crystal energy of the compound which provides the ions for the complex ion, and the greater this is the smaller will be the heat of formation of the complex and the lower its stability. From this it follows that a compound such as a sulphate or carbonate will be all the more stable, the larger the size of the positive ion and the smaller its charge. If the ion belongs to the subgroup elements or has an abnormal electronic structure, then the stability will be less because compounds containing such ions will generally have higher crystal energies.

Table XXXII

Decomposition Temperatures of the Carbonates of Alkaline-Earth Metals

carbonates	$BeCO_3$	$MgCO_3$	$CaCO_3$	$SrCO_3$	$BaCO_3$
°C	~100	230	817	1,130	1,297

The carbonates provide a very good example of these effects. The alkali carbonates should be the most stable, and, in fact, when heated they decompose to only a small extent into oxides and CO_2, with the exception of Li_2CO_3, the smaller radius of the Li ion resulting in a higher crystal energy of lithium oxide in comparison with those of the other alkali oxides. In this respect, Li_2CO_3 resembles the carbonates of the alkaline earths, which are less stable than the alkali carbonates because the crystal energy of the alkaline-earth metals is greater than that of the alkalis as a result of their higher charge. However, the alkaline-earth carbonates also show differences in stability, increasing from beryllium to barium carbonate because the radii of the positive ions increase in that order. This is clearly brought out in *Table XXXII*, which gives the temperatures at which the various carbonates exert a pressure of one atmosphere of carbon dioxide.

The carbonates of the elements of the third group of the periodic system are less stable still. $Al_2(CO_3)_3$ apparently decomposes at ordinary temperatures, for if we attempt to make this compound by reacting an aluminium salt with a carbonate, then aluminium oxide and CO_2 are formed, a well-known reaction in analytical chemistry. Only at low temperatures does a basic carbonate of aluminium appear to exist. Boron carbonate does not exist at all, while the rare earths, as a result of their larger ionic volumes, still form carbonates, and those of the tetravalent elements are not known at all.

Finally, let us compare the carbonates of some subgroup elements with those of the main groups. Although silver and sodium have almost the same ionic radii, Ag_2CO_3 decomposes at about 400°C, since the crystal energy of Ag_2O is greater than that of Na_2O. Carbonic acid itself, which contains a very small positive ion, is also extremely unstable and, as we know, H_2CO_3 only exists in very dilute solutions. Similar behaviour is shown by the sulphates, except that they are on the whole more stable than the carbonates because the value of Q is larger. Of the sulphates, those of the alkali metals are the most stable, only Li_2SO_4 showing some decomposition into Li_2O and SO_3. $BaSO_4$ is dissociated with difficulty into BaO and SO_3, while beryllium sulphate dissociates appreciably at low temperatures.

On the other hand, sulphates of tervalent metals dissociate easily. The old process for the preparation of H_2SO_4 was based on the dissociation of ferric sulphate, the SO_3 being absorbed in moderately dilute sulphuric acid. In this manner fuming sulphuric, or Nordhausen, acid can be prepared.

Aluminium sulphate decomposes on heating into Al_2O_3 and SO_3, while the rare-earth sulphates are much more stable. Tetravalent sulphates of the type $X(SO_4)_2$ occur very rarely, and of the metals of the fourth column, only thorium, because of its large ionic radius, forms a sulphate of this type.

Aluminium carbonate and H_2CO_3 are both unstable at ordinary temperatures, the instability of H_2CO_3 being due to the small H^+ ion while that of aluminium carbonate is caused by the high charge of the aluminium ion. It would therefore be expected that sulphuric acid have about the same order of stability as aluminium sulphate, which decomposes at 750°C. Actually, H_2SO_4 vapour dissociates to about 50 per cent at 350°C and one atmosphere pressure into H_2O and SO_3. These same rules must also apply to all other groups of complexes, further examples being KBF_4, which is stable, and $Ca(BF_4)_2$, which is so unstable that it cannot be prepared because it decomposes into CaF_2 and BF_3.

Most nitrates decompose on heating, but here the decomposition is somewhat more complicated. Dissociation into oxides and N_2O_5 does not occur because the latter compound further splits into lower oxides of nitrogen and oxygen. The alkali-metal nitrates decompose into nitrites and oxygen. Thus

$$2KNO_3 \rightarrow 2KNO_2 + O_2$$

We might imagine that such a reaction could be reversible under certain circumstances, and this consideration was not discussed under the heading of complex compounds. For, if a nitrite changes to a nitrate, the ions do not simply combine with a molecule, but the valency of the nitrogen changes at the same time. The process is somewhat similar to the formation of a peroxide such as BaO_2 from BaO and oxygen, in which, as will be seen later, O_2^{2-} ions are formed from the oxygen ions in BaO and free oxygen. This process is quite a different one from the formation of a CO_3^{2-} ion, because the chemical forces leading to the formation of O_2^{2-} are certainly not of a purely electrostatic kind, yet the heat which is released in the reaction

$$2BaO + O_2 \rightarrow 2BaO_2$$

can be split up in the same way as in true ionic complexes. The heat of formation can therefore be expressed

$$-U_{BaO} + Q + U_{BaO_2}$$

in which Q is now the energy released by the combination of the oxygen ions with the oxygen, and U_{BaO_2} is the energy corresponding to the formation of solid BaO_2 from the Ba ions and the O_2^{2-} ions.

Q will have the same value for all peroxides and, although it cannot be calculated in a simple manner, we can still arrive at similar rules for the stability of the peroxides as a function of charge, radius and structure of the positive ion. Again, peroxides will only be stable if the positive ion is large, has a small charge and belongs to the elements of the main groups. Magnesium peroxide will consequently be unstable in comparison with BaO_2, and, in general, the peroxides of the elements with a valency lower than two will be non-existent. The same holds true for the elements of the subgroups. The peroxides of sodium, potassium, calcium, strontium and barium are known, but those of copper, silver, zinc or cadmium, at least in the free state, could not be prepared.

There are numerous other compounds in inorganic chemistry which contain an ion composed of two or more atoms or ions as, for example, the series of persulphides containing the ions S_2^{2-}, S_3^{2-}, S_4^{2-}, S_5^{2-}, the polyiodides the ions I_3^-, I_5^-, I_7^-, and the azides the ion N_3^-. We can think of these ions as being formed by combination of the ions S^{2-} and I^- with atoms of these elements, but we do not know from our discussion so far what forces constitute the bond, and, in consequence, we cannot calculate the energy released in the formation of such ions. Nevertheless, as far as the positive ion is concerned, the same stability rules apply, namely that the compounds will only be stable when the positive ion is large and of low valency and belongs to the elements of the main groups. The azides, in general, are unstable, and even the alkali compounds are easily dissociated, while those of the subgroup elements such as AgN_3, $Hg(N_3)_2$, etc. are explosive materials.

The stability rule still holds even when the complex ion is no longer purely ionic in character, so that we cannot use its validity as an argument that CO_3^{2-} and SO_4^{2-} are built up from ions, because the rule holds for complexes to which this does not apply. The most it does show is that the bond between the complex ion and the rest of the compound is ionic in character.

Up to now we have only considered complexes with a central positive ion, but there exist some complex ions in which the central ion is negative, the best-known example being the NH_4^+ ion. Ammonium compounds differ in stability, and from the reaction.

$$NH_3 + HX \rightarrow NH_4X + \Delta H$$

it follows that the formula for the heat of formation is analogous to that of the other complexes, viz

$$\Delta H = -E_{HX} + Q - U_{NH_4X}$$

Here the dissociation energy of the acid HX or that necessary for dissociation into ions, equally well termed the molecular energy, takes the place of the crystal energy because an acid is in general not a solid substance. It follows from this that the heat of formation of the complex will be greater the smaller the dissociation energy of the acid, that is the stronger the acid is. The value of ΔH for weak acids is so low that stable ammonium compounds are not formed, and NH_4CN, for example, decomposes with great ease into NH_3 and HCN. In H_2O the dissociation energy is so large that NH_4OH cannot be formed at ordinary temperatures; H_2S, however, has a lower dissociation energy, so that the compound NH_4HS does exist.

The energy of complex formation of the H^+ compounds, which is also called the proton affinity, will depend on the properties of the negative ion. Of all hydrogen compounds, NH_3 has the highest proton affinity and therefore the most marked tendency to form positive complex ions, NH_4^+. Complex formation also occurs with PH_3, which takes up hydrogen ions to form PH_4^+, the phosphonium ion. The proton affinity, however, is smaller and consequently phosphonium ions will only be formed when the hydrogen ion is present in compounds from which it can be easily detached, as when PH_3 reacts with a strong acid. Because phosphonium ions can only be formed with strong acids, PH_4I can be produced from PH_3 and HI, but not PH_4F from PH_3 and HF under normal pressure.

Water has a much smaller proton affinity than NH_3 because of the lower charge on the oxygen ion so that there are relatively few compounds containing an H_3O^+ ion, and those that do exist are very unstable. Solid hydronium compounds, stable at room temperature, are, in fact, only formed by the reaction of water with very strong acids, the best example being $(OH_3)^+ClO_4^-$, the monohydrate of perchloric acid, which is the complete analogue of $(NH_4)^+ClO_4^-$. The justification for this formula is that both compounds have the same crystal structure. Further examples of hydronium compounds are the hydrates of the halogen acids which are formed at low temperatures from concentrated solutions. These compounds, however, generally contain more than one molecule of water, which is to be regarded as water of crystallization as in compounds such as $Na_2SO_4 . 7H_2O$. Hydrates of H_2SO_4 and H_2SeO_4 are also known, and these should probably be formulated as hydronium compounds in the same way.

The remaining hydrogen compounds have much smaller proton affinities, although HF can form a fluoronium salt $(FH_2^+)(ClO)_4^-$ by reaction with $HClO_4$. There may be further examples of proton addition with other hydrogen compounds, although $HClO_4$ behaves in quite a different way with easily-oxidizable hydrogen compounds, and reacts with HCl to give H_2O, chlorine and the lower oxides of chlorine.

The heats of formation of complex hydrogen compounds from the molecules from which they are formed confirm these conclusions (*see Table XXXIII* (*a*)). It must be pointed out that the heats of formation of these compounds from their elements have, of course, quite different values, which decrease from the fluoride to the iodide because the heats of formation of the acid also decrease from fluorine to iodine (*see Table XXXIII* (*a*)). From these figures, taking the heat of formation of 16 kcal for NH_3 and -6 kcal for PH_3, the total heats of formation then become as in *Table XXXIII* (*b*).

Table XXXIII

(*a*) *Heats of Formation in kcal*

complex hydrogen compounds (from compounds)	PH_4F ~0	PH_4Cl 15	PH_4Br 23	PH_4I 24
	NH_4F 1	NH_4Cl 37	NH_4Br 40	NH_4I 38
acids	HF 95	HCl 22	HBr 8·5	HI −6

(*b*) *Total Heats of Formation in kcal*

complex hydrogen compounds (from elements)	PH_4F 90	PH_4Cl 31	PH_4Br 25·5	PH_4I 12
	NH_4F 112	NH_4Cl 75	NH_4Br 65	NH_4I 48

33. DEPENDENCE OF STABILITY ON THE CENTRAL ION

The differing stability of various complex ions has just been discussed. As regards the dependence of stability on the central ion, the rules can be formulated very easily. When the central ion has a high charge, a small radius and not a noble-gas structure, the stability will be high because the attraction between the central and surrounding ions is then as large as it can be.

We can now state how two compounds have to be chosen in order to produce a very stable complex. One (the donor) must have a positive ion which will not be part of the non-complex ion, with a low charge and large radius and preferably a noble-gas structure; the other (the acceptor) must have a positive ion (the central ion) with a large charge and small radius, and preferably not a noble-gas structure. There is, however, a limit to the radius of the positive ion; the central ion must not be so small that there is no space left for extra ions, otherwise there will be no complex formation of any kind. It was seen earlier that no complexes of CF_4 and $SiCl_4$ exist. Because lack of space or screening only appears when an ion is surrounded by three or more ions CO_2 and SiO_2 still can form complexes. If an oxide of the type X_2O_7 takes up a further oxygen ion to form $2ClO_4^-$, there is no increase of the coordination number since in Cl_2O_7 every chlorine ion is surrounded by four oxygen ions as well, so that even this oxide still gives complexes. It is only in oxides of the type XO_4, of which only two, RuO_4 and OsO_4, are known, that the possibility of complex formation with other oxides disappears or becomes very small indeed.

There are many complexes with a central positive ion, but the number with a central negative ion is small and the reason for this is obvious. We have already seen that a central ion with a high charge and small radius is a necessary condition for high stability. Now a positive ion can have a high charge, but with increasing charge the radius diminishes. In the positive central ion, then, these two favourable factors work together. A negative ion, on the other hand, cannot have a charge greater than three, and ions with such a charge have a very large radius so that what is gained by increasing the charge is lost by increasing the radius. Finally, all negative ions have a noble-gas structure, and thus all the circumstances are unfavourable for the formation of a complex ion. While the complex KBF_4 is known and is formed thus

$$K^+F^- + B^{3+}F_3^- \rightarrow K(BF_4)$$

the analogous reaction

$$I^-Li^+ + N^{3-}Li_3^+ \rightarrow I(NLi_4)$$

probably does not take place. Only in the hydrogen compounds, where the hydrogen ion is so very much smaller than the central ion, do the arguments given above no longer hold. These compounds have been fully discussed in Section 23.

It will be seen later that the covalent bond plays an important part in those complexes containing hydrogen in the complexion. Such complexes can be considered even less than can simple hydrogen compounds as being purely ionic. Furthermore, the penetration of the hydrogen ion into the negative ion makes quantitative calculations impossible.

There is, presumably, still a group of complexes with negative central ions, among which could be cited the compound $(IAg)^{2+}(NO_3)_2^-$, formed by melting two molecules of $AgNO_3$ and one molecule of AgI, or by dissolving AgI in a concentrated solution of $AgNO_3$. The small solubility of AgI indicates a specially strong attraction between Ag^+ and I^- ions which can be attributed to the 18-electron configuration of the Ag^+ ion. This attraction leads to more than one silver ion combining with an iodine ion. The electrostatic theory cannot throw any further light on these little-known complexes.

34. COMPLEXES WITH NON-ISOLATED COMPLEX IONS

Since a complex like $KMgF_3$ does not contain isolated complex ions, the reasoning by which the stability rules for complexes were derived in the preceding sections does not hold for complexes not containing isolated complex ions. In this section it will be shown that, for the latter group, the stability rules are valid, too.

Let us consider the reaction

$$KF(s) + MgF_2(s) \rightarrow KMgF_3(s)$$

From the ionic radii, *Table V*, Section 9, it is found that the radii of K^+ and F^- are almost equal. Now it is easily seen that in an aggregate of spheres of equal radius the densest packing is obtained when one sphere is surrounded by twelve other spheres in a so-called close-packed structure (*see* Section 67). In ionic crystals, a minimum energy is to be expected if each ion is surrounded by the maximum number of ions of the opposite size, and, according to this reasoning, KF would be expected to have a structure in which each K^+ ion is surrounded by twelve F^- ions, and each F^- ion by twelve K^+ ions. However, such a structure is geometrically impossible, and K^+ and F^- ions, when coming together, cannot take full advantage of the fact that their radii would allow a twelve coordination; as has been shown, compounds *AB* must form structures in which their coordination is six (NaCl type) or eight (CsCl type). Now if there is a mixture of K^+, Mg^{2+} and F^- ions an arrangement can be formed in which each of the ions has its 'natural' coordination. In $KMgF_3$ (*Figure 20*, Section 29), each potassium ion is surrounded by twelve F^- ions, each Mg^{2+} ion is surrounded by six F^- ions, which is almost the maximum that is to be expected for the smaller Mg^{2+} ion, and each F^- ion is surrounded by two Mg^{2+} ions and four K^+ ions, which is not yet the largest possible number, but equal to that in KF and larger than in MgF_2. A large size of the positive ions with low charge will increase the stability of the complex because of the more favourable coordination in the complex.

The reason that ions with higher charge are good complex formers is the fact that in the complex the positive ions of high charge are further apart than in the single compound. $KMgF_3$ can, in a way, be visualized as MgF_2, diluted by KF, in which process the mean distance between Mg^{2+} ions has increased, and the energy is therefore lowered. In this way it can be understood that in complexes not containing isolated complex ions the heat of formation—and thus the stability—is greater the greater the difference in size, radius and configuration of the positive ions, just as in complexes with isolated groups. This rule is restricted, however, by the one that states that the stability of complexes is decreased if the ratio of the number of cations and anions strongly deviates from 1 : 1.

According to the rules concerning the properties of ions, the heat of formation of $KClO_4$ will be greater than that of $Al(ClO_4)_3$. The latter compound, in actual fact, is very unstable, probably even more than would be expected from the difference in the positive ions alone. Since, in $Al(ClO_4)_3$, more than three large ClO^- ions must surround the Al^{3+} ion to form a coordination lattice consisting of Al^{3+} and ClO_4^- ions, this structure will not be very stable, because the ClO_4 groups will come too close together. Aluminium perchlorate has a tendency to form compounds with a better cation : anion ratio by giving off Cl_2O_7, and the formation of basic salts, e.g. $AlO(ClO_4)$. Nitrates behave as perchlorates: normal nitrates of elements of a valency higher than two are very unstable and tend to form oxynitrates.

Also, according to the rules, K_3PO_4 has a higher heat of formation than $AlPO_4$, but in this case the difference is smaller than could be expected from the difference in the positive ions, alone. $AlPO_4$, in actual fact, is relatively stable because of its cation : anion ratio of 1 : 1. It can form a coordination lattice, consisting of alternating Al^{3+} and PO_4^{3-} ions, as can $KClO_4$. In K_3PO_4, however, the structure must be such that each PO_4^{3-} ion will be surrounded by more than three K^+ ions, and since K^+ and O^{2-} ions have almost the same radius, each of these K^+ ions should be in contact with twelve oxygen ions. If, in a compound $K_n(XO_p)$, n is much greater than 1, a structure in which each K^+ ion is surrounded by twelve O^{2-} ions cannot be formed. Complexes with $n > 1$ will have a tendency to reduce the cation : anion ratio by giving off the elements forming the oxide.

A Ti^{4+} ion, in reaction with O^{2-} ions, will tend to form compounds in which it is surrounded by six O^{2-} ions. In reaction with CaO, therefore, it could form isolated complex ions TiO_6, but the formula of the complex then should be Ca_4TiO_6. This complex has too unfavourable a cation : anion ratio; it reduces its CaO content, forming $CaTiO_3$, in which the Mg^{2+} ions are still surrounded by six O^{2-} ions and each Ti^{4+} ion still has a very high oxygen coordination. The TiO_6 groups, however, are no longer isolated, but interconnected by O^{2-} ions, each of these ions forming part of two MgO_6 groups exactly in the same way as the F^- ions that connect the

MgF_6 groups in $KMgF_3$, which has the same structure as $CaTiO_3$. In K_3PO_4 the cation : anion ratio is not favourable either, and the phosphates show a tendency to form complexes with a lower K_2O content. As in Ca titanate, this is effected by 'condensation' of the complex ions. In the pyrophosphates, e.g. $K_4P_2O_7$, two PO_4 groups condense to a group P_2O_7, with the structure

$$\left[\begin{array}{ccccc} & O & & O & \\ O & P & O & P & O \\ & O & & O & \end{array}\right]^{4-}$$

A further condensation occurs in the metaphosphates, APO_3, with a pseudo cation : anion ratio 1 : 1. In these compounds, phosphor has still the same coordination number, but the PO_4^{3-} ions are either condensed to rings, e.g. in the tetrametaphosphate $(NH_4)_4(P_4O_{12})$, or to chains of infinite length, the structure of the phosphates in a tetrametaphosphate being

$$\begin{array}{ccccc} & O & & O & \\ O & P & O & P & O \\ & O & & O & \\ O & P & O & P & O \\ & O & & O & \end{array}$$

or in a chain metaphosphate

$$\begin{array}{ccccccccc} & O & & O & & O & & O & \\ —O & P & O & P & O & P & O & P & O— \\ & O & & O & & O & & O & \end{array}$$

It is evident that monovalent complex ions cannot condense in this way: both NO_3^- and ClO_4^- would lose their charge and become unable to form complexes by condensation without change of their coordination number to

$$\begin{array}{ccccc} O & N & O & N & O \\ & O & & O & \end{array}$$

and

$$\begin{array}{ccccc} & O & & O & \\ O & Cl & O & Cl & O \\ & O & & O & \end{array}$$

respectively.

Condensation can occur, however, with divalent complex ions: besides the normal sulphates, pyrosulphates $A_2S_2O_7$, can be formed, either from sulphates and SO_3, or by heating the acid salts. In chromates, more than two CrO_4 groups can be combined; in the polychromates, $A_2CrO_4 \cdot nCrO_3$, n varies from 1 to 3.

Even more unfavourable than in the phosphates are the cation: anion ratios in 'ortho' silicates with isolated groups like $K_4^+(SiO_4)^{4-}$. The silicates therefore show anion condensation to an even higher degree than phosphates: in silicates rings and chains can be formed as in phosphates, but condensation can even go further, sheets of SiO_4 tetrahedra being formed, e.g. in such a way that the 'free' oxygen ions in chains

```
O       O       O       O
Si  O   Si  O   Si  O   Si
O       O       O       O
```

form the links between parallel chains.

There are several other ways in which an unfavourable cation : anion ratio can be reduced.

The I^{7+} ion is already so large that it can be surrounded by six O^{2-} ions to form the orthoperiodates K_5IO_6. These compounds are very unstable; the cation : anion ratio, however, is reduced if a number of potassium ions are substituted by ions of higher valency.

It has been found that the periodate $KNiIO_6$ is more stable, the Ni^{4+} ions in this compound having the very unusual valency of four. Phosphates are stabilized when the alkali ions are substituted by ions of the alkaline-earth metals; double phosphates, like $KBaPO_4$ and NH_4CaPO_4, are more stable than the ortho alkaliphosphates.

In the phosphates, partial substitution of oxygen by fluorine also has the effect of reducing the cation : anion ratio, e.g. in $K_2(PO_3F)^{2-}$ and $K(PO_2F_2)^-$. The first compound is easily obtained by fusion of KF and potassium metaphosphate

$$KF + KPO_3 \rightarrow K_2(PO_3F)$$

In these compounds the F^- ion can be substituted by the OH^- ion, which, because its size is almost the same as that of the F^- ion, behaves in a similar manner. The compounds $K_2\{PO_3(OH)\}$ and $K\{PO_2(OH)_2\}$ are easily formed when solutions of K_3PO_4 are hydrolysed, or slightly acidified. A more commonly seen formula of these complexes that are often described as acid salts, e.g. K_2HPO_4 and KH_2PO_4, does not show their real structure.

The different processes, condensation, substitution of positive ions and substitution of O^{2-} ions by negative ions F^- or OH^- ions by hydrolysis, may take place simultaneously and thus result in the formation of the very complicated compounds which have been observed for phosphates, borates, etc. and especially in silicates. Of the latter group, a few compounds will be discussed in somewhat greater detail.

35. SILICATES

The silicates are of the greatest importance in geology because the earth's crust is largely composed of them. The enormous variety of compositions and the complexity of these materials at one time constituted a major, and apparently insoluble, problem in chemistry. Systematic investigation by x-rays has, however, thrown much light on this subject. The first results of these investigations showed that each Si^{4+} ion in the silicates, as well as in the different natural forms of SiO_2, is always surrounded by four negative oxygen ions. A silicate of the composition $MgSiO_3$, therefore, will not contain isolated groups as does $MgCO_3$, but has SiO_4 ions that share part of their oxygen ions, thus forming chains or rings as the PO_4^{3-} groups in metaphosphates.

In the silicates, such chains actually do occur and we will now proceed to describe some of them in more detail. One example of a silicate with a free SiO_4 group is Mg_2SiO_4, olivine. In addition, there is a silicate $Sc_2Si_2O_7$, which, according to x-ray analysis, must contain a group $(Si_2O_7)^{6-}$. The structure of this group, using the coordination number four, is as follows

$$\left[\begin{matrix} & O & & O & \\ O & Si & O & Si & O \\ & O & & O & \end{matrix}\right]^{6-}$$

Actually, the four oxygen ions occupy the corners of a tetrahedron around the positive ions, but for the present purpose they have been shown in a plane. In the mineral $TiMg(Si_3O_9)$ there is, in the same manner, a hexavalent group Si_3O_9 which forms a closed ring

$$\begin{matrix} & & O\ O & & \\ & & Si & & \\ & & O\ O & & \\ O & Si & O & Si & O \\ & O & & O & \end{matrix}$$

Six SiO_4 groups in a closed ring are found in the mineral beryl, or smaragd, $Be_3Al_2(Si_6O_{18})$

```
       O O
        Si
       O O
   OSiO   OSiO
    O       O
   OSiO   OSiO
       O O
        Si
       O O
```

In some silicates these rings are so large that gaps exist in the crystal, through which water and other ions can penetrate. Such porous crystals are also found in minerals in clay, and play a very important part in plant growth because of their ability to hold such ions as potassium. The structural possibilities are not ended with the formation of rings, and infinitely long chains of SiO_4 groups can also be formed thus

```
        O     O     O     O     O
 ... O  Si O  Si O  Si O  Si O  Si  O ...
        O     O     O     O     O
```

Such a group has the composition $(SiO_3)_n$, where $n = \infty$. There must, at the same time, be $2n$ positive charges, and x-ray analysis has shown that the metasilicates A^{2+} SiO_3 do contain such chains of SiO_4 groups of infinite length. The $2n$ positive charges can then be provided by different ions, and in this way an enormous number of silicates with this grouping is possible. A well-known silicate of this type is steatite, $MgSiO_3$.

The strongest bonds in the crystal are along the Si—O—Si chains. It is remarkable that these silicate crystals, containing chains of SiO_4 groups, can be easily split into threads which are then made into fibres and textiles, e.g. the fibres from the mineral asbestos. Chains of SiO_4 groups can join together laterally to form layers, while rings can also join up in the same way. Where such layers exist, the crystals can be easily split into thin laminae, as, for example, in mica.

In such compounds the positive charge can be provided by a variety of ions. When the rings or chains interconnect, each SiO_4 group is coupled to the next by means of a common oxygen ion.

Again, the SiO_4 groups can be arranged in such a way that each of them shares an oxygen ion with four other groups, for example when SiO_4^{4-} groups form a three-dimensional lattice with the empirical composition SiO_2. Starting with the orthosilicates, one can arrive, by successive coupling of more and more SiO_4^{4-} groups, at the crystal of SiO_2, itself. Each Si^{4+} ion is surrounded by a tetrahedron of four oxygen ions which can be arranged in space in various ways; this accounts for the existence of a number of different forms of silicon dioxide.

The silicon ion in silicates can be replaced by an aluminium ion, when, of course, the charge of one of the positive ions must be increased. This means that, in a silicate, a part of the silicon can be replaced by aluminium, provided that at the same time an equal quantity of the sodium is replaced by calcium, so that the sum of the charges remains the same. Such substitutions of ions A^+ by ions A^{2+}, of about the same size, greatly increase the range of compositions of the silicates.

It is therefore quite easy to see why such a very large number of silicates is possible. In fact, the chemistry of these substances is now so developed that it can be classed next in importance to the chemistry of carbon compounds. It must not be assumed, however, that there is any direct relationship between the chemistry of silicates and that of carbon compounds. It is true that in both groups chains, rings and layers of atoms occur, but the structural features of the two groups are totally different. The silicon ions in silicates are always coupled to each other by oxygen ions, while in the carbon compounds the carbon atoms are joined directly to each other. Again, the bonds between carbon atoms are purely homopolar, while the silicates must be regarded as partly ionic compounds.

36. COMPLEXES AND DOUBLE SALTS

Complexes with isolated complex ions will always contain positive ions of high valency that form the central ions of the complex ions (KBF_4, $KClO_4$, $BaSO_4$). Positive ions of low valency will usually have a much higher coordination in the complex, and therefore will not be the central ions of isolated complex ions ($KMgF_3$, $KMgCl_3$). If complexes of both types are dissolved in water, the ions BF_4^-, ClO_4^-, etc. will not be dissociated because of the high charge of the central ions. On the other hand, in MgF_6^-, the attraction will be much smaller, the central ion being larger and having a higher charge, and these complex ions will therefore dissociate into their constituent single ions. It is evident that even $MgCl_4^{2-}$ or $MgCl_3^{2-}$ ions cannot persist in aqueous solution, since it is known that a solution of magnesium chloride in water does not contain molecules $MgCl_2$, although the repulsion between Cl^- ions in this molecule is less than in the ions $MgCl_4^{2-}$ or $MgCl_3^-$.

Since, in many cases, the complex ions persist in the solutions of complexes with isolated complex ions, and are dissociated into the single ions when complexes not containing isolated complex ions are dissolved, it was once thought that there was an essential difference between the two groups, which were distinguished as 'complexes' and 'double salts'. It is now known that there is a gradual transition between these two types, that the difference is in the charge and the size of the acceptor compound, only, and that there is, therefore, no longer any reason to make a distinction between them, all compounds formed from two binary compounds now being called complexes. It will be seen, however, that not in all combinations of two binary compounds is the essential process in the complex formation a transition of ions nor a redistribution of ions. Sometimes one of the compounds maintains part of its identity, its molecules being taken in by the lattice without formation of a complex group, or its molecules attached to one of the ions by bonds that are not electrostatic in character.

37. ACIDS AND BASES

From the point of view of practical chemistry, an important group of complexes are those obtained by the reaction of water with oxides. Starting with the oxides of the third period, in accordance with Section 29, the following complex ions can be expected to be formed

$$NaO^-, MgO_2^{2-}, AlO_3^{3-}, SiO_4^{4-}, PO_4^{3-}, SO_4^{2-}, ClO_4^-$$

in which are used the normal coordination numbers, the smallness of the central ions in SO_4^{2-} and ClO_4^- being taken into consideration. In combination with H^+ ions these will give the following neutral molecules

$$NaOH, Mg(OH)_2, Al(OH)_3, Si(OH)_4, PO_4H_3, SO_4H_2, ClO_4H$$

On solution in water, electrolytic dissociation can occur, and we now have to explain the surprising fact that NaOH is a strong base and that in the above series of compounds the basicity gradually decreases, finally giving way to an increasingly acidic character, the last compound being a very strong acid. That NaOH is a strong base is merely an expression of the fact that it will dissociate strongly in solution into the ions Na^+ and OH^-. It must be borne in mind that the OH^- behaves very much as a simple univalent ion because of the penetration of the H^+ ion. It will have approximately the dimensions of the F^- ion, so that the reason for the ionic dissociation of NaOH is related to the question of why the alkali fluorides also show marked ionic dissociation. This will be considered in detail in Section 49.

It is easy to see that NaOH will not dissociate into NaO^- and H^+, simply because the bond between O^{2-} and H^+, due to the smallness of the H^+ ion, is much stronger than that between O^{2-} and Na^+. Therefore, when NaOH dissociates, it gives the ions Na^+ and OH^-, and not NaO^- and H^+. From this it follows that NaOH is not an acid.

Considering, now, $Mg(OH)_2$, the bond between the magnesium and the oxygen is seen to be stronger because of the higher charge of the positive ion. In subsequent compounds of the series given above, the charge of the positive ion steadily increases and consequently the dissociation between positive ion and oxygen becomes increasingly more difficult, and the basic properties decrease. In $HClO_4$*, the OH group is so strongly attracted by the small, heptavalent, chlorine ion that no dissociation into OH^- ions is observable, and $HClO_4$ has, in consequence, no basic properties.

Proceeding from left to right along the series, the basic properties decrease, the splitting off of the hydrogen ions being facilitated by the repulsion of the positive ions as they become smaller and more highly charged. Therefore, while the dissociation into OH^- ions steadily diminishes, the opportunity for dissociation into H^+ ions steadily increases. This theory is in excellent agreement with the observed facts, but an exact quantitative agreement cannot be obtained. The value of the dissociation energy cannot be calculated exactly because of the difficulty introduced by the penetration of the hydrogen ion.

There is a very considerable difference between an acid, say H_2SO_4, and one of its 'salts', e.g. Na_2SO_4. It is a general rule that the acid is much more liable to decomposition into its component oxides than the corresponding sodium compound, and that the decomposition can even go so far that the acid is not stable at all, whereas the carbonates, e.g. Na_2CO_3, are perfectly stable compounds, there is no pure acid H_2CO_3. The explanation of this instability is easily found by applying the stability rule for complexes: the unstability of the acid is caused by the small radius of the hydrogen ion. Another difference between an acid and its salts is that, when dissolved in water, the salt is completely dissociated into ions,

* It is clear that the formula ClO_4H would be more rational than the accepted one.

whereas the solution of the acid, if it is weak, may contain a considerable amount of undissociated molecules. Again, there is an easy explanation: because of the much larger radius of the metal ion, the dissociation energy of the salt will always be lower than that of the acid.

It will be shown in the next section that some of the stronger acids are very stable as complexes, that is to say, do not decompose into their component oxides, but, on the other hand, may be very unstable because they form lower oxides and oxygen, e.g.

$$2HClO_3 \rightarrow H_2O + 2ClO_2 + \tfrac{1}{2}O_2$$

In such cases, the salt is always more stable than the acid: $KClO_4$, at moderate temperature, is a stable compound, but the acid is very unstable as well as explosive, even at low temperatures. In the salts, the stability is increased by the higher heat of complex formation; the total heat of formation from the elements, that determines the stability of the complex against decomposition in lower oxides, may be negative for the acid, but positive for the salts of the alkali metals.

38. STRENGTHS OF ACIDS AND BASES

The dissociation of an acid into ions depends on the magnitude of their dissociation energy in water; it has been pointed out earlier that a substantial part of the energy change on solution is caused by the hydration due to the combination of ions formed with molecules of the solvent, and the degree of ionization will therefore depend on the difference between the dissociation energy and the hydration energy. If, therefore, the acidity runs parallel with the value of the dissociation energy, it does not mean that the hydration energy is small, but merely that it is approximately the same for the different acids. This is quite reasonable, since the most important contribution to the hydration energy is made by the small H^+ ion, while the hydration energy of the large complex ion is fairly small.

In principle, the calculation of the dissociation energy is very simple. It is merely the energy of a H^+ ion related to all the other ions in the acid molecule. There is, however, the complication that the hydrogen ion penetrates the negative ion with which it is combined, and the energy between them cannot be calculated. Nevertheless, the difference in dissociation energy can be calculated easily, since it can be assumed that the error introduced in calculating the energy of the bond between the H^+ ion and the oxygen ion is practically the same in all acid ions. Making use of this assumption, a number of rules governing the dissociation energy can be derived:

1. For equal structures, the dissociation energy of an acid will increase as the central ion increases in size, because the H^+ ion is then further removed from the nucleus which repels it.

2. The higher the charge of the central ion, the smaller will be the dissociation energy, and consequently the stronger the acid, since the repulsion of the H^+ ion always increases with the charge of the central ion. This effect will be lessened, because the acid with the more highly-charged central ion contains less H^+ ions, as, for example, in the compounds H_3PO_4, H_2SO_4 and $HClO_4$, but the effect of the hydrogen ions is of less significance because they are situated farther from the hydrogen ion in question than is the central ion.

3. Replacement of a noble-gas central ion by one with another structure, but of equal charge and radius, will produce the same effect, namely an increase of acid strength.

4. For the same central ion, the dissociation energy will be smaller the fewer negative ions the acid contains; these attract the hydrogen ion.

5. If, in an acid, the negative ions are replaced by larger ones, then the acidity increases because the energy of the bond between the H^+ ion and the neighbouring negative ions decreases.

6. For the same reason, the replacement of the negative ions by ions of higher charge decreases acidity.

All these rules are naturally only true if the acids consist of ions, and when these rules are obeyed it is confirmation of the fact that the bonds in these compounds are at least partly electrostatic in character.

1. Without exception, the acidity decreases with increasing size of the central ion, as the following examples show

$$HClO_4 > HIO_4$$
$$K_2SO_4 > H_2SeO_4 > H_2TeO_4$$
$$H_3BO_3 > H_3AlO_3$$

where the sign $>$ indicates 'stronger than'.

2. Another rule, which also holds without exception, is that the acidity increases with increasing charge of the central ion, as illustrated by the following examples

$$HNO_3 > H_2CO_3 > H_3BO_3$$
$$HClO_4 > H_2SO_4 > H_3PO_4 > H_4SiO_4$$

The two strongest acids, HNO_3 and $HClO_4$, gradually change into weak acids, H_3BO_3 and H_4SiO_4, as the charge of the central ion decreases. The change in acidity in this series is undoubtedl enhanced by the increase of the radius of the central ion, which is connected with the change in charge. In the following series of compounds, in spite of the decreasing number of oxygen ions which works against reduction of acidity, the acidity diminishes with the diminishing charge of the central ion

$$HClO_4 > HClO_3 > HClO_2 > HClO$$
$$H_2SO_4 > H_2SO_3$$

The following series appears to contradict the rule

$$H_3PO_2 > H_3PO_3 > H_3PO_4$$

but this is a rather special case, since in H_3PO_2 and H_3PO_3 the hydrogen is in part bound directly to the phosphorus and is not present as H^+ ions, a point to which reference will be made later.

3. A non-noble-gas central ion, other things being equal, will give a stronger acid than a noble-gas one. Although Zn^{2+} and Ga^{3+} are somewhat larger than the ions Mg^{2+} and Al^{3+}, it is found that

$$ZnO_2H_2 > MgO_2H_2, \qquad GaO_3H_3 > AlO_3H_3, \qquad \text{etc.}$$

$Mg(OH)_2$ is exclusively basic in its properties. $Zn(OH)_2$, on the other hand, is amphoteric, while arsenious acid, H_3AsO_4, is considerably stronger than the acid derived from pentavalent vanadium.

4. The more oxygen ions an acid contains, the weaker it will be, but not many examples can be found to show this. H_6TeO_6 and H_5IO_6 are very weak acids; in addition to the size of the central ion, the large number of oxygen ions may be the cause of these acids being so very much weaker than H_2SO_4 and $HClO_4$.

5. If all the oxygen ions in H_2CO_3 are replaced by larger sulphur ions, the acidity should theoretically increase; so little is known about the acidity of thioacids that it cannot be stated with certainty whether the predictions of the theory are correct here.

6. Because of their different compositions, it is difficult to compare acids containing negative ions with different charges, but there are a number of very strong acids which contain fluorine ions in place of oxygen ions, e.g. HBF_4 and HPF_6. HBF_4 is very much stronger than boric acid, and this must be the result of the bond between the H^+ and F^- ions which, due to the lower charge of the fluorine ion, is much weaker than that between the H^+ and O^{2-} ions in boric acid. Complex acids of the type $HSbCl_6$ should be particularly strong due to the high charge of the central ion. It would probably be possible to show, with the help of such an acid, that compounds such as HCl, H_2S, AsH_3, etc. still have some proton affinity.

The behaviour of acids derived from the lower oxides of phosphorus is of particular interest. It has been seen that H_3PO_2 behaves exclusively as a monobasic acid, and H_3PO_3 as a dibasic one, from which it can be deduced that in the latter, as well as in the former, hydrogen ions are directly bound to the phosphorus. If an ionic formula is set up for these acids, taking this fact into account, then part of the hydrogen must be shown as negative, and the following structures are obtained

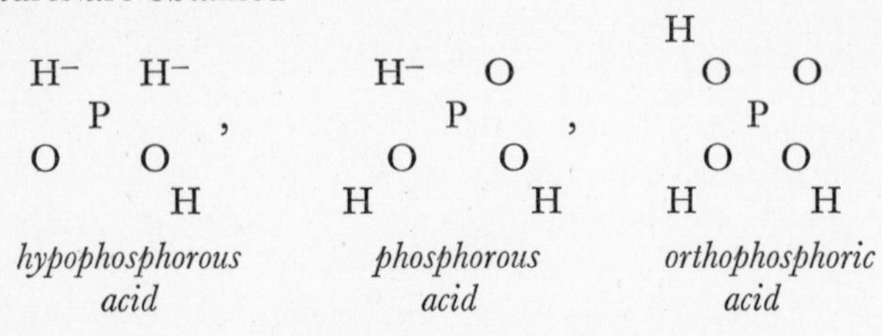

Since these acids can be derived by successively replacing an OH^- by a H^- ion, the following must hold

$$H_3PO_2 > H_3PO_3 > H_3PO_4$$

because a bivalent ion, the oxygen in $O^{2-}H^+$, is replaced by a monovalent ion H^-. These three acids can be compared with two of the acids derived from carbon, namely carbonic and formic acids. Oxalic acid also has an analogue amongst the phosphorus compounds, namely $H_4P_2O_6$.

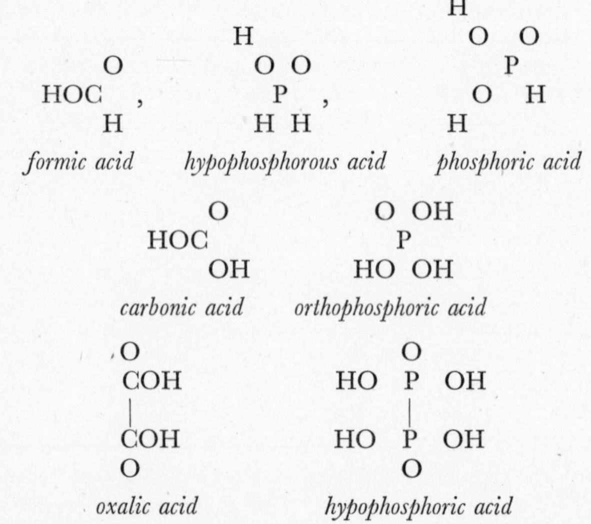

No satisfactory electrostatic formula can be devised for these latter compounds, which makes it doubtful whether it is correct to do so for H_3PO_3, H_3PO_2, H_2CO_2 and H_2CO_3.

Rules analogous to those for acids also hold for strengths of bases. It is easy to see that the dissociation of a base will be all the easier if:

1. The positive ion has a low charge.
2. The positive ion has a greater radius.

Finally, a base derived from an ion of the main series will have a smaller dissociation energy, and therefore will be stronger, than one which contains a positive ion of equal charge and radius, but with a different structure. The strongest bases are those derived from elements in the left-hand bottom corner of the periodic system, because basicity is high for large low-charged ions with a noble-gas structure. The following series

$$[B(OH)_3] < Al(OH)_3 < Sc(OH)_3 < La(OH)_3$$

$$H_2CO_3 < Si(OH)_4 < Ti(OH)_4 < Zr(OH)_4 < Th(OH)_4$$

show clearly the result of increasing basicity with increasing radius of the central ion ($<$ here meaning 'weaker base than'). $B(OH)_3$ and H_2CO_3 both have acidic properties; $Th(OH)_4$ is definitely basic while even $La(OH)_3$ is a fairly strong base. The next two series

$$Li(OH) < Be(OH)_2 < [B(OH)_3]$$

$$Cs(OH) < Ba(OH)_2 < La(OH)_3 < Hf(OH)_4\ [Ta(OH)_5, W(OH)_6]$$

also clearly show the decrease of basicity with increasing charge of the positive ion. $B(OH)_3$ and the hydrates of Ta_2O_5 and WO_3 have no basic properties at all, and have become acidic in character: this is indicated above by the use of square brackets.

In each of the four groups of compounds there must be one in which the acidic and basic properties are just about evenly balanced; it will therefore behave as an acid or a base according to the circumstances in which it is placed. Such hydroxides are called amphoteric hydroxides, a typical example being $Al(OH)_3$. In proceeding from aluminium to the compound immediately below, the basicity increases due to the larger radius of the positive ion; by moving one place to the right, the basicity decreases due to increase of the charge. In this way, therefore, $Ti(OH)_4$ is about as strong a base as $Al(OH)_3$. In fact, the amphoteric hydroxides $Be(OH)_2$, $Al(OH)_3$, $Ti(OH)_4$ and $Cb(OH)_5$ occur along a diagonal across the periodic system. The decrease of basicity with increasing charge is also the reason why, with elements which form a number of oxides, the lower members form bases and the higher ones acids, such as CrO and CrO_3, MnO and Mn_2O_7, etc. It can be deduced, therefore, that $Fe(OH)_2$ must be a stronger base than $Fe(OH)_3$, while $Ti(OH)_3$ must be stronger than $Ti(OH)_4$, even though the change in structure of the positive ion could always have a compensating influence.

The effect of the structure of the positive ion in acids has already been discussed; $Zn(OH)_2$ is weaker than $Mg(OH)_2$, while Ag(OH) is weaker than NaOH, etc. Comparing Cl_2O, which is weakly acid, with Na_2O, one would certainly expect it to have basic properties, but the fact that it is weakly acid is probably associated with the exceptional structure of the ion. Again, it must be remembered that, in general, the properties of the oxides of the nonmetallic elements do not fall into line, and CO, N_2O, NO and F_2O have neither basic not acidic properties. This proves that they are not composed of ions, which naturally raises doubts as to whether the peculiar properties of Cl_2O could not be ascribed to this fact.

39. STABILITY OF ACIDS AND BASES

A number of acids and bases decompose easily at ordinary, or slightly higher, temperatures into water and oxides. The usual stability rules for complexes govern such decompositions. Acids will lose water more easily, the smaller the charge of the central ion, which can be seen from the stability of H_2SO_4 compared with that of H_2SO_3, or $HClO_4$ with HClO. At first sight it appears rather strange that, in the basic hydroxides, this stability order is completely reversed. NaOH loses water with difficulty, while $Ca(OH)_2$ does so much more readily, and $Al(OH)_3$ and $Si(OH)_4$ both lose water with great ease, although traces of water are still very strongly held by the oxides formed.

The influence of the radius of the positive ion is also quite different for acids and bases; H_2TeO_4 loses water more easily than H_2SO_4, but LiOH does so much more readily than KOH, and $Be(OH)_2$ than $Mg(OH)_2$, which does so more easily than $Ba(OH)_2$. The reason for this apparently contradictory behaviour is that in the reaction

$$BaO + H_2O \rightarrow Ba^{2+} + (O^{2-} + H_2O) \rightarrow Ba(OH)_2$$

BaO dissociates into ions, followed by the formation of (OH^-) ions from water and O^{2-} ions. The lower the crystal energy of the oxide, the greater will be the heat of formation of this process, and the hydroxide will therefore be more stable, the greater the radius and the smaller the charge of the positive ion.

In the formation of an acid, for example H_2SO_4 from H_2O and SO_3, the SO_3 is not dissociated. Here the oxide takes up an oxygen ion and the energy which is released is greater, the larger the charge and the smaller the radius. The question of whether an oxide forms an acid or a base depends on whether the ionic dissociation of the oxide requires a greater or smaller amount of energy than the ionic dissociation of water. This can be seen in the following examples. If BaO is dissolved in water, it dissociates into ions, and the oxygen ions subsequently combine with the water to form OH^- ions. When, on the other hand, SO_3 is dissolved in water, the dissociation is certainly less than that of the water and SO_3 combines with a OH^- ion to form HSO_4^-, which subsequently dissociates further into SO_4^{2-} and H^+. It is therefore obvious that the structure of the positive ion will determine the stability. Bases become less stable and acids more stable when the noble-gas positive ion is replaced by a non-noble one. Thus, Ag(OH) and $Zn(OH)_2$ are very unstable compared with NaOH and $Mg(OH)_2$, and many other examples to illustrate this can easily be found. The explanation is quite simple: since the field of the non-noble gas ion is stronger, it reacts as if it had a higher charge or a smaller radius.

In the decompositions already described, the complex breaks up into oxides, in this instance water, and the base- or acid-forming oxide. Some acids, however, decompose in quite a different way to give oxygen and a lower oxide, and therefore have strong oxidizing properties. The reason is found in the low stability of the oxide and it is observed in acids with small highly-charged central ions; thus $HClO_4$, HNO_3 and H_2SO_4 all show this behaviour to a marked degree at high temperatures. It is not surprising that these happen to be the strong acids, since the acidity is favoured by the three factors of high charge, small radius and non-noble gas structure, each of which lowers the stability of the oxides. It is, however, noteworthy that these unstable oxidizing acids are those that hold on to water strongly and therefore form very stable complexes. Thus it follows that strong bases cannot be good oxidizing agents.

40. PROTON AFFINITY OF ACIDS AND BASES

The division between acids and bases is not a very sharp one: it has been remarked already that the borderline between the two groups is formed by the amphoteric compounds, that have both weak acid and weak basic properties, and thus behave as acids in the presence of strong bases and as bases in the presence of strong acids. To a certain degree this is true for all acids and bases. A compound that behaves as an acid under normal conditions, might show basic properties in the presence of an extremely strong acid, and vice versa. It would, therefore, be very important to prepare these extremely strong acids and bases, because with their aid it would be possible to prepare some interesting new types of compounds. Perchloric acid behaves already as an unusually strong acid: in order to understand the nature of some compounds formed by this acid it is good to use a somewhat different definition of a base.

Being the opposite of an acid, a base will be defined as a compound that has a tendency to combine with protons. In this definition the 'base' in an alkaline solution is the OH^- ion. This ion is one of the strongest bases known to exist. When combining with a proton it forms water, that itself is a weak base, since it is able to add one more proton to form an OH_3^+, hydronium ion, and a weak acid at the same time, since water can dissociate into OH^- and H^+ ions. Water being a base, too, the actual dissociation reaction will be

$$2H_2O \rightarrow OH^- + OH_3^+$$

and what are called hydrogen ions in solution are, in actual fact, hydronium ions, probably hydrated hydronium ions $(OH_3)^+(H_2O)_n$.

Acids, such as HBF_4, HPF_6 and, better still, $HSbCl_6$, fulfill these conditions very well: however, the low charge of the negative ion diminishes the stability of the compound as a complex to such an extent that these acids do not exist at all, unless perhaps at very low temperature. If, however, the H^+ ions are replaced by larger ions, e.g. H_3O^+ and H_3S^+, the stability is increased, and these strong acids that are not stable as such have been observed as 'hydrates' that in actual fact are hydronium salts, e.g. $(H_3O)_2SiF_6$, $(H_3O)SbCl_6$, $(H_3O)PF_6$ and $(H_3O)BF_3OH$. The last mentioned compound is a 'hydrate' of BF_3, $BF_3 . 2H_2O$. It is hydronium fluoroborate, in which one F^- ion is replaced by an OH^- ion. It is not impossible that, at low temperature, sulphonium salts, e.g. $(SH_3)^+SbCl_6^-$, are stable as well.

In the series NaOH, $Mg(OH)_2$, $Al(OH)_3$, $Si(OH)_4$, $PO(OH)_3$ . . ., the basic properties decrease. The OH^- ion, attached to the Na^+ ion in NaOH, is such a strong base that it reacts with the protons of any acid, i.e. any compound that can give off protons. In $PO(OH)_3$ the basicity of the OH^- ions, under the influence of the P^{5+}, is so far decreased that it will not attract protons from acids of normal acid strength. If, however, unusually strong acids were available, there would be the possibility that $PO(OH)_3$ would still withdraw a proton from this acid and form an ion $P(OH)_4^+$.

Such an acid is actually known to exist. Perchloric acid and phosphoric acid form the compound

$$\{P(OH)_4\}^+ClO_4^-$$

Since both ions in this compound are very large, the energy required for dissociation into $P(OH)_4^+$ and ClO_4^- will be small, and the compound would be expected to be completely ionized when dissolved. However, the solution in water will not be stable, since $PO(OH)_3$ is a very weak base, even weaker than water. In the presence of the latter compound it will react in such a way that one proton is transferred to a water molecule

$$P(OH)_4^+ + H_2O \rightarrow PO(OH)_3 + H_3O^+$$

and the solution of 'tetrahydroxy phosphonium perchlorate' in water will merely be a solution of orthophosphoric and perchloric acid. Perchloric acid, because of its explosive properties, is not an ideal acid to work with in the presence of oxydizable compounds, and in order to investigate the basic properties of compounds such as H_2S and AsH_3, non-explosive, strong acids are required. In order to obtain non-explosive acids, positive ions with high charge have to be avoided, and the acid should be made strong by diminishing the charge of the negative ion. Acids like HBF_4 or HPF_6 suit the purpose.

Chapter VII

POLARIZATION

41. POLARIZABILITY

THE theory of the electrostatic bond has been found satisfactory in explaining a number of phenomena in inorganic chemistry and there is scarcely any part of the subject which it fails to clarify to some extent. On the other hand, there were a few phenomena which could not be explained by the theory, for example the nature of the bond in such molecules as N_2, O_2, S_8, Cl_2, I_2 and H_2. Further, molecules such as H_2O and SO_2 were found not to have the linear structure predicted for them, and the volatility of NO, CO and similar compounds remained unexplained.

The insolubility of AgCl in water was ascribed to the strong attraction of the subgroup ion Ag^+, and this would be a plausible explanation if it were not for the fact that AgF is very soluble in water. In fact it would have been expected that this compound, containing a smaller negative ion than AgCl, would be less soluble than AgCl, itself.

With the hydrogen compounds we have seen that there are hydrides (Li^+H^-) and compounds with positive H^+ ions, but that, on the other hand, a compound such as CH_4 cannot be placed in either group. Before concluding that the electrostatic model breaks down in such cases, it must be borne in mind that its full implications have not been taken into account. While the properties of the compounds have been shown to depend on the charge and size of the ions, the phenomenon of induction has so far been ignored.

Between two charged spheres, in addition to the coulomb forces acting between them, there is another force, due to the displacement of the charges which the bodies produce in each other. Induction will occur, too, if the charged bodies are two ions, or if one of the particles is an ion and the other an uncharged atom. In fact, it is much simpler to understand the basis of induction with atoms and ions than with macroscopic bodies. In earlier chapters it was seen that in the modern atomic model one cannot speak of fixed electronic orbits. It is not possible to say precisely where a particular electron will be at a given moment, but, on the other hand, it is possible to calculate the probability of finding an electron at a given point, which will vary throughout the atom. In any position where an electron is frequently found, there will be more electricity than in one where it occurs less frequently. What, in fact, can be calculated is the mean density of the negative electricity in the neighbourhood of the atomic nucleus. In other words, the original orbits of BOHR become zones of high electric density. Quantum mechanics tells us that the charge distribution of atoms and ions with an 8- or 18-electron structure is spherically symmetrical. That is to say, the

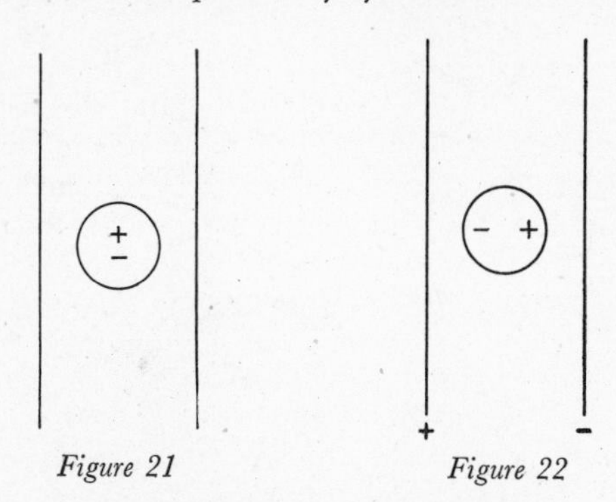

Figure 21 *Figure 22*

mean density in a spherical layer is everywhere the same. According to a well-known theorem of electrostatics, the electric intensity outside a charged sphere is the same as though all the charge were concentrated at the centre of the sphere. From this it follows that in noble-gas atoms and ions the external effect of the negative charges is the same as if they were all located within the nucleus. The centre of gravity of the negative charges is in the nucleus, so that in atoms with spherical symmetry the effects of the positive and negative charges completely neutralize one another. From this it must follow that noble-gas atoms have no external electric field (*see Figure 21*).

Now let us place a noble-gas atom in a homogeneous electric field. In such a field the positive and the negative charges of the atom will be affected, and both will tend to be displaced in different directions. As can be seen from *Figure 22*, the nucleus will be displaced to the left and the electrons to the right. The mutual attraction between nucleus and electrons will oppose displacement by the electric field, and consequently the more strongly the electrons are held by the nucleus, the smaller will be the displacement by the external field. This displacement results in the centres of gravity of positive and negative electricity no longer coinciding at the centre. The electrons will still have an external field as though they were concentrated at one point, but the nucleus and the electrons act as a combination of two point charges of opposite sign. Such a system is said to have an *electric dipole*, which is the product of the charge and the displacement, and is denoted by μ. We can assume that the distance between the two charges in the dipole is proportional to the field strength F. Just how this proportionality constant is determined will be shown later.

Let us consider the space between two plates of a condenser filled with a large number of atoms, each with a dipole induced by the field. In every atom, lines of force run from the negative to the positive pole in the opposite direction to the lines of force of the original field. If a gas is placed between the plates of a condenser, the field strength between these plates will be diminished from the value F to a value F/ε, where ε is the dielectric constant. It therefore follows that if the electrons in an atom are not so rigidly bound that they can be displaced in an electric field with respect to the positive charges, then the substance must have a dielectric constant which will exceed unity by an amount dependent on the strength of the coupling between the nucleus and the electrons. This is not only true for free atoms, but if the substance consists of molecules then a dipole is created in each atom and the effects of the dipoles have to be added together. The effect in which an electric field creates a dipole in an atom or a molecule is called *polarization;* it is easy to see that, in general, polarization will strengthen the binding between two ions of opposite charge.

The chlorine ion in a sodium chloride molecule is in the field of the sodium ion and vice versa. The electrons in both ions are displaced with respect to the nuclei, with the result that the negative charge of the chlorine ion is closer to the sodium ion, while the positive charge of the nucleus is now farther away from the sodium ion. In consequence, the sodium ion, as a result of polarization, exerts a force on the chlorine ion which is greater than that which corresponds to the charges alone. In the same way, the sodium ion is more strongly attracted by the chlorine ion. Actually, the chlorine ion is not in a homogeneous field, but, in a first approximation, it is assumed in calculations of polarization effects that the field is homogeneous and that the field strength is given by that of the actual field in the centre of the ion. This approximation is satisfactory if the two ions are widely separated from one another, and, in fact, the approximation is the same as is made when assuming that the gravitational field at the surface of the earth is homogeneous.

The calculation can be further simplified by taking into account the fact that the polarization in positive ions is in general much smaller than that in negative ones. This follows from the fact that in positive ions, in which the nuclear charge is higher than the total electron charge, the bond between the electrons and the nucleus is stronger than in the negative ions, so that it is usually sufficient to consider only the polarization of the latter.

Let us consider Na^+ and Cl^- ions at a distance r from each other (*see Figure 23*). The Cl^- ion is then in a field of which the strength is e/r^2 at the centre of the ion. The effect of the field will be to displace the $(n+1)e$ electrons by a distance d with respect to the nucleus. Let us further assume that the nucleus moves $0{\cdot}5d$ to the left, and the negative charge $0{\cdot}5d$ to the right. The potential energy of the Cl^- ion with respect to the Na^+ ion will no longer be e^2/r, since there are now in the Cl^- ion two charges $(n+1)e$ of the electrons and ne of the nucleus at distances $r - 0{\cdot}5d$ and $r + 0{\cdot}5d$, respectively, from the Na^+ ion. The potential energy is therefore

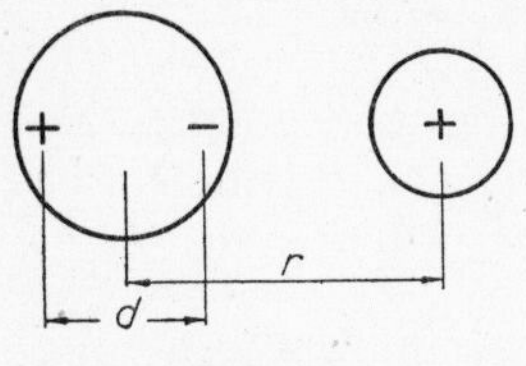

Figure 23

$$E = -\frac{e(n+1)e}{r - 0{\cdot}5d} + \frac{e\,.\,ne}{r + 0{\cdot}5d}$$

$$= -\frac{e^2}{r - 0{\cdot}5d} - n\left(\frac{e^2}{r - 0{\cdot}5d} - \frac{e^2}{r + 0{\cdot}5d}\right)$$

$$= -\frac{e^2}{r - 0{\cdot}5d} - \frac{ne^2d}{r^2 - 0{\cdot}25d^2}$$

Now d is very small in comparison with r, so that $0{\cdot}5d$ and $0{\cdot}25d^2$ can be neglected (*see Figure 23*), and the formula becomes

$$E = -\frac{e^2}{r} - \frac{ne^2d}{r^2}$$

which, however, is still not correct inasmuch as the total diminution of energy, as a result of polarization, is smaller than ne^2d/r^2 since energy is required to polarize the negative ion.

Calculation shows that this is just one-half the energy which is released by the attraction of the dipole by the positive ion. Therefore (*see* Section 71)

$$E = -\frac{e^2}{r} - \frac{ne^2d}{2r^2}$$

The second term in this expression is the energy due to polarization, E_P. The numerator can be written in the form $e\,.\,ne\,.\,d$, where d is the displacement and ne the displaced charge of the dipole induced in the negative ion. The product *ned* which occurs in all polarization calculations, is the dipole moment μ_α. Experimentally, the product $\mu_\alpha = ned$ can be measured, but not, however, the two separate factors *ne* and *d*. The dipole moment will be proportional to the inducing field F, the factor α in $\mu_\alpha = \alpha F$ being called the *polarizability*. The dipole moment is written as μ_α, rather than μ, to emphasize that it is formed by polarization. The polarization energy now can be expressed in terms of μ_α, or in terms of α and F. Substitution of $ned = \mu_\alpha = \alpha F$ in E_P yields

$$E_P = -ne^2d/2r^2 = -\frac{\mu_\alpha}{2}\cdot\frac{e}{r^2}$$

In the case of the simple molecule NaCl, the field that induces the dipole in the chlorine ion is due to the sodium ion at distance r, and is equal to e/r^2. The polarization energy then can be written as

$$E_P = -\frac{\mu_\alpha}{2}\cdot e/r^2 = -\frac{\mu_\alpha}{2}F = -\frac{\mu_\alpha^2}{2\alpha} \text{ or } -\tfrac{1}{2}\alpha F^2$$

It will be shown in Section 71 that the expressions in terms of α and F hold good for any field F, whereas $E = -\mu_\alpha/2 \,.\, e/r^2$ can be applied only if the field is due to an ion with charge e at distance r. In Section 44 a different type of dipole moment, that is not caused by polarization and thus is independent of the field, will be discussed.

The magnitude of the proportionality constant α depends on the strength of the coupling between nucleus and electrons. It can be determined by extrapolating the measured refractive index to infinite wavelength, as a result of the relations that exist between n_∞, ε (dielectric constant) and α, which are

$$n_\infty^2 = \varepsilon \quad \text{and} \quad \frac{n_\infty^2 - 1}{n_\infty^2 + 2}\cdot V = \frac{4\pi N}{3}\alpha$$

In this formula V is the volume of one gram mol of a substance containing N particles per gram mol. If the substance consists of molecules, then $\alpha = \Sigma\alpha_i$, where α_i is the polarizability of the ith atom in the molecule. In gases where n_∞ is nearly unity, the formula can be further simplified by putting $n_\infty^2 + 2 = 3$ which gives

$$n^2 = 1 + \frac{4\pi N}{V}\alpha$$

42. INFLUENCE OF POLARIZATION ON STABILITY OF CRYSTAL STRUCTURE, IONIC DISSOCIATION AND VOLATILITY

Since the energy of a molecule is diminished by polarization, one must naturally reconsider all phenomena in which use is made of this energy. Strong polarization, for example, will increase the energy necessary for the dissociation into ions and, in considering the solubility of electrolytes in water, this polarization of the ions must be taken into account.

Heats of formation will be equally well affected by polarization, since the energy of dissociation into ions, or the crystal energy, occurs in the formulae concerned. Polarization will always cause an increase in heat of formation for compounds which do not form coordinated structures, and has already been considered for a molecule A^+B^- in the preceding section. The increase will be particularly important for molecules with highly-charged ions, but unfortunately an exact calculation of the polarization energy under all circumstances is difficult, and cannot be discussed further here. Strong polarization naturally modifies, to some extent, the whole electronic structure of an atom or an ion and also, therefore, the energy with which the electrons are held in the ion. This results in a change of the absorption spectra and can lead to a change in the colour of the ion.

Halogen ions are usually colourless in combination with alkali metals, yet, on the other hand, silver iodide is yellow, HgI_2 is red and the iodides of elements of higher valency are red, russet or even black. There are also some coloured chlorides, such as WCl_6, although most of them are colourless. Most fluorides are colourless, and oxides are colourless when they are derived from the ions of higher valency in the first four columns of the periodic system. V_2O_5, however, is brown. In oxides, colour occurs in compounds containing ions of low charge if they are elements of the subgroups. Ag_2O, for example, is dark brown, HgO red and ZnO white, but yellow at high temperatures. The extra field of the subgroup ions appears to cause a strong polarization of negative ions. We shall not attempt to explain these colours, for to do so would mean analysing the whole absorption spectrum. We can, however, accept the fact that, by increasing polarization, colourless ions with 8- and 18-electron structures can become yellow, russet, brown or very dark in colour.

These coloured compounds are, in general, unstable, which would appear to be in contradiction to the fact that strong polarization increases stability. The solution of this paradox is that strong polarization occurs only when there is a strong field between the ions, which happens when one of the ions is very small or has a low charge or an abnormal structure. Without polarization such compounds would be still more unstable. It goes without saying that excluded from these considerations are such coloured compounds as the blue copper salts and the rose-coloured manganese salts in which the colour is due to the specific electronic structure of a hydrated or a non-hydrated ion.

If a compound has a coordinated structure then polarization would not be expected to produce a large effect, since each ion is symmetrically surrounded by a number of ions of opposite charge, the fields of which will neutralize one another, and thus lead to a very small resultant effect. A dipole cannot arise in an ion in a coordinated structure; the most that can occur is an overall rearrangement of the electron cloud as a result of polarization, but the energy change involved probably is small and it is difficult to calculate. Under certain special circumstances, it could lead to a lower coordination number. What, however, is of greater importance is that strong polarization can cause a coordinated structure to disappear. In Section 12 it was shown that in screened compounds the lines of force from the positive ion terminate practically at the negative ions, and there is little or no external field. In such, polarization plays a very important part. In CCl_4 the field of the positive ion attracts the electrons of the Cl^- ions inwards, thereby reducing the external field of the molecule. In this way polarization has a big influence in bringing about the existence of molecular crystals. The effect will, however, not be a sudden change from a coordinated to a molecular structure, but will involve a number of transitional forms between these two extremes.

Let us consider a compound not belonging to either group, having neither a typical unscreened structure with small polarization energy, such as NaCl, nor a typical screened structure such as CCl_4. Molecules between these two extremes take a middle course in crystal formation and show some of the characteristics of both types. They can be said to profit from the favourable coulomb energy of the coordinated crystal without giving up the benefits of polarization energy.

Consider a crystalline compound which no longer satisfies the requirements of a coordinated structure, but in which now each ion is symmetrically surrounded by a number of ions of opposite charge. Such a crystal is shown in *Figure 24*, and is actually that of cadmium iodide. In this crystal every cadmium ion is still surrounded in a symmetrical manner by six ions of opposite charge, but this is not true for the iodine ions, as can be seen from the figure.

The energy content corresponding to the attraction between the oppositely-charged ions is not as favourable as it could be. This part of the total energy would certainly be lower if the cadmium ions were arranged in a regular manner round the iodine ions. However, what would then be gained as electrostatic energy would be lost as polarization energy, because a regular arrangement with the iodine ions surrounded by cadmium ions would mean that the dipoles in the iodine ions could no longer exist.

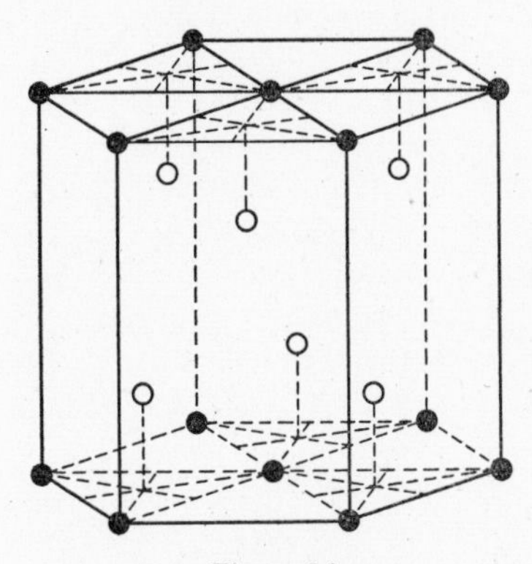

Figure 24

In cadmium iodide the crystal energy consists of two parts, electrostatic and polarization, and in a coordinated structure the electrostatic energy would undoubtedly be lower, but the term corresponding to polarization energy would be absent . The magnitude of the latter will therefore determine whether the total energy is lower in a coordinated crystal or in a crystal of the cadmium iodide type. Since the polarization energy has the form $-\frac{1}{2}aF^2$ and since the main contribution to this energy is due to the field caused by the nearest ions at a distance r, it is apparent that the polarizability and the radius of the ions will determine whether either a coordinated crystal or a crystal without complete coordination will be formed. The polarization term will be large when α is large and r is small, so that there is a strong tendency for the formation of incompletely coordinated structures when strongly-polarizable negative ions occur in conjunction with a small positive ion of high charge, e.g. in the sulphides and selenides of zirconium and hafnium, or a subgroup ion as in cadmium iodide. Various forms of such structures are known, but we will merely note the peculiarities of crystals of the cadmium iodide type. As can be seen from *Figure 24*, the crystal is made up of a layer of metal ions followed by two layers of negative ions and then a further layer of metal ions, etc. The two layers of negative ions will repel one another, but are prevented from increasing their distance from one another by the attraction of the layers of positive ions and by the van der Waals forces (*see* Section 51), which act between two adjacent layers of iodine ions. Under such circumstances it is clear that the distance between the layers of negative ions will be fairly large, and the bond between them weak. All crystals of this type, therefore, have the property of being easily split along planes parallel to those of the layers of atoms. This tendency is so great that the crystals can be broken up by hand to form very thin plates which feel soft to the touch. This property is often a sufficient indication that the substance has this particular type of structure, while x-ray analysis proves it conclusively.

Where there is very strong polarization, such as in hydrogen compounds, it can happen that molecules of the type AB no longer have coordinated structures; this is so in hydrogen compounds such as HCl, HBr, HI and H_2O. The strong polarization in these molecules would disappear if they were arranged in a coordination lattice of the NaCl or zinc-blende type.

In compounds crystallizing in coordination lattices, the energy in the solid state is not affected by polarization, but the energy of the molecules in the gaseous state is lowered. Since the heat of sublimation is the difference between the energies in the solid and gaseous states, respectively, the heat of sublimation is reduced, and the volatility increased by polarization of the gaseous molecules. The heats of sublimation of the lithium halides LiCl, LiBr, LiI and of CsF are too low when calculated without making a correction for polarization. In the Li salts the large halogen ions are polarized by the small Li^+ ions. CsF is an unusual case, however, because in this instance there is polarization of a large positive ion (Cs^+) by a small negative ion (F^-). The polarization in free molecules will always be stronger than in the crystal lattice, even if it is not a coordination lattice, and polarization will therefore always tend to increase the volatility.

43. MOLECULES OF LOWER SYMMETRY

Water belongs to the group of compounds AB_2 which, contrary to expectation, were proved by measurements of the dielectric constant not to possess a linear molecule. In a water molecule the oxygen ion, which is strongly polarizable, has two extremely small hydrogen ions that can approach it very closely. It would be more accurate to say that they actually penetrate the oxygen ion, but this we can neglect for the moment and discuss the problem as though the hydrogen ions were on the surface of the oxygen ion, as small ions with a normal electron shell as in Li^+ would be. Obviously, the polarization of the oxygen ion will depend on the positions of the positive ions. If all three ions were arranged linearly there would be no polarization effects at all, because the effects of the two symmetrically-placed hydrogen ions would cancel. This, however, would not occur if the two hydrogen ions were not symmetrically situated; each of them would then tend to induce a dipole in the oxygen ion, as illustrated in *Figure 25.* The effect of these two displacements would produce a resultant moment, as shown in

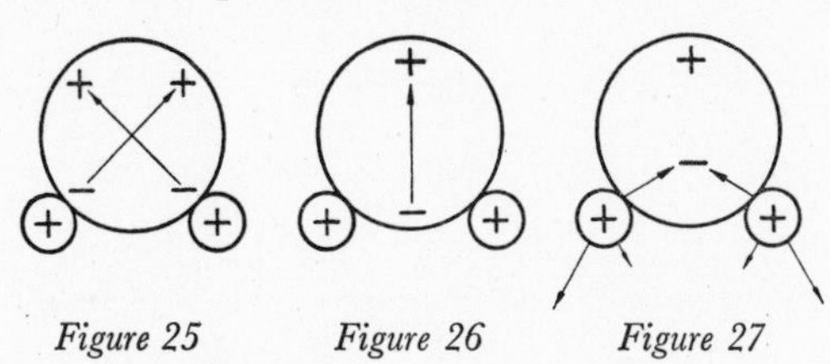

Figure 25 *Figure 26* *Figure 27*

Figure 26. In this position the hydrogen ions will be more strongly attracted by the oxygen than when in the original position because the negative charges of the oxygen are closer to the two positive ions and the positive charge of the nucleus is farther away. A force will act on both ions which will tend to bring them closer together, and they are attracted more strongly by the negative charge than they are repelled by the positive one (*see Figure 27*). The resultant tendency is that the two ions will try to get as close together as the mutual repulsion of their own charges allows. Polarization of the central O^{2-} ion, therefore, may lead to a non-linear structure of the water molecule, but a quantitative calculation is required to show that the polarization effects are strong enough to overcome the mutual repulsion of the H^+ ions. In the Appendix, Section 71, it will be shown that a molecule $A^{2-}B_2^+$ will not be linear if A^{2-} is strongly polarizable, and the distance AB small. For water, this result is not conclusive, because the necessary correction for penetration of the oxygen ion by the hydrogen cannot be applied.

It is also possible to visualize, in a qualitative way, that this penetration effect alone will lead to a non-linear molecule. Let us suppose that we put three positive charges in a sphere uniformly filled with negative charges. The three charges will be attracted to the centre of the sphere and at the same time will repel one another.

If the charges are equal, then at equilibrium they will form an equilateral triangle. In water, where the charge of the oxygen nucleus is much greater, the triangle will be flatter.

Polarization is one of the reasons for the asymmetrical form of the water molecule, and also may be partially responsible for the non-linearity of H_2S molecules. Polarization would lead to the pyramidal shape observed for the molecules NH_3 and PH_3, but it is very doubtful whether it can be held responsible for the asymmetrical form of molecules such as PCl_3 and SO_2. In these molecules, the central ion is positive, if it is assumed that the bonds in these compounds are ionic, and since positive ions have not a large polarizability, the distortion of the molecule can scarcely be due to polarization effects. Indeed, we cannot continue to consider these compounds as purely ionic in character, but will find it necessary to explain their asymmetry on the basis of the homopolar bond (*see* Section 53). Even in hydrogen compounds such as H_2O and NH_3 we shall find we have to take into account their partial homopolar structure in order to arrive at a really satisfactory explanation of their structures.

44. PERMANENT DIPOLE MOMENT

Free ions occurring in a solution will move under the influence of a homogeneous electric field, the negative ions going to the positive pole, and the positive ions to the negative one. Measurement of the electrical conductivity of such solutions is the best method of determining the number and kinds of ions present, even when the ions are associated with solvent molecules. Molecules of the solvent will, of course, be transported with the ions, and special experiments can be made to determine the quantity being transported and hence arrive at the number of molecules of solvent associated with each ion.

According to the theory of ARRHENIUS the ions obtain their charge at the instant the molecules dissociate, but the picture that we have formed of the chemical bond leads to a completely different view in which ions are always present, as in solid NaCl, and on solution are separated from one another by the solvent. The question now arises whether it is possible to determine experimentally the size and charge of the particles making up the molecule. We have already established that solid NaCl is built up from ions. This follows *inter alia* from the agreement between observed and calculated crystal energies, but there is, so far, no experimental proof that gaseous NaCl, in which free molecules occur, consists of ions.

Let us suppose that a molecule of HCl consists of a Cl^- ion and a

H^+ ion and that, neglecting the question of penetration of the Cl^- ion by the H^+ ion, it can be represented by *Figure 28*. It is clear that if such molecules are placed in a homogeneous electric field no electric current will result, because equal forces will act on both ions in opposite directions. The force which acts on an ion of charge e is eF, if F is the field strength. It might be thought that the molecule could be dissociated by the field, but a simple calculation shows that this is impossible with the field strengths which are experimentally available. In electrostatic units the force to separate the ions is eF, while the coulomb force between them is e^2/a^2, where a is the distance between the ions in the molecule, from which it follows that only when $F > e/a^2$ will the molecule be dissociated by the field. The charge of an electron is $4{\cdot}8 \times 10^{-10}$ e.s.u., a can be given the value 3×10^{-8} cm, so that the field must be greater than $4{\cdot}8 \times 10^{-10}/9 \times 10^{-16}$, or greater than 5×10^5 e.s.u or 5×10^7 V/cm. Such voltages can only be produced under very special conditions, so that the possibility of splitting the molecule by an electric field is excluded.

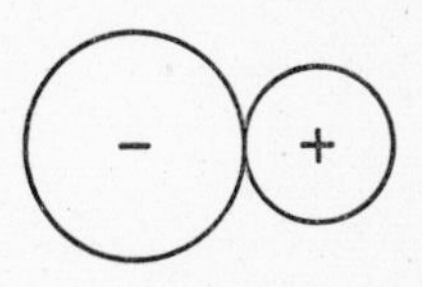

Figure 28

As the centres of gravity of the positive and negative charges in a molecule of HCl do not coincide, it must have a dipole moment which, in a symmetrical molecule, can only be produced by polarization by an external field. It is worth while to accentuate the difference of a *permanent* dipole in a molecule HCl, which exists independently of the field, and the *induced* dipole moment in an atom, which is proportional to the field $\mu_\alpha = \alpha F$. In this example there are two charges e at a distance r giving a dipole moment of er. For NaCl, where the charges and the distance are known, μ can be calculated thus

$$\begin{aligned}\mu &= e(r_{\mathrm{Na}} + r_{\mathrm{Cl}}) \\ &= (4{\cdot}178 \times 10^{-10}) \times (2{\cdot}76 \times 10^{-8}) \\ &= 13{\cdot}2 \times 10^{-18} \text{ e.s.u} \times \text{cm}\end{aligned}$$

Therefore, with a means with which to measure the dipole, it could be found whether or not the molecules really consist of ions.

It was seen above that a polar molecule in a homogeneous field is not displaced, but that a couple is exerted by the field of strength F, the moment of which is $eF \,.\, d$, which will tend to turn the molecule in a direction against the field. The significance of the word 'moment' now becomes clear; the dipole moment is the couple corresponding to unit field strength.

The forces which act on each charge tend to rotate the molecules against the field and, in consequence, the molecules will become aligned in the field. This alignment must, however, not be thought of as complete. A molecule originally at an angle to the field will be turned by the field, but it will also be undergoing vibration, with the result that the mean position of the molecule will form a smaller angle with the direction of the field than it did before. There is, therefore, only a partial alignment of molecules.

In order to further elucidate the effect of such an orientation let us suppose that all the molecules lie exactly in the direction of the field. The position will become that shown in *Figure 29*, in which all the molecules have positive and negative charges. The only difference is that in the figure the dipole was created by the field, whereas in our assumed arrangement the molecules are aligned because of their permanent dipole moments. Here also the lines of force of the molecules are opposite in direction to those between the plates of the condenser. As a result of the alignment of molecules, the field strength between the plates is diminished and the orientation of the dipoles thus contributes to the dielectric constant. For a non-polarizable material, the relation between dielectric constant and dipole moment is

$$\frac{\varepsilon - 1}{\varepsilon + 2} V = \frac{4\pi N^2}{3} \cdot \frac{\mu^2}{3RT}$$

where R is the gas constant and N is Avogadro's number. The influence of the dipoles on the dielectric constant therefore depends on the temperature and diminishes as the temperature rises. This is easily appreciated when it is remembered that a rise in temperature tends to destroy the alignment of the dipoles, the higher temperature producing greater molecular movement.

In general, polar molecules will be polarizable and the expression for the dielectric constant when both α and μ are taken into account is as follows

$$\frac{\varepsilon - 1}{\varepsilon + 2} V = \frac{4\pi N}{3} \alpha + \frac{4\pi N^2}{3} \cdot \frac{\mu^2}{3RT}$$

and if a new constant (Boltzmann's) is introduced such that $k = R/N$, then for a single dipole

$$\frac{\varepsilon - 1}{\varepsilon + 2} = \frac{4\pi N}{3V} \left(\alpha + \frac{\mu^2}{3kT}\right)$$

Since, for gases, ε differs little from unity, $\varepsilon + 2$ may be made equal to 3, so that the relationship for a gas becomes

$$\varepsilon = 1 + \frac{4\pi N}{V}\left(\alpha + \frac{\mu^2}{3kT}\right)$$

By carrying out two experiments at different temperatures, α and μ can be found, and, similarly, the magnitudes of α and of μ can be determined for all other substances, since similar formulae apply to both dilute solutions and to pure liquids. If a substance has no permanent dipole, then according to the theory

$$\varepsilon = n_\infty^2$$

so that

$$\frac{\varepsilon - 1}{\varepsilon + 2} V = \frac{n_\infty^2 - 1}{n_\infty^2 + 2} V = \frac{4\pi N}{3} \alpha$$

which is the same formula as that given in Section 36.

45. DIPOLE MOMENT AND STRUCTURE

It is to be expected that all molecules of type *AB* have dipole moments if they consist of ions, yet it is found that the molecules H_2, O_2, N_2, Cl_2, Br_2 and I_2 are non-polar. It is therefore clear that these molecules are not composed of ions, and that the formulae H^+H^-, Cl^+Cl^-, etc. must be discarded. The chemical bond in these molecules must be of an entirely different kind from that in purely ionic compounds. It is to be remembered that it was expected that NaCl has a moment of $13{\cdot}2 \times 10^{-18}$, whereas the experimental value is 10×10^{-18}. In view of the great experimental difficulties in measuring the dipole moment of NaCl in the vapour state, this agreement can be considered satisfactory.

HCl has a moment of $1{\cdot}0 \times 10^{18}$, which is very much lower than expected for a compound built up from two ions with charge e at a distance of 2 Å from one another. Two effects contribute to this lower value, the first of which is the penetration of the H^+ which reduces the distance between the charges, and the second the polarization of the Cl^- ion by the H^+ ion which creates a dipole opposed to that created by the ionic charges. Both these effects, however, are quantitatively insufficient to explain the large discrepancy. CO and NO are still more baffling. If we assume the existence of two divalent ions, then the dipole moment should be about $2e(r^+ + r^-)$. If for $r^+ + r^-$ a value of 3 Å is taken, then $\mu = 29 \times 10^{-18}$, while the actual moment is only $0{\cdot}10 \times 10^{-18}$ for CO, and $0{\cdot}16 \times 10^{-18}$ for NO. There is, therefore, even less reason to regard the structures of these gases as ionic.

Molecules of the type AB_2 should be linear and, whatever the size or charge of A and B, the three particles should lie in a line and the electric field should exert no couple on the molecule (*see Figure 29*). If, on the other hand, for some reason they are not linear, then there will be a moment (*see Figure 30*). This can be appreciated from the fact that in the linear structure the centres of gravity of the positive and negative charges coincide in the middle of the molecule, while in the less symmetrical structure the centre of gravity of the positive

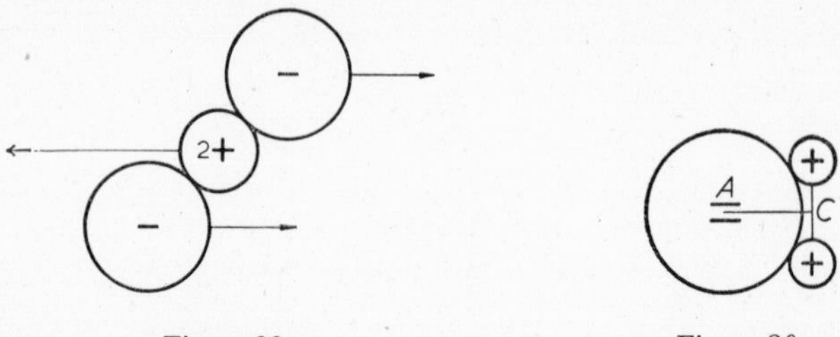

Figure 29 *Figure 30*

ions is at C, and of the negative at A (*see Figure 30*). From measurement of the dipole moment, therefore, it can be determined whether or not a structure is linear. In this way it has been found that CO_2, CS_2 and $HgCl_2$ are of this form, while H_2O, H_2S and SO_2 have the less symmetrical form. The results obtained from measurements of dipole moments are completely confirmed by the results of electron-diffraction experiments. It is easy to see that in a molecule AB_3, where the three B ions form a triangle, there will be no moment if atom A is in the plane of the B ions, but the moment will most certainly not be nil for any other arrangement, e.g. for a molecule with the shape of a trigonal pyramid. Dipole measurements show that BCl_3 has a planar structure, but that NH_3, PH_3, AsH_3, PCl_3, PBr_3, $AsCl_3$, $AsBr_3$, AsI_3, $SbCl_3$, $SbBr_3$ and SbI_3 are pyramidal.

Doubt can arise at this point as to whether molecules with unusual shapes are really ionic compounds. It must be remembered, however, that dipoles arise because the particles still retain some charge, otherwise the moment would be zero. The problem still remains as to how the particles in HCl, NO and CO can have charges which are only fractions of that of an indivisible electron. The difficulty is partly resolved by bringing the polarization of the ions into consideration, for if both ions in NaCl are polarized, then in both ions dipoles are created, which are opposite to the dipole caused by the charges (*see Figure 31*). What, in fact, is measured is the resultant of these three dipoles. The observed dipole is therefore always smaller than the dipole which is caused by the ionic charges. This explains the difference between the measured and calculated dipoles of the alkali halides. There is, however, no reason why there should

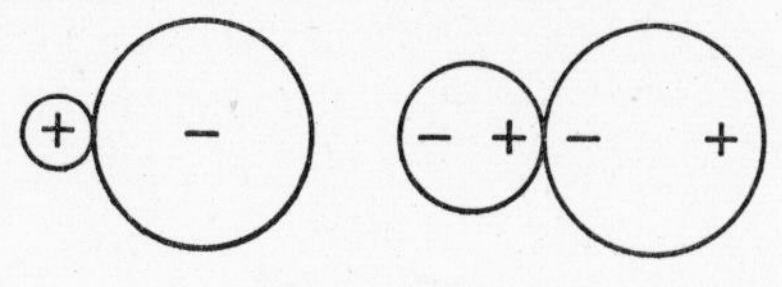

Figure 31

be any such strong polarization in CO and NO, and the low value of the measured dipole, 0·005 of the calculated value, cannot be explained by polarization effects alone.

46. INFLUENCE OF DIPOLES ON BOILING POINT

There will be an attraction between two polar molecules, the energy being a minimum, when the two dipoles are as shown in *Figure 32*. If the two dipoles are equal, then the corresponding energy is $-2\mu^2/r^3$. This formula can easily be derived by considering the system as a combination of four charges (*see Figure 32*). The expression for the energy will then consist of the following terms

$$-\frac{e^2}{r-d}+\frac{2e^2}{r}-\frac{e^2}{r+d}=\frac{-2e^2d^2}{r(r^2-d^2)}=-\frac{2e^2d^2}{r^3}=-\frac{2\mu^2}{r^3}$$

in which it is assumed that the dipole distance is small compared to the distance between the molecules. The expression becomes more complicated for any arbitrary position of the dipole; the energy can, however, be expressed as $K\mu^2/r^3$, where K depends on the angles made by the dipoles with the line joining their centres.

In a liquid consisting of polar molecules this mutual attraction will give rise to an increase in the latent heat of evaporation. Between two polar molecules there is, in addition, an atttraction due to the fact that the field of one will induce a dipole in the other molecule, this induced dipole being attracted by the one that has produced it. We shall not investigate this phenomenon further, but note the fact that a dipole raises the boiling point of a compound. We will examine first the boiling points of a number of screened, symmetrical and non-polar compounds such as CF_4, CCl_4, $SiCl_4$, etc. The boiling points in such a series rise from the fluoride to the iodide. The explanation for this will appear later.

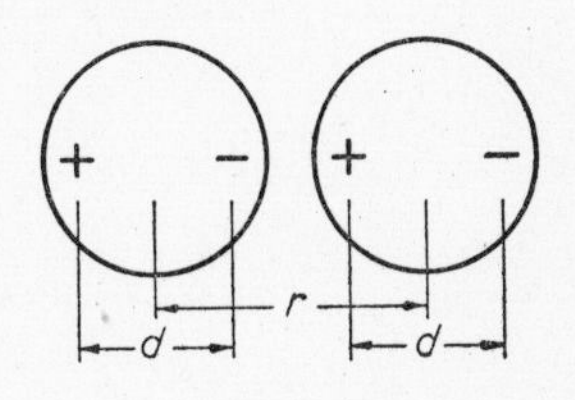

Figure 32

Halides of carbon, other than those given in *Table XXXIV*, are known, and mixed halogen compounds also exist; the boiling points of these compounds are given in *Table XXXV*. In this series the boiling point rises by equal increments when one halogen in a compound is replaced by another, and the calculated values given in the table assume equal increments. It appears that the mixed

Table XXXIV

Boiling Points in °K of Screened Compounds

BF_3 172	BCl_3 286	BBr_3 363	BI_3 483
CF_4 143	CCl_4 349	CBr_4 463	CI_4 —
SiF_4 187	$SiCl_4$ 330	$SiBr_4$ 426	SiI_4 564
POF_3 233	$POCl_3$ 378	$POBr_3$ 466	
PF_5 188	PCl_5 α 435	PBr_5 —	

Table XXXV

Boiling Points in °K of some Mixed Halides of Carbon

	CF_4	CF_3Cl	CF_2Cl_2	$CFCl_3$	CCl_4
observed	143	193	248	298	349
calculated	—	194·5	246	297·5	—
	CF_4	CF_3Br	CF_2Br_2	$CFBr_3$	CBr_4
observed	143	—	298	380	463
calculated	—	223	303	383	—
	CCl_4	CCl_3Br	CCl_2Br_2	$CClBr_3$	CBr_4
observed	349	377	408	433	463
calculated	—	377·5	406	434·5	—

halogen compounds have very small dipole moments. Each of the C—halogen bonds have moments which, however, together form a moment equal to zero. The compounds which also contain hydrogen have a moment because the moment of the C—H bond is smaller than that of the C—halogen bond. The total moment is, however, again nearly independent of the particular halogen present. For example, the compounds in the series $CHCl_3$, $CHClBr_2$, $CHCl_2Br$, $CHBr_3$ have practically the same values, but these are quite different from those of the series CH_3Cl, CH_3Br, etc.

Table XXXVI

Boiling Points in °K of Compounds of Carbon, Hydrogen and a Halogen

	CF_4	CHF_3	CH_2F_2	CH_3F	CH_4
observed	143	189	~212	199	112
calculated	—	135	127·5	120	—
	CCl_4	$CHCl_3$	CH_2Cl_2	CH_3Cl	CH_4
observed	349	334	314	249	112
calculated	—	290	230·5	171	—
	CBr_4	$CHBr_3$	CH_2Br_2	CH_3Br	CH_4
observed	463	419	371	277·5	112
calculated	—	375	287·5	200	—
	CI_4	CHI_3	CH_2I_2	CH_3I	CH_4
observed	—	—	455	318	112
calculated	624	496	368	240	—

The boiling points no longer rise in a regular manner if the halogen is replaced by hydrogen, as can be readily seen in *Table XXXVI.* In order to determine the correct boiling points for molecules of the type CX_3H, 45°C, for CX_2H_2 about 85°C and for CXH_3 about 80°C must be added to the calculated values. By substituting hydrogen in CF_4, the boiling point rises as a result of the creation of a dipole, and decreases again from CH_3F to CH_4, when again there is a symmetrical molecule with zero moment. Finally, in *Table XXXVII*, the boiling points and dipole moments of the hydrogen compounds of the last four groups of the periodic system are given.

Table XXXVII

Dipole Moments $\times 10^{18}$ and Boiling Points in °K of Hydrogen Compounds and the Noble Gases

	CH_4	NH_3	H_2O	HF	Ne
$\mu \times 10^{18}$	0	1·46	1·84	~2	0
b.p.	112	240	373	293	27
	SiH_4	PH_3	H_2S	HCl	Ar
$\mu \times 10^{18}$	0	0·55	0·93	1·03	0
b.p.	161	187	213	188	87
	GeH_4	AsH_3	H_2Se	HBr	Kr
$\mu \times 10^{18}$	0	0·15	~0·4	0·78	0
b.p.	183	218	231	206	122
	SnH_4	SbH_3	H_2Te	HI	Xe
$\mu \times 10^{18}$	0	~0·1	~0·2	0·38	0
b.p.	221	256	271	238	164

From this table the effects of the dipoles are immediately apparent. The hydrogen compounds of the fourth group have low boiling points just as does the noble gas which follows them in the periodic system. If they contained no dipoles it would be expected that the boiling points of the hydrogen compounds between those of the fourth group and the subsequent noble gas have intermediate values. The dipole moments, however, raise the boiling points, especially in the smaller molecules of the first row, in which the effect will be greatest since the energy of the dipole attraction is inversely proportional to the third power of the radius of the molecule. It can also be seen from *Table XXXVII* that the boiling point of water is particularly high.

Chapter VIII

WATER AS A COMPONENT OF COMPOUNDS AND SOLUTIONS

47. THE SPECIAL PROPERTIES OF WATER

WATER has a number of exceptional properties, one of the most striking being that ice has a lower density than water. There are very few other substances in which the liquid is denser than the solid, the best known being bismuth. Water is the only substance which shows a maximum in its density, and the expansion coefficient is negative between 0° and 4°C. In other words, in this temperature range, water contracts on heating. We have already seen from the table of boiling points of hydrogen compounds that water has a fairly high value in comparison with those of the other compounds, and therefore the heat of vaporization must also be fairly large.

Water also possesses the property of dissolving a variety of substances and causing their ionic dissociation. There are very few other compounds which compare with water in this respect, with the exception perhaps of liquid HF, HCN and $HCONH_2$, although these compounds have been far less investigated because of the experimental difficulties encountered in using them.

Lastly, water has the property of forming chemical compounds with other substances, which was dealt with in Chapter VI. Next to the acids and bases there are also crystal hydrates, such as $CuSO_4.5H_2O$ and $CaCl_2.6H_2O$, and the hydrates of a range of organic compounds, for example $CCl_3COH.H_2O$, all of which differ markedly from the complex compounds considered earlier.

The peculiar properties of water are as important in biology as in chemistry; life on this planet would be quite different were it not for these properties. For example, if ice were heavier than water, a large part of the earth would have quite a different climate. When water freezes an ice crust forms on its surface and to a large extent prevents further freezing, since the heat in the water is lost by conduction and radiation through the ice crust, a much slower process than if its surface were water. Again, the maximum in the density prevents the formation of ice. If water had a normal coefficient of expansion, cold water would sink and the warmer water rise to the surface. Actually, this process occurs only until a temperature of 4°C is reached, after which the colder water remains above and the heat from the lower depths is lost only through conduction and radiation. Both these phenomena have the effect of preventing the formation of ice; a far greater cooling of the earth's surface would result if ice were formed at the bottoms of lakes and seas. Calculations show that a large part of the earth, under such conditions, would have a polar climate.

The great solvent power of water, especially for ionic compounds, is due to its dielectric constant. If this were only, say 10, instead of the actual 80, it would mean that water could dissolve only a trace of sodium chloride. This solvent action of water naturally plays an important role in geology. In biology, water functions as a means of conveying salts and other substances which circulate in the bodies of animals and plants. It is outside the scope of this book to discuss any further the function of water on this planet, a subject which could fill many volumes. It is important in this context that we now know water molecules to possess a dipole moment and to discover whether perhaps this fact can provide an explanation of the unique properties of water.

48. WATER AND ICE

In Section 41 it was shown that attraction between two dipoles in the vapour state can lead to the formation of double molecules. This phenomenon is called association and is observed with water, acetic acid and other substances containing a polar OH group.

In the liquid state the situation is quite different; each molecule is in almost continuous contact with a number of its neighbours. In attempting to visualize a liquid it is in most respects possible to liken it to a gas. In a crystal, or in the solid state in general, the molecules or ions can be arranged neatly in the lattice, while in a gas they are in a state of complete disorder. It is natural to think of a liquid in a similar state of disorder because of the difficulty of imagining it to have any structure at all. It is, however, quite incorrect to assume that no structure exists. Let us consider a molten salt, e.g. NaCl. Its electrical conductivity shows it to be almost completely dissociated into ions. If attention is focused on a single ion then, if complete disorder reigned in the liquid, there would be in the immediate neighbourhood of the ion an even chance of encountering a similarly-charged ion or one of opposite charge. This, however, cannot be correct since, as a result of the electrostatic forces, there will always be a tendency for the positive ion to be in the immediate neighbourhood of the negative ions, and vice versa. There must therefore be some residual structure in the liquid whereby each positive ion is surrounded by negative ones, etc. Such a structure is, of course, not as regular as a crystalline one. On the average, each ion in the molten sodium chloride will be surrounded by six ions of opposite charge, yet at any given moment there may only be four or five ions surrounding a Na^+ ion and at another seven or eight, and their arrangement will never be completely regular. In other words, the immediate environment of each ion will be similar to that in a crystal, but farther away from the ion the environment will be quite different and there will be no long-range order as is found in a crystal. However, x-ray investigation has definitely shown that liquids possess a somewhat disordered structure in which only the immediate environment of each particle is in any way similar to that of the same particle in a crystal.

When water crystallizes, the dipoles will be so arranged that their energy is as low as possible, but it is not a simple matter to calculate what this arrangement will be. The problem can, however, be approached in another way by examining the structure of ice by x-ray analysis. This shows that each water molecule is surrounded by four others, two of which attach themselves by the negative ends of their dipoles to the two H^+ ions, while the H^+ ions of the other two molecules attach themselves to the negative end of the molecule in question. Such a structure is very open, as can be realized from the fact that when spheres are packed as closely as possible, each one is surrounded by twelve others. Ice, therefore, has a low specific gravity. It melts at 0°C, or, in other words, the thermal movement becomes so strong that the dipole attractions can no longer keep the crystal in an ordered state. This presumably will take place as a result of the increasing rotation of the molecules. When a molecule rotates while its dipole is opposite another one, it will be as frequently in the position of attraction as of repulsion, so that the mutual attraction of the dipoles vanishes altogether. In addition to the mutual attraction of the dipoles there are other forces acting between molecules, namely the polarization forces which have already been discussed, and the van der Waals forces which will be described later. These latter forces are not affected by the rotation and whereas the dipoles strive to produce a definite structure, these other forces cause the molecules to come as close as possible to one another. Therefore, as soon as the dipole forces cease to act after melting has taken place, the cohesion in the lattice is determined mainly by the van der Waals forces which make the substance denser. After the structure of ice has disappeared, the liquid still retains some residual structure so that the density will continue to increase as the temperature rises. It is only after the temperature 4°C is reached that this contraction is compensated by the normal coefficient of expansion, but even then the structure has not completely disappeared. This is true even at the boiling point when there is still a residue of coherence to produce the rise in boiling point which was mentioned earlier.

It still has to be explained why the boiling points of NH_3 and HF are not also high. This is due to the fact that water, with its two positive poles, can easily form a lattice, whereas HF molecules, with only one positive and one negative pole in each, can at most only form chains or rings. In ammonia, which has three positive poles, a structure similar to that of water cannot be formed and it is again apparent that it is only a very special combination of circumstances which gives rise to the properties of water.

49. HYDRATES AND ELECTROLYTE SOLUTIONS

It was remarked in Section 13 that the solution of an electrolyte in water is not a simple dissociation and that a quantity of energy of the same order of magnitude as that of the dissociation energy is released on solution, for it is known that even if the heat of solution is negative this is many times smaller than the dissociation energy. Since water has a dipole moment, it is reasonable to assume that this energy is released through the attraction of the dipoles by the charges of the ions. Water molecules therefore combine with the ions, a process called hydration, or, for solvents other than water, solvation.

The potential energy of a dipole with charges e' and $-e'$ at a distance d from one another, and an ion with charge e at a distance r from the dipole, *Figure 33*, will be

$$E = -\left(\frac{ee'}{r-0{\cdot}5d} - \frac{ee'}{r+0{\cdot}5d}\right) = -\frac{ee'd}{r^2-0{\cdot}25d^2} = -\frac{e\mu}{r^2}$$

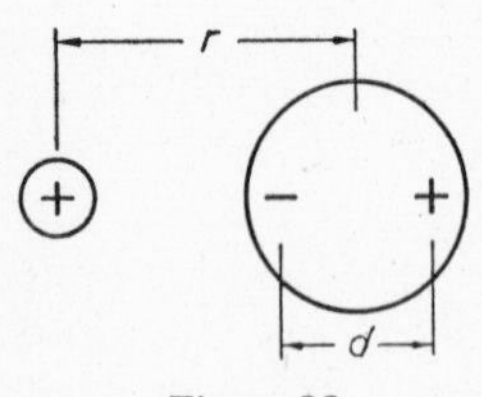

Figure 33

in which it is assumed that the dipole lies at the mid-point of the molecule.

The least distance to which the ion and dipole can approach each other is equal to the sum of the radii of the two. If a value of 3 Å is assumed for this, then the energy is

$$E = -\frac{(4{\cdot}8\times10^{-10})\,(2\times10^{-18})}{(9\times10^{-16})} = -1{\cdot}1\times10^{-12}\,\text{erg}$$

If, therefore, 1 gm mol of NaCl is dissolved in water in which $2N$

ions are formed, and if it is further assumed that on the average each ion combines with n dipoles, then the total hydration energy obtained is

$$H = (1 \cdot 1 \times 10^{-12})\, n \times 2N \text{ erg} = 1 \cdot 3 \times 10^{12}\, n \text{ erg} = 30n \text{ kcal}$$

In Section 13, it will be remembered, a value of 188 kcal was found for the dissociation energy, or crystal energy, per mol. If, therefore, each of the ions combines with six water molecules, an amount of energy is released which almost compensates for the dissociation energy. In any exact calculation of hydration energy, account must be taken of a number of factors, including the mutual repulsion of the dipoles, polarization effects and thermal movement, etc., but the order of magnitude of the hydration energy is not altered by these factors. Small highly-charged ions, as a result of their stronger field, are hydrated to a greater extent than large ions of low charge.

NaBr dissolves completely in an excess of water, but with less water a hydrate $NaBr.H_2O$ is formed. The hypothesis could be put forward that the dipole of the water penetrates between the ions of the lattice. Such a process will require energy in order to move the ions sufficiently far apart to provide space for a water molecule, but by the same process energy would be released because the positive ion would then come close to the negative, and the negative ion close to the positive pole of the water molecule. The calculation of the energy of a crystal hydrate is extremely complicated, and in order to understand under what conditions this process can occur, we will not consider a crystal but the single molecule A^+B^-. Taking the radii of the ions as r^+ and r^-, the energy of the molecule is $-e^2/(r^+ + r^-)$. In order to introduce a water molecule between the ions, the distance between them must be increased from $r^+ + r^-$ to $r^+ + r^- + 2r_d$, in which r_d is the radius of the dipole molecule, considered as a sphere. For such a process the necessary energy is

$$e^2/(r^+ + r^-) - e^2/(r^+ + r^- + 2r_d)$$

By introduction of the dipole, the positive pole is now at a distance $r^- + r_d$ from the negative ion; this corresponds to a release of energy of amount $e\mu/(r^- + r_d)^2$ and, because the negative pole is now close to the positive ion, the energy gained is $e\mu/(r^+ + r_d)^2$. The total energy gain in the formation of a hydrate is therefore

$$-\frac{e^2}{r^+ + r^-} + \frac{e^2}{r^+ + r^- + 2r_d} + \frac{e\mu}{(r^+ + r_d)^2} + \frac{e\mu}{(r^- + r_d)^2}$$

On introducing the values for the ionic radii of Na^+ and Br^-, and the value of $1{\cdot}84 \times 10^{-18}$ for μ, and giving r_d the reasonable value of 1 Å, the heat of formation of $Na^+(H_2O)Br^-$ amounts to $+0{\cdot}24 \times 10^{12}$ erg $= 6$ kcal.

The result depends to a large extent on the radii of the ions, small changes of which can easily alter the sign of the energy. When the radii become smaller, the first term of the expression will be mainly affected and the energy of formation of the hydrate can very easily have large negative values, or, in other words, hydrates are not to be expected from compounds containing small ions. Thus the alkali halides, LiF and NaF, form no hydrates. High ionic charges of both ions will influence the first two terms more than the last two because of the occurrence of the squared term. Since the first term is always larger than the second, an increase of charge must always tend to prevent the formation of a crystal hydrate; in fact, there are no hydrates of MgO, CaO and AlN; and, while $Mg(OH_2)$ can be called a hydrate of MgO it is actually not a true one in the sense that the water molecule does not penetrate between the ions, but forms two OH^- ions.

Absorption spectra of the compound $NaBr.H_2O$ show water molecules, as such, to be present in the compound, although the bands are of course somewhat altered. Formation of crystal hydrates can be considered as a first stage of solution. The first water molecules are taken up in a regular manner in the lattice and surround the positive ions. From x-ray analysis it is known that in many hydrates containing six molecules of water, such as $CaCl_2.6H_2O$, the water molecules are arranged around the positive ion, and the formula $Ca(H_2O)_6Cl_2$ is thus reasonable in view of the structure. When more water molecules are taken up, then the ions are loosened from the structure and each of them goes into solution with its portion of water molecules attached to it. From this very simplified picture of the formation of crystal hydrates and of solution we can for the moment conclude only that small ionic radii and high charge of both ions will tend to prevent the formation of crystal hydrates and solutions. It will now be shown that those cases which have proved difficult to comprehend, such as the insolubility of the halides and chalcides of subgroup elements AgCl, AgI, ZnS, CdSe, etc. will become clearer when a correction for polarization phenomena is introduced.

The extra field of the subgroup ions certainly plays a part in the low solubility of these compounds, but it cannot be said that this alone reduces solubility since AgF, in which the fluorine ion is particularly small, is freely soluble in contrast to AgCl and the other silver halides. It must be kept in mind that, in general, lattice energy and hydration energy tend to balance one another to within a few kcal. The magnitude of this small difference will be influenced by a number of other conditions, including polarization. The strong field of the subgroup ion will mean that a silver ion will try to surround itself with strongly polarizable particles. If a silver ion in water is brought into contact with chlorine ions then these will be strongly attracted, but since the negative ions, such as F^-, ClO_4^- and SO_4^{2-}, are only weakly polarizable, this effect will be small and the water molecules will be still more strongly attracted due to polarization. The silver ion then remains in the water and does not form a lattice, so that AgF and $AgClO_4$ are soluble, and AgCl, AgBr and AgI are insoluble. It is important to note that, in the subgroups, the order of solubility is quite different from that of the ions of the principal groups. Thus, for example, of the potassium salts, the fluoride is soluble but not the perchlorate, while the small lithium ion forms a fluoride of low solubility and a perchlorate of high solubility. A complete and satisfactory explanation of these complicated phenomena cannot be given unless all factors such as polarizability, size, etc. are taken into account.

We will not discuss them further here, but we still must consider the effect of the positive ion on the lattice energy of the solid and on the hydration energy. The perchlorate ion contains a highly-charged central ion and, since this repels positive ions strongly, $HClO_4$ is a strong acid. This positive ion will not only repel the H^+ ions but also other small ions, especially when they have an extra strong field as do the silver ions. This repulsion must lower the crystal energy in the solid salt and is one reason why $AgClO_4$ is so soluble.

If silver is combined successively with the ions of progressively lower acidity, ClO_4^-, SO_4^{2-} and PO_4^{3-}, then the solubility should decrease, which in fact it is found to do. With a large ion, such as caesium, this effect is no longer present because the centre of the caesium ion is further removed from the central ion of the negative complex ion so that the order becomes reversed and $CsClO_4$ is very insoluble, Cs_2SO_4 moderately soluble and Cs_3PO_4 very soluble.

Finally, it must be remembered that the hydration is also influenced by the structure of the ion. In view of the fact that the positive pole of a water molecule attaches itself to the negative ion, the molecule will be repelled by the positive nucleus of the positive ion. This means that the ion of a strong acid has a small hydration energy and will therefore have a smaller heat of solution and hence the tendency to form insoluble compounds. This effect is shown when ClO_4^- combines with a large ion, and must be taken into account in explaining the solubility behaviour of caesium salts, which increases in the order $ClO_4^- \rightarrow SO_4^{2-} \rightarrow PO_4^{3-}$. From what has been said, it appears that the phenomenon of the solubility of electrolytes in water is so complicated in view of the many factors which must be taken into consideration that no complete description of it, as a whole, can be given. Van der Waals forces, which will be dealt with in Section 46, also have an important effect on the dissociation, especially on compounds of the ions of the subgroups.

It is obvious that a non-polar molecule cannot penetrate into the crystals of an electrolyte, nor dissolve it. This explains why, for example, NaCl is insoluble in benzene, CCl_4, CS_2, etc., which are non-polar. On the other hand, nitrobenzene is not a solvent for salts either, yet its dipole moment of 4×10^{-18} is larger than that of water. It must, however, be remembered that the molecule $C_6H_5NO_2$ is also much larger than that of water, and consequently the larger dipole cannot approach as closely to the charges of the ions. A liquid, to produce easy dissociation, must have small molecules with large dipole moments.

Although ethyl alcohol, C_2H_5OH, is a much larger molecule than water, it is nevertheless a good solvent, which is due to the fact that the dipole in alcohols between the O^{2-} and H^+ ions lies in the OH group, which, in turn, determines the property of these compounds. This dipole lies on the surface of the oxygen ion and not, as in a chloride, in the group $—C^+—Cl^-$ behind the relatively large Cl^- ion. Thus, in the alcohols, the dipole can come close to the charges of the ions or to other dipoles in spite of the size of the molecule. To decide whether one liquid is a better solvent for salts than another with an equally large dipole moment, it is necessary to look into the details of the structure of the two molecules to see where the dipoles are located.

A further complicating effect in the problem of solubility is that not all compounds decompose into ions on solution. A typical example of such a compound is $HgCl_2$, and obviously the energy is lower in a solution containing undissociated molecules. The energy change in the solution of a compound to undissociated molecules is

$$O_M = -S + H$$

in which S is the heat of sublimation of the compound and H the hydration energy of the whole molecule. On the other hand, it is to be remembered that the heat of solution to ions is

$$O^{-+} = -U + H^+ + H^-$$

Now $(H^+ + H^-)$ is unquestionably much greater than H, so that O_M can only be greater than O^{-+} if S is small. Thus only those compounds with a small heat of sublimation, and which are therefore relatively volatile, will dissolve as complete molecules, and $HgCl_2$, as its name 'sublimate' implies, has this property. Here it is the strong polarization of the molecule which lowers the heat of sublimation; mercuric chloride does not have a true coordinated structure.

The insolubility of AgCl is due to the increased crystal energy caused by the extra field of the subgroup ions, but AgCl still forms a coordinated structure. If the extra field of the subgroup ion is stronger, it can lead, by polarization of the negative ion, to the formation of the molecular crystal with a lower heat of sublimation. The circumstances are then favourable for solution to a non-dissociated molecule, especially if the polarization is still insufficiently strong to reduce the electrical field of the molecule to a negligibly low value, for then the hydration energy of the molecule always has a value high enough to cause solubility. If the polarization is so great that the molecule can no longer be considered as ionic, then the molecule becomes insoluble in water.

When we look at the series $NaCl \rightarrow AgCl \rightarrow HgCl_2 \rightarrow CCl_4$, then we see that by increasing polarization or transition to a more covalent type of bond, the solubility is first decreased, followed by the formation of solutions containing undissociated molecules, and finally the compound becomes completely insoluble.

50. HYDRATES AND AMMONIATES

A molecule, to have the same property as water of solvating ions, must have a dipole of the same order of magnitude and not be much larger in volume. We would naturally choose HF and NH_3 as the most likely compounds. HF is not easy to work with, and consequently has not been investigated to any great extent. With NH_3, however, we know that, like water, it penetrates between the ions of a crystal or a molecule, and that a number of very interesting compounds are formed in this way.

When $CrCl_3$ is dissolved in liquid ammonia, the NH_3 molecules penetrate between the ions until the Cr^{3+} is completely surrounded by ammonia. The final state is represented by the solid compound $Cr(NH_3)_6Cl_3$, which is built up of $Cr(NH_3)_6^{3+}$ and Cl^- ions. This compound is comparable both with hydrates of the type $Ca(H_2O)_6Cl_2$ and with a complex composed of ions. The only difference is that here the Cr^{3+} is combined, not with ions, but with whole molecules through their dipoles.

A compound $Pt(NH_3)_6Cl_4$ can be formed from $PtCl_4$. In addition, Cu^{2+} ions can easily form compounds of this kind, and the deep blue colour observed when an excess of NH_3 is added to a cupric salt is due to the formation of the $Cu(NH_3)_4^{2+}$ ions. By the choice of experimental conditions, complexes can be formed containing water as well as ammonia, and also containing weakly polar molecules such as NO and even CO. There are, therefore, innumerable possibilities of this kind of complex formation, especially as penetration between the ions does not necessarily have to be complete. Besides the compound $Pt(NH_3)_6Cl_4$, another occurs with only five NH_3 molecules, in which there is still room for one chlorine ion attached to the Pt^{4+} ion so that its formula is $[Pt(NH_3)_5Cl]^{3+}Cl_3$. The series can be extended as far as a compound with the ion $[PtCl_6]^{2-}$, which amounts to the same thing as successive substitution of NH_3 by chlorine. The following ions are also obtained in this way: $[Pt(NH_3)_6]^{4+}$, $[Pt(NH_3)_5Cl]^{3+}$, $[Pt(NH_3)_4Cl_2]^{2+}$, $[Pt(NH_3)_3Cl_3]^{+}$, $[Pt(NH_3)_2Cl_4]^{0}$, $[Pt(NH_3)Cl_5]^{-}$ and $[PtCl_6]^{2-}$.

We have already met the last of these ions in the complex salt K_2PtCl_6. We also know that the bond between Pt^{4+} and Cl^- ions is so strong that practically no dissociation occurs, but when the chlorine is not directly bound to the platinum it will dissociate very easily, indeed. The series of compounds, proceeding from $[Pt(NH_3)_6]^{4+}Cl^-$ to $K_2(PtCl_6)$, will give successively 5, 4, 3, 2, 0, 2 and 3 ions. The conductivities, therefore, of solutions of these compounds containing the same number of molecules must be proportional to these numbers. $Pt(NH_3)_2Cl_4$ is not an electrolyte, and this compound corresponds to a minimum in the conductivity curve, as shown in *Figure 34*. The gap in the series is due to the fact that it has not yet been possible to prepare $Pt(NH_5)Cl_4$.

Analogous curves have been found for the series derived from $PtCl_2$ and $CoCl_3$. Most alkali halides form ammoniates with ammonia in an analogous manner to hydrates; when they are dissolved in water the ammonia is replaced by water, because the hydrate is the more stable. With the cupric salts, behaviour is reversed, and the hydrate even in the presence of excess water is decomposed by NH_3 to form the ammoniate. On closer investigation, it appears that, in general, the hydrates are more stable with a large positive ion of low charge and a noble-gas structure, while with an ion of small radius, high charge and abnormal structure, the ammoniates are the more stable. An ion with a strong field favours the formation of ammoniates.

It might at first sight be thought that, since the dipole moment of water is larger than that of ammonia, the hydrates would be more stable, which is certainly true when the field of the ions is weak and polarization consequently has little effect. The energy of an ion with respect to a dipole was found to be $e\mu/r^2$, which can be written $-F\mu$ since the field of the ion is given by e/r^2. The energy due to polarizability is equal to $-F\mu_\alpha$, but μ_α is now the induced dipole which is superimposed on the permanent one. Therefore, μ_α is equal to αF, so that the attraction of the molecule, as a result of polarizability, is

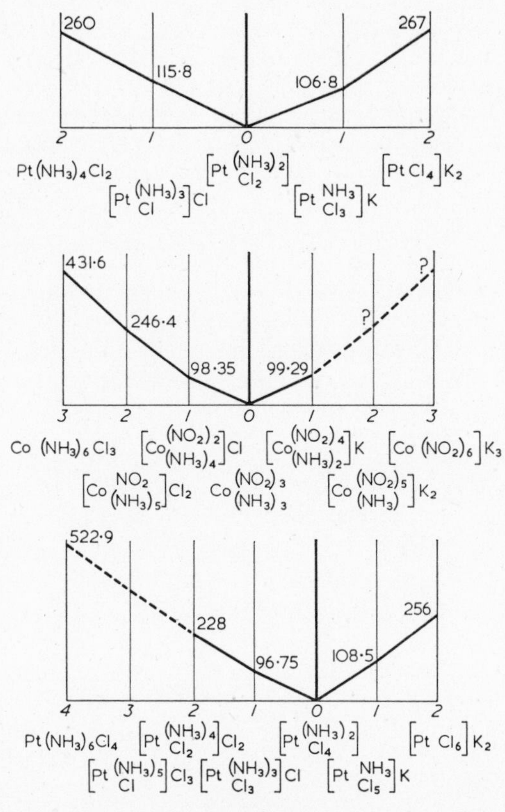

Figure 34

given by a term $-\frac{1}{2}\alpha F^2$, which is particularly important for high field-strengths. When field strengths are large, one must not seek the molecule with the greater dipole but the one which is the more polarizable. In particular, the α value for NH_3 is $2{\cdot}4 \times 10^{-24}$, while the polarizability of water is $1{\cdot}5 \times 10^{-24}$.

There is thus a qualitative explanation for the differences between hydrates and ammoniates. The question does arise, however, whether they are, in fact, explicable by polarization effects alone, since certain phenomena indicate that the ammoniates are not true ionic compounds. There was, as well, some doubt whether the low symmetry of some molecules could be explained on the basis of polarization effects. One reason for doubt arises from the fact that there are complexes with CO, wherein the CO can displace ammonia. The dipole of CO is, however, very small and it therefore seems impossible that the stability of complexes containing CO is determined exclusively by the electrostatic attraction of permanent and induced dipoles.

These uncertainties are increased when the existence of compounds of CO with metals, the carbonyls such as $Fe(CO)_5$, for which no electrostatic model is conceivably possible are considered. The iron obviously is not present in the compound as an ion; how then can the attraction for the CO molecules be explained? Even in the straight ammoniates there is some doubt regarding the validity of the simple electrostatic representation of the structure for it is found experimentally that the magnetic properties of halides are radically altered by the taking up of molecules of ammonia. This shows that some of the electrons of the positive ions are influenced by the ammonia molecules in a way which an electrostatic picture cannot explain.

Chapter IX

NON-ELECTROSTATIC BONDS

51. VAN DER WAALS-LONDON FORCES

THE conception of the electrostatic bond has been found to be most valuable in the field of inorganic chemistry and has helped to clarify a great many phenomena. It has frequently made it possible to predict properties both of unknown compounds and of those which have been little investigated. Nevertheless, a number of difficulties have been encountered. For example, in Section 43, it was shown that the theory did not really provide a satisfactory explanation of the low symmetry of molecules. Again, the theory failed to explain the volatility and small dipole moment of the compounds CO, NO, Cl_2O, etc., and lastly, it threw no light whatever on the reason for the existence of molecules of elements such as H_2, Cl_2, O_2, N_2, etc., especially as dipole measurements show that the formulae H^+H^-, Cl^+Cl^- are excluded.

Another explanation must therefore be found. Now we know that besides forces of an electrical character there are others which act between atoms. Even the noble gases attract one another, although they are non-polar and have spherically symmetrical electronic structures. These so-called van der Waals forces cannot be explained on the basis of classical mechanics and LONDON was the first to find an explanation of them with the help of wave mechanics. He reached the conclusion that two particles at a distance r have a potential energy which is inversely proportional to the sixth power of the distance, and directly proportional to the square of the polarizability, and to a quantity φ which is a function of the ionization and excitation energies of the atom, so that

$$U_L = -\varphi\alpha^2/r^6$$

The energy for two different atoms is

$$U_L = -\sqrt{\varphi_1\varphi_2}\alpha_1\alpha_2/r^6$$

This formula explains why the boiling points of shielded halides increase from the fluorides to the iodides (*see* Section 41). As the polarizability increases in this order more strongly than the third power of the distance, the energy required to separate the molecules in the liquid increases from the fluorides to the iodides. The increase of the boiling point of the series of noble gases from He to Rd, of the halogens from F_2 to I_2 and of the screened calcides from the oxides to the sulphides, depends on the same effect. The formula also provides an explanation for the systematic linear progression of boiling points in the series CCl_4, CCl_3Br, CCl_2Br_2, $CClBr_3$, CBr_4, etc.

Can the van der Waals forces lead to the formation of chemical compounds? The two Cl atoms in a molecule Cl_2 will certainly be attracted to one another by a van der Waals-London force but it can be very simply shown that these forces alone can never lead to the formation of a chemical compound. The peculiar property of these forces is that they always strive to bring like atoms together. Suppose we have a dilute gas mixture containing N atoms of A and N atoms of B; further let us imagine that the van der Waals-London forces lead to the formation of molecules AB from these atoms; the energy of the system is then

$$\Delta H_1 = -N\sqrt{\varphi_A \varphi_B \alpha_A \alpha_B}/(r_A + r_B)^6$$

If we were to form $0{\cdot}5N$ molecules of A_2 and $0{\cdot}5N$ molecules B_2 then the energy would be

$$\Delta H_2 = -\{0{\cdot}5N\varphi_A\alpha_A^2/(2r_A)^6 + 0{\cdot}5N\varphi_B\alpha_B^2/(2r_B)^6\}$$

If it can be shown that $\Delta H_1 > \Delta H_2$, then the molecules AB will not be formed, and this may be proved. From

$$(a - b)^2 > 0$$

it follows that

$$Nab < 0{\cdot}5N(a^2 + b^2)$$

Substitute

$$a = \sqrt{\varphi_A \alpha_A}/(2r_A)^3 \qquad \text{and} \qquad b = \sqrt{\varphi_B \alpha_B}/(2r_B)^3$$

and thus

$$N\,\frac{\sqrt{\varphi_A\varphi_B\alpha_A\alpha_B}}{2^6 r_A^3 r_B^3} < 0{\cdot}5N\left(\frac{\varphi_A\alpha_A^2}{(2r_A)^6} + \frac{\varphi_B\alpha_B^2}{(2r_B)^6}\right)$$

and since

$$(r_A - r_B)^2 > 0$$

it follows that

$$(r_A + r_B)^2 > 4r_A r_B \qquad \text{and} \qquad (r_A + r_B)^6 > 2^6 r_A^3 r_B^3$$

Therefore

$$N\,\frac{\sqrt{\varphi_A\varphi_B\alpha_A\alpha_B}}{(r_A + r_B)^6} < N\,\frac{\sqrt{\varphi_A\varphi_B\alpha_A\alpha_B}}{2^6 r_A^3 r_B^3} < 0{\cdot}5N\left(\frac{\varphi_A\alpha_A^2}{(2r_A)^6} + \frac{\varphi_B\alpha_B^2}{(2r_B)^6}\right)$$

from which is obtained

$$-N\frac{\sqrt{\varphi_A\varphi_B}\alpha_A\alpha_B}{(r_A+r_B)^6} > -0{\cdot}5N\left(\frac{\varphi_A\alpha_A^2}{(2r_A)^6}+\frac{\varphi_B\alpha_B^2}{(2r_B)^6}\right)$$

The energy of the combination *AB* is thus higher than that of $0{\cdot}5A_2 + 0{\cdot}5B_2$. This result can be proved equally well for other combinations. Van der Waals-London forces, therefore, although very important in the mutual cohesion of atoms and molecules, can never lead to an actual chemical combination.

The forces causing chemical combination must be of a completely different kind and must lead to a definite saturation. When two chlorine atoms combine to form a molecule Cl_2, a third atom can not be added whereas the van der Waals-London forces will always tend to add still further particles to an existing combination. These forces can lead to the formation of lattices, but not to separate molecules with a fixed number of particles.

Strictly speaking, the van der Waals-London forces should be taken into account in any consideration of energies of compounds. In general, the correction is small because the α of the positive ion is usually small. Only in compounds of the subgroup elements are the effects of these forces perceptible because the polarizability of the subgroup ions is appreciably greater than that of the ions of the main groups. This effect contributes to the low solubility of the halides and calcides of elements of subgroups, such as AgCl, AgI, CdS, CdSe, etc. (*see* Section 49). The effect of the van der Waals-London forces is to surround each particle with the highest possible number of like neighbours, and this effect will lead to the formation of lattices with higher coordination numbers if the ions are strongly polarizable. The fact that CsCl, CsBr and CsI crystallize in the CsCl system is mainly due to this. A correction must accordingly be made to the hypothesis of GOLDSCHMIDT governing the relation between lattice structure and ionic radii (*see* Section 71).

The van der Waals-London forces play a particularly important part in the formation of molecular lattices even when the molecules still have an ionic structure; screening and polarization diminish the effect of electrostatic forces to a great extent, and the van der Waals forces are therefore preponderant. Examples of substances which form molecular lattices are those of the type XY_4, such as CCl_4, CI_4, $SnCl_4$, etc. In these a small positive ion is surrounded by four large halogen ions in the form of a tetrahedron, with the result that the external electric field of the positive ion is very weak. Mutual attraction of molecules is often exclusively the result of the van der

Waals forces, which act between all atoms and ions, and therefore the molecules of the halogens, oxygen and nitrogen, etc. combine to form molecular crystals at sufficiently low temperatures. In this way all atoms attract all others, and the van der Waals forces strive to surround every particle with as many others as possible. If the particles are spherical, then this leads to a dense spherical packing, as shown in *Figure 35*. This arrangement is a cubic one, but there is still a further type of packing, equally closely packed, which corresponds to the symmetry of a crystal of the hexagonal class (*see Figure 36*).

Figure 35 *Figure 36*

We shall be concerned mostly with the regular packing which occurs when spheres are placed together two by two, or joined three by three in such a way that the mid-points form an equilateral triangle, just as four spheres are placed in a tetrahedral arrangement. Thus molecules of the type XY_3 and XY_4 can form molecular lattices with the closest packing of the negative ions as long as those ions are spherical and the positive ions are small so that the mutual contact of the negative ions is not prevented. In so far as the structures of such substances have been investigated, they show the negative ions to have the closest-packed structures, or very nearly so.

52. MUTUAL SOLUBILITY

A hydrocarbon is negligibly soluble in water, but, equally well, water is insoluble in the hydrocarbon. Methyl alcohol is soluble in water in all proportions, but not in a hydrocarbon. A higher alcohol is only slightly soluble in water, but is freely soluble in hydrocarbons. Water and hydrocarbons, so far as their solubilities are concerned, are opposites; what is soluble in one is insoluble in the other. Thus, sodium chloride dissolves in water, but not in a hydrocarbon, sulphur is insoluble in water, but soluble in a hydrocarbon. It can reasonably be inferred that these differences largely arise from the fact that water is a polar substance while the hydrocarbon is not.

Let us consider the addition of the hydrocarbon hexane to water. The water molecules are held together by dipole forces, so that energy must be expended to detach one molecule; this energy would not, however, be regained if the water molecule were in the hexane, because the water molecule could find no polar point of attachment. The dipole attraction in the water therefore prevents the water mixing with the hexane. Similarly, the hexane molecules will not mix with the water, because the energy required to remove a water molecule is not regained if a hexane molecule is brought into the new environment where the water molecule will exert no attraction on the non-polar hexane molecule. The dipole attraction thus prevents not only the separation of the water molecules, but also the ingress of non-polar molecules. A substance with a strong dipole does not mix with a non-polar one, and vice versa.

In fact, the problem is a great deal more complicated because, in addition to the dipole-dipole attractions, the van der Waals-London forces resulting from the polarization of non-polar molecules by polar ones have also to be taken into account. The energy required to remove a molecule from the liquid can in general be split into three separate parts

$$\Delta H = L + D + K$$

where L, D and K correspond to the names of those who first investigated the forces theoretically: KEESOM, the dipole-dipole interaction, DEBYE, the action of dipoles on polarizable molecules, and LONDON, the mutual attraction of non-polar molecules and atoms.

We will now proceed to calculate the energy changes when two substances are mixed. If a large negative value is found it will mean that no mixing occurs, or that the solubility will be very small. In order to simplify the calculation, we will assume that there is only one kind of energy, namely L, which we choose because the van der Waals forces are always present. Consider two non-polar liquids A and B, in which it will be assumed that the molecules are approximately of equal size. Since the van der Waals energy decreases rapidly with the distance, it can be assumed that there will only be attraction between a molecule and its nearest neighbours. We can therefore say that when N molecules are evaporated a certain number, p, bonds per molecule will be broken, or $Np = P$ per gram mol. The energy required for this process is the heat of evaporation per mol. We proceed now to mix $(1 - \alpha)$ molecules of A with α molecules of B; in the first place the two components must be evaporated; this requires an amount of energy

$$(1 - \alpha)\, \Delta H_A + \alpha\, \Delta H_B$$

or, if $\Delta H = L$, then it becomes

$$(1 - \alpha) L_A + \alpha L_B$$

Altogether, P bonds have had to be broken since we have assumed that the molecules are of equal size, and, consequently, the molecules of A and B have the same number of neighbours.

The gas in now mixed and recondensed. The P bonds are all reestablished but now each molecule has a number of neighbours consisting of A and B and not, as before, neighbours of the same kind. For every bond formed between two like atoms, an energy L_A/P or L_B/P will be released, and for bonds between unlike atoms there will be a different value which we will call L_{AB}/P.

We now further assume that a molecule A, on condensation, has an equally good chance of finding itself in the neighbourhood of a molecule B as of another molecule A, which means that the distribution is determined completely by chance. On the average, therefore, the proportion of molecules of A and B, as immediate neighbours of an atom B, will be in the ratio of the concentrations of A and B in the mixture, or $(1 - \alpha) : \alpha$. Therefore the number of A—A bonds is equal to $P(1 - \alpha)^2$, because the number of A molecules is proportional to $(1 - \alpha)$ and the number of A neighbours of an A molecule is proportional to $(1 - \alpha)$. In the same way, the number of bonds B—B is proportional to $P\alpha^2$, that of the A—B bonds to $P(1 - \alpha)\alpha$ and that of the B—A bonds to $P\alpha(1 - \alpha)$. Now, the the number of A—B bonds is equal to the number of B—A bonds, the total number of this kind therefore being $2P\alpha(1 - \alpha)$. The total number of bonds is again P. For the three kinds we therefore obtain

$$(1 - \alpha)^2 P, \qquad 2\alpha(1 - \alpha)P, \qquad \alpha^2 P$$

and the energy released in the formation of the P bonds is

$$(1 - \alpha)^2 L_A + 2\alpha(1 - \alpha) L_{AB} + \alpha^2 L_B$$

Now it is immediately apparent from the preceding section that L_{AB} can be replaced by $\sqrt{L_A L_B}$, so that the condensation energy of the gas mixture is

$$(1 - \alpha)^2 L_A + 2\alpha(1 - \alpha)\sqrt{L_A L_B} + \alpha^2 L_B$$

but the heat of evaporation of the components was

$$\{-(1-\alpha)L_A - \alpha L_B\}$$

so that the total heat of mixing is found to be

$$\begin{aligned}\{(1-\alpha)^2 - (1-\alpha)\}L_A + 2\alpha(1-\alpha)\sqrt{L_A L_B} + (\alpha^2 - \alpha)L_B \\ = -\alpha(1-\alpha)(L_A - 2\sqrt{L_A L_B} + L_B) \\ = -\alpha(1-\alpha)(\sqrt{L_A} - \sqrt{L_B})^2\end{aligned}$$

The heat of mixing is therefore always negative, that is to say, two liquids of this particular kind will always be immiscible at low temperatures. As the heat of sublimation actually involves Debye and Keesom energies, as well, when the two molecules have dipoles, then, by a similar argument, the heat of mixing can be expressed by the formula

$$\Delta H_M = -\alpha(1-\alpha)\{(\sqrt{L_A} - \sqrt{L_B})^2 + (\sqrt{D_A} - \sqrt{D_B})^2 + (\sqrt{K_A} - \sqrt{K_B})^2\}$$

an expression which is, however, still always negative*. According to this formula, therefore, all pairs of liquids are immiscible at low temperatures, and only when ΔH_M is small will any appreciable mixing take place at temperatures where ΔH_M can be compensated by the product of the change in entropy

$$\Delta S = R(\alpha \ln \alpha - (1-\alpha)\ln(1-\alpha))$$

ΔH_M will be zero when the two liquids are identical, and it is obvious that under such conditions the two liquids must be completely miscible. Also, liquids which are very similar to one another and have practically identical values of L, D and K will be miscible. It is, however, not a sufficient condition for solubility that the two molecules have equal heats of evaporation. We now return to the example of water and hexane. The boiling points are not markedly different and consequently their heats of evaporation are of the same order. For hexane $\Delta H = L$, and D and K are both zero, while for water the K term is so predominant that, as a good approximation, $\Delta H = K.\Delta H_M$, which then has its largest possible value

$$-2\alpha(1-\alpha)(K_{H_2O} + L_{Hex.})$$

* In chemistry, heat of reaction is given a positive sign when heat is given out, that is, when the mixture gets warmer. NaCl has therefore a positive heat of formation and a negative latent heat of vaporization. In physics, on the other hand, it is usual to describe a heat of vaporization as positive because the energy of the system increases in the process, that is, energy has been added to the system as heat.

and the miscibility in this system must be minute. If hexane had a dipole, and if water were somewhat more polarizable than it is, then the miscibility would immediately increase. The hydrocarbon can be given a dipole by replacing one of the hydrogen atoms by a halogen, an OH or a NO_2 group. The question still remains whether the solubility of a monochlor hydrocarbon will be greater than that of a corresponding hydrocarbon. The solubility of the former will increase by virtue of the introduction of the dipole, yet it will decrease because the chlorine atom is strongly polarizable, which increases the L value of the chloride. With F, which has low polarizability, the dipole effect predominates. C_6H_5F is more soluble than C_6H_6, while C_6H_5Cl is less soluble. An even more marked effect would be expected from the introduction of an OH group. This group is less polarizable and, in addition, the dipole is close to the surface since the H^+ ion is so small. If an H in CH_4 is replaced by an atom, or a group of atoms, then the solubility in water of the compounds would be expected to increase in the following order:

$$I \rightarrow Br \rightarrow Cl \rightarrow F \rightarrow NO_2 \rightarrow OH$$

The smallest effect will be that of iodine because of its large polarizability; the NO_2 group has a fairly large effect because of its large dipole (4×10^{-18}) just as does that of the CN group, but the effect of the OH group is by far the largest because of its small polarizability and the peripheral position of the dipole. Experimentally observed values of the solubilities are given in *Table XXXVIII*.

Table XXXVIII

Solubilities in millimol per 100 *gm of Water*

solvent	CH_3	C_2H_5	nC_3H_7	$isoC_3H_7$	C_6H_5
OH	∞	∞	∞	∞	90
NO_2	—	—	—	—	1·7
CN	∞	190	—	—	—
F	—	—	—	—	1·6
Cl	—	—	3·5	3·9	0·43
Br	—	8·2	1·9	2·6	0·28
I	10	2·6	0·6	0·8	0·17
H	—	—	—	—	0·9

Table XXXVIII brings out very clearly the rules we have derived for solubilities; the order of solubility in the phenyl compounds is what would be expected from the magnitudes of the moments and polarizabilities of the substituent groups. All the solubility values decrease with increasing length of the hydrocarbon chains, which is accompanied by an increase of van der Waals energy. The shape of the molecule has some influence, as can be seen from the fact that the *iso*propyl compounds are more soluble than the normal ones, but we will not discuss this detail any further here.

By the introduction of an OH group into CH_4, the resulting methyl alcohol is completely miscible in water. Also, by a similar substitution in the hydrocarbons C_2H_6 and C_3H_8, completely miscible alcohols are obtained. This does not apply in still longer chains. When one OH group is not sufficient to promote solubility of the hydrocarbon it can only be brought about by introducing several OH groups, the effect of which is seen in the high solubilities of the sugars.

The introduction of dipoles increases solubility in water, but diminishes it in a non-polar liquid, glycol, glycerol and the sugars having negligible solubility in hydrocarbons, CCl_4, CS_2, etc. Substitution in the water molecule, leading to an increase of polarizability or decrease of the dipole, will increase the solubility in non-polar liquids; thus in $H_2O \rightarrow C_2H_5OH \rightarrow C_2H_5OC_2H_5$, the miscibility with hydrocarbons steadily increases in that order. It now becomes quite clear why sulphur is more soluble in hydrocarbons than in water. Accurate determinations of the very small solubility of mercury have shown that it is higher in benzene than alcohol, and higher in alcohol than water. The large polarizability of the mercury atom accounts for this effect.

With regard to the previous discussion, there are several observations to be made; thus, in the derivation of the formula for the heat of mixing it was assumed that the molecules were of equal size, which is not true in all the examples cited. However, it can be shown that the variation in size does not make much difference provided the molecules can be considered as approximately spherical. A more difficult point occurs when, in contradiction to the theory, the heat of formation is positive, as, for example, with alcohol and water. This arises from the fact that in the calculation it was postulated that the molecules in the mixture were distributed according to chance. This is no longer true if the energy of the two molecules, as a result of their particular structure, is favourable to combinations with low energies which occur to a greater extent than if they were determined by probability alone. If, however, this effect is included in the calculation, then the theory becomes far too complicated. We shall therefore have to exclude cases of positive heats of mixing from these considerations.

We will, however, just examine one mixture in which these particularly favourable combinations are such that the probability distribution plays no part at all, e.g. in the solution of an electrolyte in water. It is in just such solutions that there is frequently a positive heat of mixing, because the hydration energy is often greater than the crystal energy. Under such conditions, each ion usually has water molecules as its immediate neighbours, very seldom other ions and never any of equal charge. We can, if we wish, regard the formation of NaCl from sodium and chlorine as a 'mixing', but here there is no question of the arrangement being determined by probability. The low energy of the Na^+Cl^- bond means that only this type of bond occurs, and the chance distribution is entirely replaced by the complete order of the crystal. Because this mixing leads to order, it is no longer described in this way, but instead is called a chemical combination.

It was seen in Section 46 that the van der Waals forces alone could never lead to the formation of molecules, and yet it appears that they prevent mixing. In fact, the van der Waals-London forces always tend to add like to like. It is due to the change in entropy that mixing still takes place, except where the heat of mixing is positive under the influence of dipole forces.

53. CHEMICAL BINDING BY ELECTRON PAIRS

The simplest chemical reaction is that between two hydrogen atoms

$$H + H \rightarrow H_2$$

in which only two protons and two electrons take part. To explain why a molecule H_2 is formed, one must show that a system of two protons and two electrons has a minimum energy when these four particles are in combination. This problem can be solved with the aid of wave mechanics, the details of which will not be discussed in this book, but instead a schematic picture of the result of such a calculation will be given. The picture is that of two electrons of a system moving in such a way around two protons as to produce a coupling between them. This can be represented by the symbol H : H, but it must not be thought that this electron pair is stationary between the two protons. Both electrons describe very complicated paths, but their common centre of gravity, on the average, lies midway between the two H nuclei. Such a pair of electrons correspond to a valency, a bond produced by an electron pair being called a covalent bond. The concept of an electron pair is an essential part of the theory. The electrons, therefore, occur in the atoms in pairs; the completed *K* shell contains one pair, and the completed *L* shell four pairs, etc.

Two chlorine atoms can also react so that their two unpaired electrons form a pair. Since this pair of electrons is common to both atoms, the *L* shell of each chlorine atom of eight electrons is complete. Further pairing cannot then occur, and molecules larger than Cl_2 are not formed. The electron pair therefore is used in place of the old valency link of organic chemistry. The great advantage, however, of the newer concept is that from the distribution of the electrons in the atom, especially of those in the outer shell, the valency of the atom can be determined. Hydrogen and the halogens have an electron missing from the outer shell, and they can therefore, form one pair, that is, they are univalent. The chalcogens are divalent, elements of the nitrogen group tervalent, and elements of the carbon group tetravalent. Boron, however, is not pentavalent. As there are only three electrons in its outer shell more than three pairs cannot be formed unless the electrons in the *K* shell are included. These are already in a state of low energy which cannot be still further lowered by bringing them into the *L* shell.

We will in the first place examine the consequences of this concept of reactions between like atoms. Together with modern ideas on the structure of molecules and crystals we can learn a good deal more from this concept than from the original valency links. Further development of the theory of the covalent bond provides information on the directions of the valencies in space. The probability of finding an electron in the hydrogen atom on the surface of a sphere, with its centre in the nucleus, is everywhere equal, but it is a function of the distance from the nucleus. It can therefore be said that the electrons are so arranged around the nucleus that the mean density diminishes with decreasing distance from the nucleus, and is therefore spherically symmetrical. The second electron of the *K* shell has the same spherical distribution as have the first two electrons (*s* electrons) of the *L* shell, but the other six, or rather the three remaining pairs (*p* electrons), have a different distribution. They are not spherical and are all at right-angles to one another. When these electrons form covalent bonds they are at right-angles; thus, in a purely covalent H_2O molecule, the valency lines O—H will be at right-angles. Of the valency electrons of carbon, one is an *s* electron and the other three are *p* electrons, which can give a new distribution in which there are four valency directions arranged in such a way that they make angles of 109° with one another. These valency angles are modified by other effects, such as Born repulsion, van der Waals-London forces and partial ionic bonds; in actual fact, they are about 110° with variations of approximately 10°.

The halogens can combine in one way only, namely to form molecules $X—X$, as in H_2, F_2, Cl_2, Br_2 and I_2, larger molecules being unknown. An ion can still be formed from such a molecule; thus the ion H_3^+ exists, which, however, in reaction with negative ions or electrons always forms only H_2 molecules. Two atoms of the chalcogens can combine to give molecules of the type $X = X$, as O_2 and S_2, the latter molecule occurring in sulphur vapour at high temperatures. Then, again, there is the possibility of ring formation and a third possibility, the formation of infinitely long chains.

$$—X—X—X \ldots\ldots\ldots X—X—X—$$

This structure is met in the crystals of selenium and tellurium, in which the atoms occur in chains twisted into spirals. This spiral formation is caused by the fact that valency bonds make angles of 105° with one another, and these can lead to chains of various shapes, but if a spiral is formed the atoms are closely packed in the chain so that the energy of the van der Waals forces, which are always acting, can assume a low value.

The structure of such a crystal can be obtained very easily by dividing a surface into equilateral triangles and then placing, at each apex of the triangles, a spiral of atoms with its axis at right-angles to the surface.

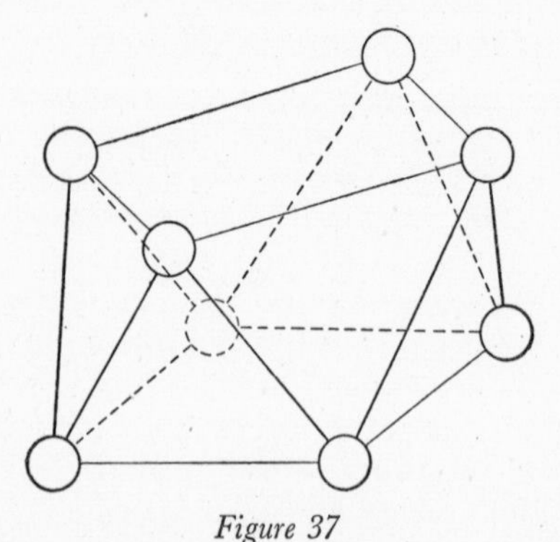

Figure 37

Sulphur vapour, at low temperatures, mostly contains the molecules S_8; because the angle between the S—S bonds must be about 100°, the S atoms cannot lie in a flat ring but must be folded in a so-called Archimedian antiprism (*see Figure 37*). In the nitrogen group there are more numerous possibilities, such as:

1. Molecules with tervalent bonds, for example N≡N.
2. Ring-forming systems with single and double bonds. Systems of this type consisting of like atoms are not known.
3. Series of atoms with double and single bonds. These are only known in combination with other groups, as for example in the tetrazoles *X*N=N—N=N*X*.
4. Tetrahedral molecules X_4, such as P_4 and As_4. In these compounds each atom has three neighbours with valency lines joining each of the neighbours, so that all the atoms are just saturated. All bonds include angles of 60°, which is much smaller than is to be expected from the valency directions in free atoms. These molecules do not have a minimal energy.
5. Infinitely extended layers of the kind shown in *Figure 38*.

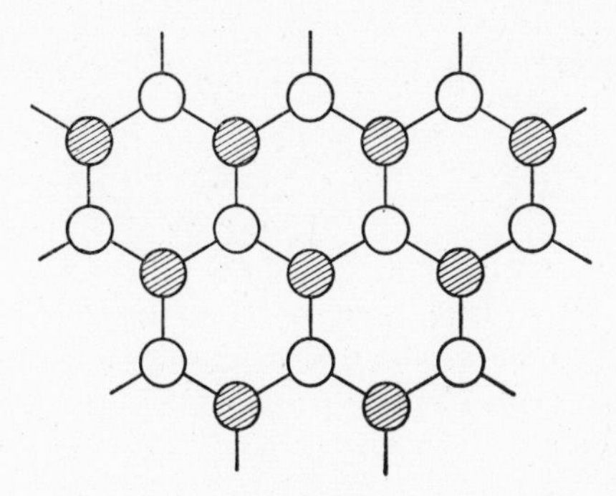

Figure 38

In the latter, the valency angles must be about 100°, so the layers cannot be flat. Their shape is obtained if, in *Figure 38*, the atoms shown with the clear circles are displaced somewhat below the plane of the paper and the shaded ones similarly, above it. If the layers formed in this way are then arranged on top of one another, the crystal structure of the elements arsenic, antimony and bismuth are obtained in their normal forms in which they have metallic properties. There also exists a modification of phosphorus with a similar structure. In addition, there are other forms of arsenic and antimony, the properties of which correspond to those of yellow phosphorus; these forms contain molecules P_4, As_4 and Sb_4.

The number of possible structures in the elements of the carbon group is still greater. Molecules *X*≡*X* are not known. In all probability this is because the maintenance of the tetrahedral valency angle prevents their formation. Ring systems and chains of all kinds with uni-, di- and tervalent bonds are extensively found in organic chemistry in carbon compounds in combination with other atoms. The graphite crystal provides an example of a layer-forming structure, which was met in the previous group. Here, however, we have to assume a number of double bonds (*see Figure 39*), or leave a free valency for every atom. This difficulty also had to be faced in organic chemistry; the formula of benzene, as put forward by KEKULÉ, is not satisfactory since it leads to two di-ortho substitution products

```
       Cl                      Cl
       C                       C
      // \                    / \\
   HC     CCl              HC     C
   |      ||               ||     |
   HC     CH               HC     CH
      \\ /                    \ //
       C                       C
       H                       H
```

The solution of this problem is that the double bonds are continuously changing in the molecule, so that on the average the six C—C bonds are equivalent. The best structural formula for benzene is therefore

```
       H
       C
      /⁄ \\
   HC     CH
   |ı     ı|
   HC     CH
      \\ /⁄
       C
       H
```

in which the bond ═ sign indicates the particular bond in benzene, with on the average three electrons per bond, which is produced by 3/2 normal C—C bonds.

In graphite, four valencies must be divided between three bonds and therefore there are, on the average, 8/3 electrons per bond, the type of bond thus being 4/3 of a normal C—C bond. By transition of the bonds, the three structures shown in *Figure 39* are continuously changing from one to another. A feature of the quantum mechanical theory of the chemical bond is that the simultaneous existence of states of equal or nearly equal energy, called 'resonance' (*see* Section 55), lowers the energy of the system. This resonance energy plays an important role in many chemical reactions.

A further structural possibility, which exists in the elements of the fourth group, is a lattice infinitely extended in space in which each atom is surrounded by four others in a tetrahedron, and in which the

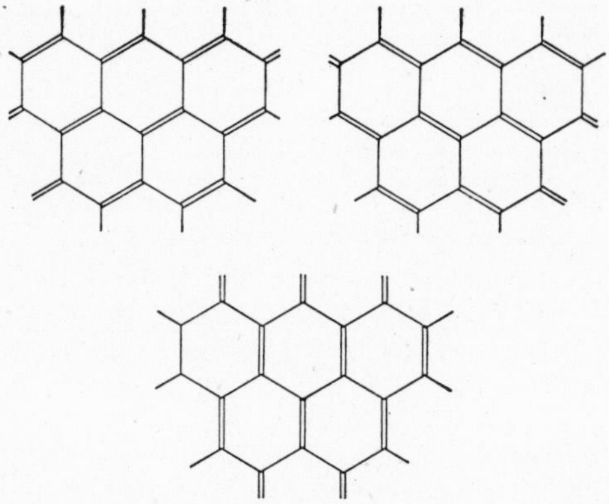

Figure 39

theoretical valency angle is maintained. The diamond structure can be derived from the cubic form of Zns (Section 14), if the two kinds of atoms are substituted by carbon atoms. Diamond, which is the second form of carbon, has such a structure, as have also silicon, germanium and grey tin, into which form the normal metallic tin changes at 13°C. White tin has a somewhat deformed diamond lattice that is obtained when the normal diamond lattice is compressed in a direction parallel to the edges of the unit cell.

All the other elements except boron, which has a very complicated structure, are metallic, and the only kind of molecular formation known is the occurrence of small concentrations of A_2 molecules in the vapours of the alkali metals. Such molecules are analogous to those of hydrogen, but their dissociation energy is small and their existence in the crystalline state is unknown. In the metallic state we have to assume a third kind of bond, which will be dealt with at a later stage.

From the survey of the structures of non-metallic elements it is seen that not all elements form stable multiple bonds. Whereas, in oxygen and nitrogen, multiple bonds are the more stable, with a lower energy than the equivalent number of single bonds, as follows from the existence of the molecules O═O and N≡N and the non-existence of chains or rings O_n and N_n, in the other elements the single bonds are the more stable. In carbon, the difference is small: chains ═C═ C═C═C═ or —C≡C—C≡C—C≡C, containing carbon atoms only, are not stable, but in graphite the double bonds become stable, their energy lowered by resonance. Sulphur molecules, S_2, with structure S═S, have a higher energy that the chains S_n or rings S_8; the same holds true for selenium and tellurium, and in phosphorus, arsenic, antimony, bismuth, silicon and germanium, too, the stable forms only contain single bonds. Molecules with multiple bonds, like P≡P or Si≡Si, when occurring at all, are only to be found in the vapour state at high temperature, where the higher energy is compensated by a higher entropy.

No explanation will be given as to why oxygen and nitrogen are the only elements for which multiple bonds are more stable than single bonds, and in carbon multiple bonds are only slightly less stable than single bonds; this experimental fact is very important, for in compounds, as well, stable multiple bonds are only formed if they contain one of these elements.

54. COVALENT BONDS BETWEEN DIFFERENT ATOMS

Covalent bond formation between two different atoms A and B is usually possible, and the number of electrons of each atom that will partake in the bond formation will be determined by the energy. At low temperature the combination of atoms A and B, with a minimal energy, will be stable. Many types of bonds can be formed: they may be single or multiple electron pairs, but bonding by one or three electrons has been observed in a few cases.

To predict what kind of bond will be formed by two kinds of atoms, A and B, is a problem of quantum mechanics. Since the calculation of the states of minimum energy for a given pair is completely beyond the scope of this book, we will try to find out empirically what kind of bonds will be formed.

When looking at the compounds formed by two elements near the end of the periods, viz. the negative, non-metallic elements preceding the rare gases, it is found that a very common type of bond is that in which a complete electron octet is formed, as in combinations of two equal atoms. In a molecule Cl_2, one electron pair is formed by the two unpaired electrons, and each Cl atom has still three pairs of electrons, the electron formula of the molecule being

$$:\underset{\cdot\cdot}{\overset{\cdot\cdot}{\mathrm{Cl}}}:\underset{\cdot\cdot}{\overset{\cdot\cdot}{\mathrm{Cl}}}:$$

By this sharing of two electrons, four electron pairs then belong to each Cl atom, all eight electrons residing in the *L* shell.

Octet structures are found in almost all stable hydrogen compounds, and

$$\mathrm{HF},\quad \mathrm{H_2O},\quad \mathrm{H_3N},\quad \mathrm{H_4C}$$

can each be represented by an electron formula, in which the other atom has an electron octet

$$\mathrm{H}:\underset{\cdot\cdot}{\overset{\cdot\cdot}{\mathrm{F}}}:,\qquad \mathrm{H}:\underset{\cdot\cdot}{\overset{\cdot\cdot}{\mathrm{O}}}:\mathrm{H},\qquad \mathrm{H}:\underset{\mathrm{H}}{\underset{\cdot\cdot}{\overset{\cdot\cdot}{\mathrm{N}}}}:\mathrm{H},\qquad \mathrm{H}:\underset{\mathrm{H}}{\underset{\cdot\cdot}{\overset{\mathrm{H}}{\overset{\cdot\cdot}{\mathrm{C}}}}}:\mathrm{H}$$

Since the H atom contains a *K* electron only, it can only form a *K* electron pair, and therefore in hydrogen compounds one electron pair only is connected to the hydrogen atom.

In a molecule formed by two elements, complete octets can also result from bond formation between two equal atoms: besides the compounds given above there exist others

H_2O_2	H_4N_2	C_2H_6	C_2H_4	C_2H_2
hydrogen peroxide	*hydrazine*	*ethane*	*ethene*	*acetylene*

and all the other hydrocarbons which clearly have complete octet structures, too

$$\mathrm{H}:\underset{\cdot\cdot}{\overset{\cdot\cdot}{\mathrm{O}}}:\underset{\cdot\cdot}{\overset{\cdot\cdot}{\mathrm{O}}}:\mathrm{H},\qquad \mathrm{H}:\underset{\mathrm{H}}{\underset{\cdot\cdot}{\overset{\cdot\cdot}{\mathrm{N}}}}:\underset{\mathrm{H}}{\underset{\cdot\cdot}{\overset{\cdot\cdot}{\mathrm{N}}}}:\mathrm{H},\qquad \mathrm{H}:\underset{\mathrm{H}}{\underset{\cdot\cdot}{\overset{\mathrm{H}}{\overset{\cdot\cdot}{\mathrm{C}}}}}:\underset{\mathrm{H}}{\underset{\cdot\cdot}{\overset{\mathrm{H}}{\overset{\cdot\cdot}{\mathrm{C}}}}}:\mathrm{H},$$

$$\mathrm{H}:\underset{\mathrm{H}}{\underset{\cdot\cdot}{\overset{\cdot\cdot}{\mathrm{C}}}}::\underset{\mathrm{H}}{\underset{\cdot\cdot}{\overset{\cdot\cdot}{\mathrm{C}}}}:\mathrm{H},\qquad \mathrm{H}:\mathrm{C}:::\mathrm{C}:\mathrm{H}$$

It is somewhat more difficult to see that the third nitrogen—hydrogen compound, azoic acid N_3H, also has only complete octets. By the study of the solid azides, e.g. KN_3, it has been shown that the

N_3^- ion has a linear configuration, and a possible electronic configuration for the acid, therefore, is

$$H:\underset{\cdot\cdot}{N}::N::\underset{\cdot\cdot}{N}:$$

in which each N atom has an octet structure.

Only for boron hydride does another type of bond formation have to be assumed. For this compound an octet structure is impossible, since boron has only three valency electrons. The compound BH_3 thus would have a sextet structure

$$\begin{array}{c} H:\underset{\cdot\cdot}{B}:H \\ H \end{array}$$

the *K* electrons having such a low energy that they cannot be used in bond formation. The sextet in BH_3 is not stable, the molecules are always dimeric, and it is still a point under discussion what the bond type in B_2H_6 and some other boron hydrides really is.

Many halides also have octet configurations, as, for example, in the following compounds

$$:\overset{\cdot\cdot}{\underset{\cdot\cdot}{F}}:\overset{\cdot\cdot}{\underset{\cdot\cdot}{F}}:, \qquad :\overset{\cdot\cdot}{\underset{\cdot\cdot}{F}}:\overset{\cdot\cdot}{\underset{\cdot\cdot}{O}}:\overset{\cdot\cdot}{\underset{\cdot\cdot}{F}}:, \qquad \begin{array}{c} :\overset{\cdot\cdot}{\underset{\cdot\cdot}{F}}:\overset{\cdot\cdot}{\underset{\cdot\cdot}{N}}:\overset{\cdot\cdot}{\underset{\cdot\cdot}{F}}:, \\ :\underset{\cdot\cdot}{F}: \end{array} \qquad \begin{array}{c} :\overset{\cdot\cdot}{F}: \\ :\overset{\cdot\cdot}{\underset{\cdot\cdot}{F}}:\overset{\cdot\cdot}{\underset{\cdot\cdot}{C}}:\overset{\cdot\cdot}{\underset{\cdot\cdot}{F}}: \\ :\underset{\cdot\cdot}{F}: \end{array}$$

that are analogous to hydrogen compounds, except for the fact that the halogen atom has an octet configuration, as well. Compounds with bonds between equal atoms also occur

$$F:\overset{\cdot\cdot}{\underset{\cdot\cdot}{O}}:\overset{\cdot\cdot}{\underset{\cdot\cdot}{O}}:F, \qquad \begin{array}{c} Cl:\overset{\cdot\cdot}{\underset{\cdot\cdot}{P}}:\ \overset{\cdot\cdot}{\underset{\cdot\cdot}{P}}:Cl, \\ Cl\ \ Cl \end{array} \qquad \begin{array}{c} Cl\ \ Cl \\ Cl:\overset{\cdot\cdot}{\underset{\cdot\cdot}{C}}:\ \overset{\cdot\cdot}{\underset{\cdot\cdot}{C}}:Cl, \\ Cl\ \ Cl \end{array}$$

$$\begin{array}{c} Cl:\underset{\cdot\cdot}{C}::\underset{\cdot\cdot}{C}:Cl \\ Cl\quad Cl \end{array}$$

In the latter formulae the octets of the halogen atoms are not marked. Recently a second nitrogen fluoride, N_2F_2, has been prepared: the only possible structure is

$$F:\underset{\cdot\cdot}{N}::\underset{\cdot\cdot}{N}:F$$

It is remarkable that in P_2Cl_4, which can be obtained from PCl_3 by reduction with zinc vapour, the bond between the two phosphor atoms is a single one, whereas in the lower nitrogen fluoride it is double, nitrogen, as was noted in the preceding section, forming stable multiple bonds.

The boron halides again can form sextets only, e.g.

$$\begin{array}{c} \mathrm{Cl : B : Cl} \\ \cdot\cdot \\ \mathrm{Cl} \end{array}$$

It will be shown below that these compounds are able to react with certain other compounds in such a way that the sextet is graduated to an octet. Boron, alone, has not enough electrons to form a complete octet with halogen atoms.

There are halides for which it is impossible to construct a strictly covalent model with all atoms in octet configuration, because they contain too many halogen atoms, e.g. PF_5, SF_6, IF_7, PCl_5, SCl_4, $SeCl_4$ and ICl_3. If, in PF_5, five P : F bonds are accepted, ten electrons would belong to each P atom: the S atom in SF_6 would have 12 electrons, and the I atom in IF_7 14 electrons.

The valency electrons in phosphor are *M* electrons: since the *M* shell contains *s*, *p* and *d* electrons, it can be assumed that in PF_5 not only the *s* and *p* electrons are active in bond formation, but that *d* orbitals may participate, as well. In the gaseous state, where it is shown by electron diffraction that the five bonds in PCl_5 are almost equivalent and certainly cannot be described as four covalent and one ionic bond, the bond formation by *d* orbitals must be accepted. It is in agreement with the idea that the *d* orbitals contribute to the bond formation that the higher fluorides (e.g. NF_5 and OF_6) of nitrogen and oxygen which have *L* shells in which *d* electrons do not occur cannot be obtained.

Another electronic configuration is also possible, and the crystal structure of solid phosphor pentabromide suggests what this configuration will be like. The structure of PBr_5 is a combination of alternating PBr_4 groups and Br particles. Since it is very improbable that free Br atoms will occur, it is reasonable to assume that the Br particles actually are Br^- ions, and that the structure of PBr_5 in the solid state is $PBr_4^+Br^-$. This partially ionic structure has normal octets, its configuration being

$$\left[\begin{array}{c} \mathrm{Br} \\ \cdot\cdot \\ \mathrm{Br : P : Br} \\ \cdot\cdot \\ \mathrm{Br} \end{array}\right]^+ \mathrm{Br}^-$$

Similar positive complex ions may occur in fluorides, e.g. BrF_3; in chlorides, PCl_5, SCl_4, $SeCl_4$, $TeCl_4$ and ICl_3; and in the corresponding bromides and iodides, with structures like:

$$\left[\mathrm{F : \overset{..}{\underset{..}{Br}} : F}\right]^+, \quad \left[\begin{array}{c}\mathrm{Cl} \\ \mathrm{Cl : \overset{..}{\underset{..}{P}} : Cl} \\ \mathrm{Cl}\end{array}\right]^+, \quad \left[\begin{array}{c}\mathrm{Cl : \overset{..}{\underset{..}{S}} : Cl} \\ \mathrm{Cl}\end{array}\right]^+, \quad \left[\mathrm{Cl : \overset{..}{\underset{..}{I}} : Cl}\right]^+$$

all of them with normal octet configurations.

If a sulphur atom forms three covalent bonds with Cl atoms, a total of nine electrons are involved in bond formation. In order to arrive at an octet, one electron must be given off, the group formed from this process being the ion SCl_3^+. In this ion the S atom can be regarded as the seat of the positive charge; since it is connected with one electron pair, and shares three electron pairs with chlorine ions, it is in full possession of $(2 + \frac{1}{2} \times 6) = 5$ electrons. As this is one electron less than in the free sulphur atom, the S atom in SCl_3^+ may be said to have a formal charge of one unit, as expressed by the formula

$$\left[\begin{array}{c}\mathrm{Cl : \underset{..}{S^+} : Cl} \\ \mathrm{Cl}\end{array}\right]^+$$

The compounds BrF_3, PBr_5 and PCl_5 are remarkable because here, for the first time, the coexistence of covalent and ionic bonds in one compound must be assumed.

All the partially ionic halides have one remarkable property in common; in reactions with other halides they form complexes, in which reaction they behave as strong halogen donors. A molecule $PCl_4^+Cl^-$ consists, in fact, of a very large (complex) positive ion PCl_4^+ and a Cl^- ion. Like other large complex ions, e.g. NH_4^+, or, more especially, like the tetramethylammonium ion $N(CH_3)_4^+$ which has about the same size as PCl_4^+, they are excellent complex formers. If a chloride forms a complex with CsCl, it is able to form complexes of the same type with PCl_5, SCl_4, $SeCl_4$ and $TeCl_4$, too. For example

$$2CsCl + SnCl_4 \rightarrow Cs_2SnCl_6$$
$$2PCl_4^+Cl^- + SnCl_4 \rightarrow (PCl_4)_2SnCl_6$$
$$2SCl_4 + SnCl_4 \rightarrow (SCl_3)_2SnCl_6$$

PCl_5 is an even stronger complex former than CsCl: it reacts with BCl_3 to form $PCl_4^+BCl_4^-$. The corresponding Cs compound cannot be prepared.

In order to make the complexes of PCl_5, care has to be taken that the phosphor chloride is not hydrolysed. These complexes cannot be prepared in aqueous solution, but are easily formed by mixing solutions of PCl_5 and the second halide in suitable solvents, e.g. $POCl_3$ or $AsCl_3$.

BrF_3 reacts with fluorides of polyvalent elements, e.g. SbF_5 and TaF_5, the structure of these compounds being $BrF_2^+SbF_6^-$ and $BrF_2^+TaF_6^-$, respectively.

Octet formation is less pronounced in oxides; among the oxides of the halogens (Cl_2O, ClO_2, ClO_3, Cl_2O_7; Br_2O, BrO_2; IO_2, I_2O_5) and nitrogens (N_2O, NO, N_2O_3, NO_2, N_2O_4, N_2O_5) there are some, with an uneven number of electrons, that evidently cannot be arranged in octets. In actual fact, for Cl_2O, Br_2O and N_2O_3, only formulae in which all bonds are covalent and all atoms have an octet structure can be given

$$\mathrm{Cl : \underset{\cdot\cdot}{\overset{\cdot\cdot}{O}} : Cl} \qquad \mathrm{\vdots O : : \dot{N} : \underset{\cdot\cdot}{\overset{\cdot\cdot}{O}} : \ddot{N} : : O \vdots}$$

For N_2O_5, the older type of a structure formula, in which a dash represents a 'valency', would be

```
O              O
  ⟍          ⟋
    N—O—N
  ⟋          ⟍
O              O
```

Substitution of a dash by two electrons yields the electronic formula

$$\mathrm{\vdots O : : \underset{\vdots\vdots}{N} : O : \underset{\vdots\vdots}{N} : : O \vdots}$$
$$\mathrm{.\underset{\cdot\ \cdot}{O}. \qquad .\underset{\cdot\ \cdot}{O}.}$$

but this formula cannot be correct, since ten electrons belong to each N atom. This formula can, however, be changed into a correct one by a simple trick: by removing one pair of electrons shared by an O and a N atom to the O atom, a formula is obtained in which each atom now has a complete octet

$$\mathrm{: \underset{\cdot\cdot}{\overset{-\ \cdot\cdot}{O}} : \underset{\vdots}{\overset{+}{N}} : O : \underset{\vdots}{\overset{+}{N}} : \underset{\cdot\cdot}{\overset{\cdot\cdot\ -}{O}} :}$$
$$\mathrm{.\underset{\cdot\ \cdot}{O}. \qquad .\underset{\cdot\ \cdot}{O}.}$$

In this process an electron pair, shared by a N and an O atom, is moved completely to the O atom. This is equivalent to the transfer of one electron from the N to the O atom, and by this process the N atom acquires a positive charge of one unit, whereas the oxygen atom obtains a negative charge: the double covalent bond is transformed into one single covalent bond plus an ionic one. This type of bond is called a *semipolar* bond. By assuming a sufficient number of semipolar bonds, all the other oxides with an even number of electrons can be written as compounds with complete octet configurations, too

$$\begin{array}{c} \overset{-\,\cdot\cdot}{:\text{O}:}\quad \overset{\cdot\cdot\,-}{:\text{O}:} \\ \overset{-\,\cdot\cdot}{:\text{O}}:\text{Cl}:\overset{\cdot\cdot}{\text{O}}:\text{Cl}:\overset{\cdot\cdot\,-}{\text{O}}:, \\ :\underset{\cdot\cdot}{\text{O}}:\quad :\underset{\cdot\cdot}{\text{O}}: \end{array} \qquad \begin{array}{c} \overset{-\,\cdot\cdot}{:\text{O}}:\overset{2+}{\text{I}}:\overset{\cdot\cdot}{\text{O}}:\overset{2+}{\text{I}}:\overset{\cdot\cdot\,-}{\text{O}}:, \\ :\underset{-\,\cdot\cdot}{\text{O}}:\quad :\underset{\cdot\cdot\,-}{\text{O}}: \end{array}$$

Cl_2O_7 $\qquad$ I_2O_5

$$\overset{-\,\cdot\cdot}{:\underset{\cdot\cdot}{\text{O}}}:\overset{+}{\underset{::}{\text{N}}}:\overset{+}{\underset{::}{\text{N}}}:\overset{\cdot\cdot\,-}{\underset{\cdot\cdot}{\text{O}}}:$$

N_2O_4

It is evident that the formal charge is one for the N atoms in N_2O_4, two for the I atoms in I_2O_5 and three for the Cl atoms in Cl_2O_7, and, further, it can be understood that the bond between the two N^+ atoms is very weak because of electrostatic repulsion.

In the oxides with semipolar bonds we have a second example of the coexistence of covalent and ionic bonds in one molecule. The oxide N_2O is a very unusual compound. By electron diffraction measurements it has been discovered that the molecule is linear, and that the two N atoms are directly connected. For this molecule, then, the following electronic structures are possible

$$:\overset{\cdot\cdot}{\underset{\cdot\cdot}{\text{N}}}:\text{N}:::\text{O}:, \qquad :\text{N}::\underset{\cdot\cdot}{\text{N}}::\dot{\underset{\cdot}{\text{O}}}:, \qquad :\text{N}:::\text{N}:\overset{\cdot\cdot}{\underset{\cdot\cdot}{\text{O}}}:$$

all with octet structures, only. The charges on the different ions are

$$\overset{2-}{\text{N}}\ \overset{+}{\text{N}}\ \overset{+}{\text{O}}, \qquad \overset{-}{\text{N}}\ \overset{+}{\text{N}}\ \text{O}, \qquad \text{N}\ \overset{+}{\text{N}}\ \overset{-}{\text{O}}$$

as can be easily verified by remembering that each free electron pair counts for two negative charges and each shared pair for one. Which of these formulae is the correct one will be discussed in the next chapter.

The occurrence of molecules with an odd number of electrons can be understood in the following way. Nitrogen and oxygen both have a tendency to form stable multiple bonds, and it is not surprising that stable double bonds will also be formed between a N and an O atom. In the molecule

$$.\underset{\cdot\cdot}{\text{N}}::\dot{\underset{\cdot}{\text{O}}}:$$

there remains one single electron, that can form only a very unstable bond with a further oxygen atom. However, a stable single bond can be formed with the monovalent halogens, and NOF and NOCl, therefore, are relatively stable compounds.

Chlorine also forms double bonds with oxygen, as can be seen from the compounds ClO_2 and ClO_3 that form weak bonds, only, by the sharing of their unpaired electrons.

There are combinations of covalent and ionic bonds other than those observed in PCl_5 and the semipolar bonds in N_2O_5. For the ion NO_2, different electron configurations can be constructed, but since this compound has an odd number of electrons, these configurations cannot have only normal octets. If, however, one electron is taken away, the ion NO_2^+ can be given different structures with normal octets, e.g.

$$\left(:\underset{\cdot\cdot}{\overset{\overset{-}{\cdot\cdot}}{O}}:\overset{+}{N}:::\overset{+}{O}:\right)^{+} \quad \text{and} \quad \left(\dot{\underset{\cdot}{:}}O::\overset{+}{N}::O\dot{\underset{\cdot}{:}}\right)^{+}$$

of which the first has one triple bond and one semipolar. The fact that the ion has a normal octet structure may be the reason that it is so easily formed. It occurs in a number of complexes, $NO_2^+ClO_4^-$, $NO_2^+SO_4H^-$ and $NO_2^+BF_4^-$, in which the complex ion is the ion of a strong acid.

Another electron donor is NO: here the ion can have the configurations

$$\left(:N:::\overset{+}{O}:\right)^{+} \quad \text{and} \quad \left(:\overset{+}{N}::O\dot{\underset{\cdot}{:}}\right)^{+}$$

of which the former has complete octets only, and no repulsion of two equal charges as in the first state of NO_2. Since an O atom has one electron more than a nitrogen atom, NO^+ has the same number of electrons as (i.e. is isoelectronic with) the N_2 molecule. The stability of this molecule shows that the ten electrons must form a very stable configuration, and the ten electrons in NO^+ can do the same.

In actual fact, NO is a very strong electron donor, the ion occurring in dozens of complexes, such as $NO^+ClO_4^-$, $NO^+SO_4H^-$, $NO^+BF_4^-$, $NO^+BCl_4^-$ and $(NO)_2^+ SnCl_6$. The oxide complexes of NO^+ can be prepared from a mixture of N_2O_3 and the acid. In the old base-acid-salt theory, $NO.ClO_4$, or nitrosylperchlorate, is the salt of a base NO.OH, belonging to the oxide N_2O_3 and the acid $HClO_4$, and the reaction therefore, is

$$N_2O_3 + 2HClO_4 \rightarrow 2NO.ClO_4 + H_2O$$

The halide complexes are more easily made from the nitrosyl halides and halides, thus

$$2NOCl + SnCl_4 \rightarrow (NO)_2^+SnCl_6^{2-} \quad \text{or} \quad NOF + BF_3 \rightarrow NO^+BF_4^-$$

The positive NO_2^+ ion occurs in compounds like nitroxyl perchlorate, $NO_2^+ClO_4^-$, but there is a negative NO_2^- ion in nitrites. This negative ion, NO_2^-, can be given a structure with only octets, as well, e.g.

$$\left[\dot{\underset{\cdot}{O}} : : \underset{\cdot\cdot}{N} : \underset{\cdot\cdot}{\overset{\cdot\cdot}{O}} : \right]^-$$

and if there are two NO_2 molecules, they can react as follows

$$2NO_2 \rightarrow NO_2^+ + NO_2^- \rightarrow NO_2^+NO_2^-$$

according to which the molecule would be nitroxyl nitrite. If there is oxygen present, the nitrite ion NO_2^- is easily oxidized to a nitrate ion NO_3^-, and a compound $NO_2^+NO_3^-$, nitroxyl nitrate, is formed. It has been shown by x-ray analysis that, in actual fact, solid N_2O_5 has this structure.

It is evident that the molecule N_2O_4, formed from NO_2 at low temperatures, may have the structure $NO^+NO_3^-$ (nitrosyl nitrate), too. Both $NO^+.NO_3^-$ and $NO_2^+.NO_2^-$ in the liquid and solid states seem more probable than the formula $O_2N.NO_2$ given earlier, because in the ionic forms there is not the repulsion between the two positively-charged N atoms.

The formation of two complex ions gives a reasonable explanation of the dimerization of NO_2 to N_2O_4, and also of ClO_3 to Cl_2O_6.

$$2ClO_3 \rightarrow ClO_2^+ClO_4^-$$

The oxides NO and ClO_2, however, cannot form the stable complex ions NO_3^- and ClO_4^-, and thus do not dimerize.

The transition of the molecules N_2O_5, NO_2 and ClO_3 into more ionic forms on solidification can be readily explained. In the solid state, the lattice energy gives a strong contribution to the total energy if the compound is ionic, and therefore enhances the formation of the ionic form.

55. RESONANCE

In the preceding section many molecules were mentioned in which a shift of electron pairs was possible, and for which, therefore, different electronic structures could be given. According to quantum mechanics, the two states of the molecule CO, viz.

```
 −       +                        .
: C : : : O :      and    : C : : O :
     I                         II  .
```

are not two isomers that can both be prepared in the pure state. Actually, the configuration contains these two states, and all that can be done to visualize this somewhat mysterious phenomenon is to describe the two states as rapidly transforming into each other. It may be that, according to this picture, the molecule taken over a long time t, would have the configuration I over a time $a.t$ and the configuration II over the time $(1 - a).t$. It then would be said that the real molecule occurs in the two states, with weight a for I and $(1 - a)$ for II.

It may be that, according to a quantum mechanical calculation, one of the n states, let us say ψ_i, has an energy much lower than all others. In that case, a_i will be very near to unity, and there will be practically no contribution of the other states. On the contrary, if all energies are practically equal, the weights of the different states will be equal, too, and the n states will give almost equal contributions. In that case, quantum mechanics has revealed a surprising phenomenon: if there are n states with equal energy, the energy of the molecules will be lower than it would be if it were in one of the n states, only. The different states that contribute to the total state of the molecule are called 'resonating states', and the decrease of the energy due to this resonance is called 'resonance energy'.

We will now see what the effect of resonance is on the stability of compounds. There are four states for the molecule N_2O_5 with octet structures only

```
 − ..  +  ..  +  .. −            .    +  ..  +  .. −
 : O : N : O : N : O :          :O : : N : O : N : O :
   ..  ..  ..  ..  ..    ,       .    ..  ..  ..  ..
       ..      ..                        :O :   ..
      .O.     .O.                     − ..     .O.
       .       .                                .

 − ..  +  ..  +      .           .    +  ..  +       .
 : O : N : O : N : : O :        :O : : N : O : N : : O :
   ..  ::  ..  ..     .   ,      .    ..  ..  ..      .
      .O.    : O :−                  : O :−  : O :−
       .       ..                      ..      ..
```

Since all these states have the same number of double bonds and semipolar bonds, the energy of the four states will be almost equal, and the different states will occur with almost the same frequency.

There will be a large resonance energy that gives an appreciable contribution to the stability of the molecule. The situation is different in two molecules that probably are stabilized by resonance, as well, e.g. N_2O and N_3H. For the first, three electronic formulae with complete octets can be written

$$:N:::\overset{+}{N}:\underset{\cdot\cdot}{\overset{\cdot\cdot\,-}{O}}:\,, \qquad :\underset{\cdot\cdot}{\overset{-}{N}}::\overset{+}{N}::\underset{\cdot\cdot}{O}:\,, \qquad :\underset{\cdot\cdot}{\overset{2-}{\overset{\cdot\cdot}{N}}}:\overset{+}{N}:::\overset{+}{O}:$$

I II III

Here the energies will be different, and without a detailed calculation it is impossible to say which will be the lower one (it may be somewhat higher in III because in this state two positive atoms come close together).

For the compound N_3H, three formulae in which all atoms have octets only, can be given,

$$:\underset{\cdot\cdot}{\overset{2-}{\overset{\cdot\cdot}{N}}}:\overset{+}{N}:::\overset{+}{N}:H, \qquad :\underset{\cdot\cdot}{\overset{-}{N}}::\overset{+}{N}::\underset{\cdot\cdot}{N}:H, \qquad :N:::\overset{+}{N}:\underset{\cdot\cdot}{\overset{-}{\overset{\cdot\cdot}{N}}}:H$$

Ia IIa IIIa

For the ion N_3^- the formulae are

$$\left[:\underset{\cdot\cdot}{\overset{2-}{\overset{\cdot\cdot}{N}}}:\overset{+}{N}:::N:\right]^- \qquad \left[:\underset{\cdot\cdot}{\overset{-}{N}}::\overset{+}{N}::\underset{\cdot\cdot}{\overset{-}{N}}:\right]^- \qquad \left[:N:::\overset{+}{N}:\underset{\cdot\cdot}{\overset{2-}{\overset{\cdot\cdot}{N}}}:\right]^-$$

Ib IIb IIIb

Now the three formulae Ia to IIIa all have different energies, but for Ib and IIIb the energies are identical. In the ion, therefore, there can be a stronger resonance, which will increase its stability. Azides, like N_3K, in which the bond between N_3^- and K^+ is ionic, are therefore more stable than azides N_3H or N_3CH_3, in which this bond is covalent.

There are many organic compounds stabilized by resonance. As a first example we may cite benzene, in which there is resonance between the two Kekulé structures. In this case, the resonance energy could be calculated to give good agreement with the experimental data on the heat of formation of the molecule. Perhaps even more remarkable is the compound KC_5H_5, which is formed when potassium reacts with *cyclo*pentadiene.

Hydrocarbons usually do not exchange hydrogen for metals when in contact with the latter; the compound KC_5H_5 is an exception, because the ion $C_5H_5^-$ contains five exactly-equal CH groups that are connected by three single and two double bonds. One of these states is

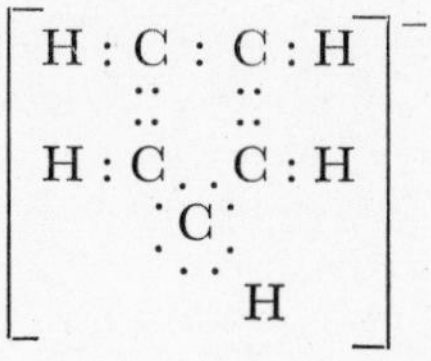

```
┌                  ┐ −
│ H : C : C : H    │
│     ::  ::       │
│ H : C . . C : H  │
│       :C:        │
│       . . .      │
│         H        │
└                  ┘
```

and in total there are five different states of the ion that are formed by electron transitions without a change in the position of the atoms.

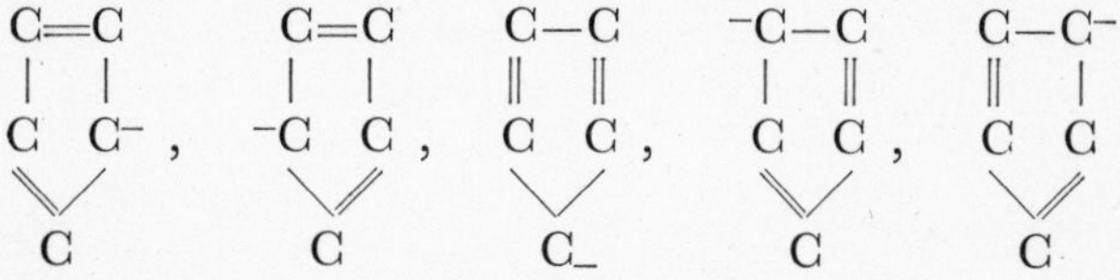

```
C═C          C═C          C—C          ⁻C—C         C—C⁻
|  |         |  |         ‖  ‖          |  ‖        ‖  |
C  C⁻ ,     ⁻C  C ,       C  C ,        C  C ,      C  C
 ⫽ \          \ ⫽          \ /          ⫽ \          \ ⫽
  C            C            C₋           C            C
```

Because of this resonance, the energy of $K^+C_5H_5^-$ is lower than in the hydrocarbon, where no resonance occurs.

56. RELATION BETWEEN COVALENT AND IONIC BONDS

There can be resonance between covalent and ionic states. In the molecule H : H a complete shift of the electron pair to the left would have the effect to make the left-hand H atom a negative ion, leaving the right-hand one as a positive ion. Next to the state H : H there will be two others, H^-H^+ and H^+H^-, which closely resemble the electrostatic model for the H_2 molecule. Since the three states are resonating, the states H^-H^+ and H^+H^- will make a contribution to the bonding energy, too: in this case, however, their contribution will be relatively small, because the energy of the covalent state H : H certainly is much lower than that of the ionic states H^-H^+ and H^+H^-.

The existence of the states H^-H^+ and H^+H^- is not in disagreement with the properties of the hydrogen molecule, e.g. the absence of a dipole moment. Since the states H^+H^- and H^-H^+ certainly have the same energy, they are equally frequent and the total state

$$a\mathrm{H : H} + b\mathrm{H^+H^-} + b\mathrm{H^-H^+}$$

has no dipole moment because the switching of electrons occurs too fast to be detected by any measurement of the dielectric constant.

Now let us consider the compound HF, for which again there are different states, H : F, H^+F^- and H^-F^+. Since hydrogen has a smaller electron affinity than fluorine, and a higher ionization energy, the energy of state H^+F^- will be much lower than that of H^-F^+, and the latter will make practically no contribution at all. On the other hand, the energy of the ionic state H^+F^- will be not as far above that of H : F as the energy of H^-H^+ is above H : H, and in HF the contribution of the ionic state will be more important than in hydrogen. HF, therefore, will be a 'resonance' hybride of HF and H^+F^-, for which calculation gives $\sim$30 per cent ionic character.

Now that we know that every compound is to some extent a resonance hybrid, it is possible to explain many properties by taking into account both the ionic and covalent character of the compound. This explanation of the properties, however, is not very convincing, if, to any compound, one could arbitrarily assign a certain ionic and covalent character. There will be some advance if means can be found by which it becomes possible to predict to what extent a compound AB_n will be ionic and to what extent it must be considered a covalent compound. This cannot yet be done in a quantitative way: in a qualitative way, however, it is clear that a compound will be more ionic, the smaller the ionization energy of the atoms that form the positive ion, and the greater the electron affinity of the atoms that form the negative ion. Since, from an atom that easily attracts electrons, it will be difficult to withdraw electrons, a large electron affinity is almost equivalent to a high ionization energy, and it can be stated that the compound will be more ionic, the greater the difference in ionization energies of the two component elements. Since the ionization energy is associated with size and electron configuration, as shown in Section 10, it is always possible to predict whether, in a series of compounds, the covalency will decrease or increase and to make a rough estimate of the degree of covalency, when it is known that the first term of the series is almost completely ionic and the last term almost completely covalent. Such a series are LiCl, $BeCl_2$, BCl_3, CCl_4 and CCl_4, $SiCl_4$, $TiCl_4$, $ZrCl_4$, $ThCl_4$.

In the series SiF_4, $SiCl_4$, $SiBr_4$, SiI_4 or TiO_2, TiS_2, $TiSe_2$, $TiTe_2$ the covalency will increase, but it cannot be said that the first term is completely ionic, and the last completely covalent; here the degree of covalency is more difficult to estimate than in the former series.

57. STABLE ELECTRONIC CONFIGURATIONS (NON-OCTET)

In the preceding sections it was found that the octet configuration, either with single or multiple bonds, is very often observed in the compounds of the elements in the end of the periods. Octet configurations, however, can occur, as well, in the first subgroups, where compounds like CuBr, ZnSe, GaAs and GeGe have eight valency electrons for each pair of atoms, and each atom therefore can form four covalent bonds with atoms of the other kind. Assuming this octet formation, the crystal structure of all these compounds is easily understood; the first three crystallize according to the cubic zinc-blende type (*see* Section 14), in which each ion is surrounded by four of the other component, and the fourth is the element germanium, itself, that has a diamond structure (*see* Section 53). There may be an admixture of ionic bonds: the ionic character will increase from germanium, where it is zero, to CuBr, and will be very considerable in the fluorides and oxides in this group, e.g. in AgF and CdO.

Yet octets are not the only stable electron configurations. It was remarked before that *d* electrons probably contribute to the bond formation of molecules like IF_5, TeF_6, etc. (*see* Section 54). Electronic configurations, in which *d* electrons play a part, are of great importance in the bond formation of all elements between the aluminium and the copper group, all of which elements have deficient *d* shells.

Let us consider an iron atom, with the following electron distribution

$$\underset{K}{1s^2} \,.\, \underset{L}{2s^2p^6} \,.\, \underset{M}{3s^2p^6d^7} \,.\, \underset{N}{4s^1}$$

Evidently the *K* and *L* shells will not take part in any bond formation, but it can be imagined that, with the aid of electrons of other atoms, the *M* shell may be completed and the *N* shell filled with eight s^2p^6 electrons. This would require ten electrons for iron, eight for nickel and twelve for chromium.

In Section 50 it was remarked that these metals form the carbonyls, with formulae $Cr(CO)_6$, $Fe(CO)_5$ and $Ni(CO)_4$. These formulae can be easily explained if it is assumed that each CO molecule contributes two electrons: in each of the carbonyls eighteen valency electrons are then involved in the bond formation. This is just sufficient to fill the five orbitals of the 3*d* and the four orbitals of the $4s^2p^6$ shells. Later on it will be shown why just two electrons of the CO molecule are active in the bond formation.

According to a theory by Pauling, other stable electron configurations can be formed from 3*d*, 4*s* and 4*p* orbitals in the fourth period, and, similarly, of 4*d*, 5*s* and 5*p* in the fifth and 5*d*, 6*s* and 6*p* electrons in the sixth period. There is, first of all, a configuration in which eight electrons are involved, 2*d*, 2*s* and 4*p* electrons that form four stable bonds. This configuration is called the dsp^2 hybridization. Unlike the four bonds in an octet, the four bonds formed by dsp^2 hybridization radiate to the corners of a square. If, by this type of bonding, groups AX_4 are formed, these groups have a square configuration.

There is another configuration, d^2sp^3 with twelve electrons forming six bonds, radiating in the directions of the corners of an octahedron, and one with sixteen electrons, d^4sp^3, with formation of eight bonds.

If each of the *d*, *s* and *p* orbitals is represented by a circle, the situation in the carbonyls, where all orbitals are filled, can be represented by

In $PdCl_2$, ten electrons are available from the Pd atom and two from the chlorine atoms. They are sufficient for dsp^2 hybridization. This compound, in actual fact, has square groups $PdCl_4$, each Cl atom

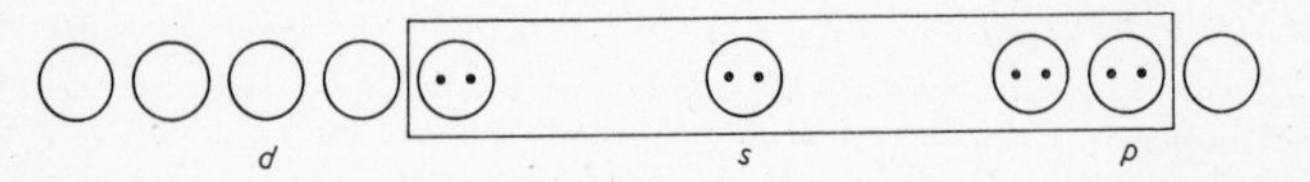

being shared by two such groups. It cannot so far be decided where the two remaining electrons should be located. It is probable that they will be in the empty *d* shell, since there they will have a lower energy than in the empty *p* orbitals.

Hund has given a general rule for the way the available electrons will be distributed over the *d* orbitals. If there are five electrons, or less, they will all occupy different orbitals, with the spins of the electrons parallel, and all electrons will be unpaired. If there are more than five electrons, these will be located in the half-filled orbitals, with opposite spins. For three and seven electrons, the situations are as follows

So if there are

1, 2, 3, 4, 5, 6, 7, 8, 9, 10

electrons in the *d* orbitals, respectively

1, 2, 3, 4, 5, 4, 3, 2, 1, 0

of these will be unpaired.

We now can get further information on the electronic configuration by studying the magnetism of the compounds. Any electron revolving around a nucleus in a closed orbital is equivalent to a circular electric current, and thus produces a magnetic moment. Usually these orbital magnetic moments are directed in such a way that they just cancel each other, in which case the orbital moments are of no further interest for our present purpose.

Each electron, however, has a moment of its own because of its rotation along an axis. If two electrons occupy one orbital, the moments have opposite directions and thus cancel. If all electrons are paired, there is no resultant magnetic moment and the compound is diamagnetic. If, however, there are unpaired electrons, their moments will form a resultant moment, that will depend—in a rather complicated way—on their number, which number can be calculated, in a way that cannot be explained here in more detail, from the measured susceptibility. What matters is that the number of unpaired electrons can be determined by magnetic measurements.

Let us take the compound $CoCl_3$. This may be ionic or have one of the *dsp* configurations. If it is ionic, the Co^{3+} ion will have six electrons and a magnetic moment corresponding to four unpaired electrons would be observed, the configurations of the *d*, *s* and *p* shells in the Co^{3+} ion being

In total, twelve electrons are available, nine from the Co and three from the Cl atoms. Covalent bonds may be formed in different ways:

1. In an sp^3 octet.
2. In a dsp^2 square configuration.
3. In a d^2sp^3 hybridization.

It is evident that the three possible configurations are

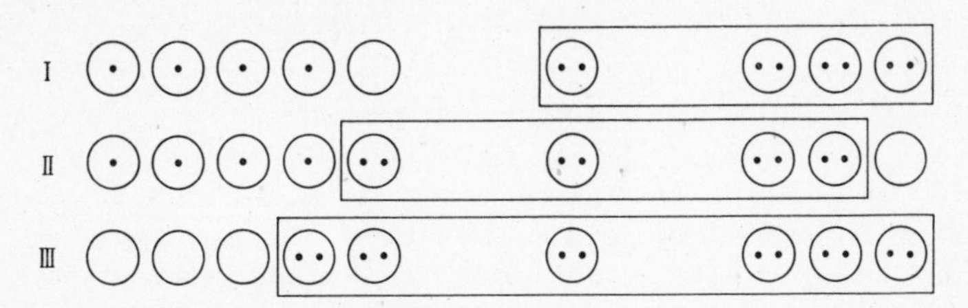

The magnetic moments of configurations I and II would be equal,

with strong paramagnetism, caused by four unpaired electrons as in the ion; the s^2pd^3 configuration, however, would be diamagnetic.

It has been found that the compound $\{Pt(NH_3)_6\}^{4+}Cl_4^-$ is diamagnetic. Just as CO in carbonyls, the NH_3 group will donate two electrons. Since the Pt atom has ten valency electrons, the group $\{Pt(NH_3)_6\}$ has twenty-two electrons. Of these, four are required to form the four negative Cl^- ions, which leaves eighteen electrons available for bond formation. These eighteen electrons can just fill the *d*, *s* and *p* orbitals. Since, in the platinum ammoniates, the Pt atom has six ligands (*see* Sections 50 and 62), there probably is s^2pd^3 hybridization, and the configuration is

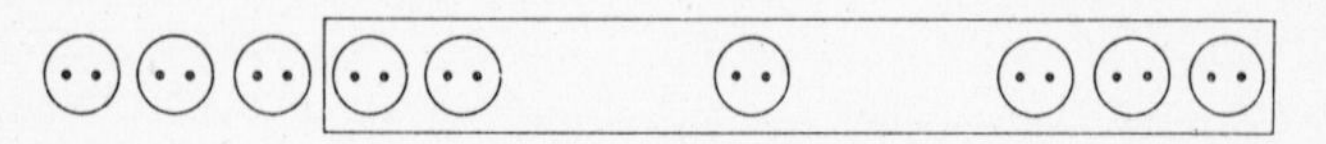

If the compound were ionic, all electrons in Cl^- and NH_3 would be paired: the Pt^{4+} ion would have six electrons, four of them unpaired, and the compound would show strong paramagnetism due to these four unpaired electrons.

The covalency by *dsp* hybridization is of primary importance in the complex formation of all elements in the groups between aluminium and copper, the latter group included.

The different electronic configurations of $CoCl_3$ can be transformed into each other by a shift of electrons, and thus there may be resonance between the different states. However, this resonance is restricted by a number of rules, one of the most important being that, by resonance, the number of unpaired electrons should not change. Thus there cannot be resonance between the ionic form $Co^{3+}Cl_3^-$ and the diamagnetic covalent configuration III, and in $Pt(NH_3)_6Cl_4$ there can be no resonance between the paramagnetic ionic state $Pt^{4+}(NH_3)_6Cl_4^-$, with four unpaired electrons, and the covalent diamagnetic one with all orbitals occupied and all electrons paired.

58. STRUCTURE OF OXIDES

It has been shown in this chapter that most inorganic compounds are neither purely covalent nor purely ionic, but have a bond type intermediate between the two extremes. The bond will be more ionic the lower the ionization energy of the atom that has to form the positive ion and the greater the electron affinity of the other.

In a certain group of compounds, with the same negative ion, the ionic character of the bond will be more pronounced, the larger the atom that has to form the positive ion. Keeping this in mind, it will be easier to understand the different properties and structures of the members of one such group, e.g. the oxides, where the bond type will become more ionic in a series such as N_2O_5, P_2O_5, As_2O_5, Sb_2O_5, Bi_2O_5.

The non metallic and semi-metallic elements may be divided into different groups, according to the way they react with oxygen

C	N	O	F
Si	P	S	Cl
Ge	As	Se	Br
Sn	Sb	Te	I
Pb	Bi		

These groups are:

I. Fluorine, which forms a class apart. With oxygen, this element forms single bonds only; double or semipolar bonds would give the fluorine a positive charge which probably is prevented by the high ionization energy of the fluorine atom.

II. The next group comprises the elements that, like nitrogen, form stable multiple bonds with oxygen, all of them elements with high electron affinity.

III. The third group contains the elements that still form strongly covalent bonds, which are, however, always single in so far as this can be reconciled with the formation of complete octets.

IV. The last group contains the elements which form the more ionic compounds.

In Section 54 ample evidence was given for the existence of stable multiple bonds in the oxides of group II. In this group, sulphur forms a transition to the following group. In the lower oxide SO_2 two double or semipolar bonds must be assumed

$$:\overset{-}{\underset{\cdot\cdot}{\ddot{O}}}:\overset{+}{\ddot{S}}::\underset{\cdot}{\dot{O}}\cdot, \qquad O::\ddot{S}::O, \qquad \underset{\cdot}{\dot{O}}::\overset{+}{\ddot{S}}:\overset{-}{\underset{\cdot\cdot}{\ddot{O}}}:$$

and the molecule has no tendency, as SeO_2 (v.i.), to form single bonds by polymerization. In the higher oxide SO_3, as it occurs in the vapour state, all bonds must be double or semipolar, but in the solid state the molecule polymerizes. In one of the modifications, molecules $(SO_3)_3$ are formed. In this trimeric molecule the three S atoms and three O atoms form a hexagonal ring

```
          -O .   . O-
             : S :
              . . .
           O        O
           ..       ..
     _O : S .    . S : O_
     _O  ˙ :O: ˙  O_
             . .
```

in which $\frac{1}{3}$ of the double or semipolar bonds is replaced by single bonds. Each S atom can be given an octet structure by assuming that all bonds that are not single are semipolar.

In Group III a similar polymerization, leading to a reduction of the number of double bonds, is observed for all oxides. Whereas CO_2, with two double bonds, has no tendency to polymerization, SiO_2, as a monomeric molecule O=Si=O, is only stable in the vapour at very high temperature and forms a three-dimensional aggregate in the solid state, each Si atom forming four single bonds with the O atoms.

In the different forms of silicon dioxide (quartz, tridymite, cristobalite, etc.), each silicon is surrounded by four oxygen atoms, each oxygen atom of a tetrahedral group SiO_4 being shared by two such groups.

Of the oxides of phosphor and arsenic, P_2O_3, P_2O_5, As_2O_3 and As_2O_5, the first three are known to be dimeric in the vapour state. Whereas the monomeric molecule P_2O_3, or

```
 .        ..  ..  ..        .
  O : : P : O : P : : O
 .             ..             .
```

would have two double bonds and two single bonds, and the pentoxide

```
 .                         .
  O : : P : O : P : : O
 .                         .
        ..       ..
      : O :    : O :
        ..       ..
```

contains two single bonds and four double or semipolar bonds, the dimeric molecule P_4O_6 has single bonds only, and in P_2O_5 there are twelve single bonds and four double or semipolar bonds, only.

The molecules P_4O_6 are probably *iso*morphous with As_4O_6; the latter consists of six O atoms arranged in an octahedron that has the four As atoms in the centre of four of the faces, where they are connected by single bonds to the three surrounding O atoms, each As atom forming three single bonds, each O atom two. From P_4O_6 the molecule P_4O_{10} is obtained by adding one oxygen atom to each P atom: this connection is by a double or semipolar bond.

The structure SeO_3 in the gaseous or solid state is unknown, but in the lower oxide there is polymerization. In SeO_2 there are two double or semipolar bonds, but in the solid state the compound forms chains

$$\begin{array}{ccccccccccc} O & : & \ddot{Se} & : & \ddot{\underset{\cdot\cdot}{O}} & : & \ddot{Se} & : & \ddot{\underset{\cdot\cdot}{O}} & : & \ddot{Se} & : & O \\ & & :\ddot{\underset{\cdot\cdot}{O}}: & & & & :\ddot{\underset{\cdot\cdot}{O}}: & & & & :\ddot{\underset{\cdot\cdot}{O}}: & & \end{array}$$

in which one-half of all bonds are single and each Se atom has an octet structure if the other bonds are supposed to be semipolar.

The oxides in Group IV do not show an octet structure: TeO_2 has a distorted rutile structure, in which each Te atom is surrounded by six oxygens and thus resembles the more ionic oxides TiO_2 and SnO_2. In TeO_3, too, each tellurium is surrounded by six oxygen atoms as in oxides like WO_3 and CrO_3. It is not quite clear how much of the higher coordination in Group IV is caused by a more ionic character, by the contribution of bonds by *d* orbitals as in IF_5, etc. (*see* Section 54) or by a combination of both effects.

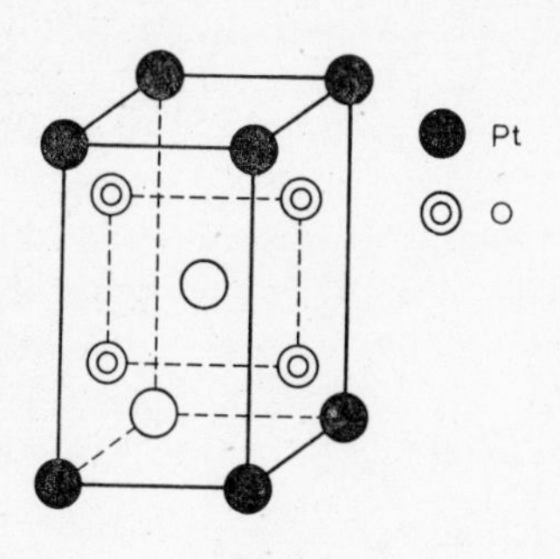

Figure 40

The covalency in the metal oxides is less pronounced than in the oxides of the non-metallic elements, and the oxides of the first three groups of the periodic system may be regarded as essentially ionic. When, however, the *d* shells in the next groups begin to contain more electrons, the tendency to complete these shells by covalent bond formation increases, and becomes evident in the oxides of the platinum metals, which often have crystal structures that can only be understood when it is assumed that the bonds are covalent rather than ionic.

In the oxides PdO and PtO, twelve electrons are available for bond formation. This number is sufficient for dsp^2 hybridization, and from the fact that each Pt atom is surrounded by four oxygen atoms, forming a square group PtO_4, it is evident that this hybridization actually occurs. The unit cell of PtO is represented in *Figure 40*.

Square configurations (*see Figure 40*) have been observed in other oxides, too, e.g. in the very complicated triclinic CuO structure, but it is not known exactly how many electrons partake in the bond formation, and in what way the remaining are distributed over the different orbitals. The oxides of copper and silver, Cu_2O and Ag_2O, also have structures different from ionic coordination lattices, each metal ion being surrounded tetrahedrally by four oxygen only, and each O atom lying between two metal atoms. But, again, it is not known what type of bonds are formed. The main difficulty for the correct interpretation is that we do not know whether, or, if so, to what extent, electrons can be used for bond formation between metal atoms. It is because of this interaction between metal atoms that our knowledge of the structure of all compounds of the metals with deficient *d* shells, which are all the metals between the aluminium group and the copper group, is still very limited (*see* Section 68).

59. COVALENT BONDS IN COMPLEXES

It has been shown in Chapter VI that the stability of most complexes formed by two halides, oxides or hydrides follows the rules for complex formation of two ionic compounds. The formation of the complex ions BF_4^- and NH_4^+ was described as an addition of the ions F^- and H^+ to the molecules BF_3 and NH_3, caused by the attraction of the highly-charged ions B^{3+} and N^{3-}. However, this complex formation can be given quite a different interpretation, and it can be argued that F^- ions combine with BF_3 because, in this process, the octet of the B atom is completed

$$:\underset{\cdot\cdot}{\overset{\cdot\cdot}{F}}: + \begin{array}{ccc} F & & \\ \cdot\cdot & & \\ B & : & F \\ \cdot\cdot & & \\ F & & \end{array} \rightarrow \left[\begin{array}{ccccc} & & F & & \\ & & \cdot\cdot & & \\ F & : & B & : & F \\ & & \cdot\cdot & & \\ & & F & & \end{array}\right]^-$$

and that in the reaction

$$H^+ + \begin{array}{cccc} & H & & \\ & \cdot\cdot & & \\ : & N & : & H \\ & \cdot\cdot & & \\ & H & & \end{array} \rightarrow \left[\begin{array}{ccccc} & & H & & \\ & & \cdot\cdot & & \\ H & : & N & : & H \\ & & \cdot\cdot & & \\ & & H & & \end{array}\right]^+$$

the lone electron-pair of NH_3 is used to form a $1s^2$ shell for the hydrogen atom. Since both complex ions would have a tetrahedral structure in the ionic and in the covalent form, and would be diamagnetic, as well, in both forms, it is very difficult to decide which description is correct. It may well be that both are resonance hybrids

$$\left[\begin{matrix} & F & \\ & \cdot\cdot & \\ F : & B & : F \\ & \cdot\cdot & \\ & F & \end{matrix}\right] \leftrightarrow \left[\begin{matrix} & F^- & \\ F^- & B^{3+} & F^- \\ & F^- & \end{matrix}\right]$$

In the group of halide complexes there are a few compounds that certainly cannot be normal ionic complexes. It was remarked earlier that PBr_5 and PCl_5 react as halides with a very large positive ion. By forming four covalent bonds with Cl atoms, the P atom completes its octet, and the complex formation, e.g. in

$$PCl_5 + BCl_3 \rightarrow PCl_4^+BCl_4^-$$

is due to the strong covalency in the PCl_4^+ ion.

As a weak chlorine-ion acceptor PCl_5, in reaction with CsCl, does not form ions PCl_6^-: these ions however can be formed if PCl_5 reacts with the strongest Cl^- donor known to exist, to wit PCl_5, itself. The resultant product would be $PCl_4^+PCl_6^-$. The crystal structure of PCl_5 shows that it actually does have this structure.

Phosphortrichloride does not react with CsCl, either: it evidently is a very weak Cl^- ion acceptor, which is not very surprising since it is known from the geometrical form of the molecule that it is a strongly covalent compound with a complete octet. Contrary to all rules for ionic complex formation, it reacts with BCl_3, forming a compound $Cl_3P.BCl_3$. Remembering that the B atom in BCl_3 has not a complete octet, it seems reasonable to assume that PCl_3 uses its lone electron-pair to complete the B octet

$$\begin{matrix} & Cl & & Cl & \\ & \cdot\cdot & & \cdot\cdot & \\ Cl : & B & : & P & : Cl \\ & \cdot\cdot & & \cdot\cdot & \\ & Cl & & Cl & \end{matrix}$$

It seems likely that, in an analogous way, the lone electron-pair of PCl_3 can be used to complete the *d* shell in the compounds of the platinum metals. There can be hardly any doubt but that this happens in compounds like $PtCl_2.PCl_3$ and $PtCl_2.2PCl_3$, which can be formed by heating platinum metals with PCl_5. For example

$$Pt + PCl_5 \rightarrow PtCl_2.PCl_3$$

Since all bonds in these compounds are covalent, these molecules do not have strong electric fields, and are therefore soluble in non-polar and weakly polar solvents, like benzene. Ionic complexes, if soluble at all, would only dissolve in water or other strongly polar solvents.

The complexes $Cl_3P.BCl_3$ and $Cl_2Pt.PCl_3$ are radically different from ionic complexes in that a bond is formed between the P atom and the B or Pt atom. In ionic complexes, the positive ions are never connected by direct bonds, the cohesion in the crystal being maintained by the alternations of positive and negative ions.

There are a large number of molecules besides PCl_3, e.g. NH_3, CO, NO, CN, that can use their lone electron-pairs for bond formation with atoms with incomplete electron configurations. In the following section various groups of complexes formed in this way will be discussed.

60. HALIDE COMPLEXES

From the formula alone, one would never suspect K_2PtCl_6 to be quite different from many complexes with the same form as K_2ZrF_6 and K_2ZrCl_6, which have been described as ionic complexes. The diamagnetism of the compound, however, shows that there must be a coupling of the electrons of the Pt ion with those of the chlorine ions in such a way that all electrons form pairs. By counting the electrons it is found that eighteen electrons are available, ten from platinum, six from chlorine, and two from potassium. All 5*d*, 6*p* and 6*s* orbitals thus can be filled. Since each Pt atom is surrounded by six Cl atoms, it is probable that bond formation is caused by s^2pd^3 hybridization. There is another compound, K_2PtCl_4, in which the covalency is more apparent than in K_2PtCl_6. In K_2PtCl_4 the crystal lattice is built of square $PtCl_4^{2-}$ ions and K^+ ions. It is evident that bond formation in this compound is due to spd^2 hybridization. Sixteen electrons are available and the configuration clearly is

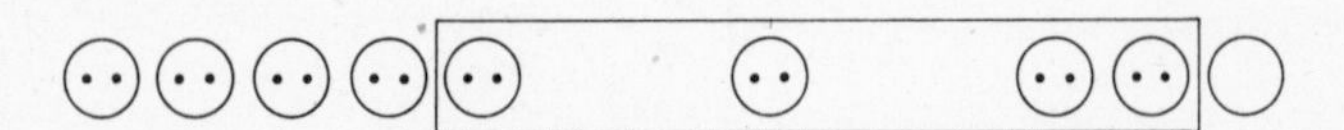

with all electrons paired. The compound is thus diamagnetic. Covalency is observed for all halides of the platinum group: the compound K_2IrCl_6 has seventeen electrons, one of which, at least, must be unpaired. From the susceptibility, it can be calculated that there is only the contribution of one spin moment, the configuration being

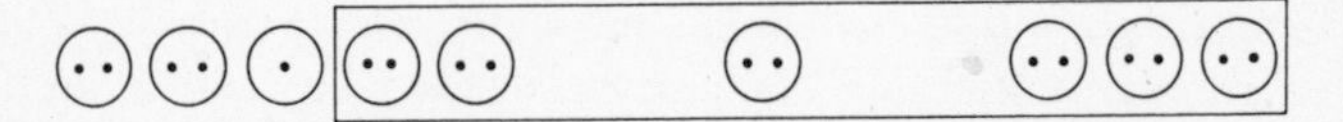

In K_3IrCl_6, that can be formed by reduction of K_2IrCl_6, e.g. in the remarkable reaction

$$2KCl + 2K_2IrCl_6 \rightarrow 2K_3IrCl_6 + Cl_2$$

there are eighteen electrons, and the compound is diamagnetic.

The elements iron, cobalt and nickel, and the elements preceding the platinum-iron group, have not as strong a tendency to form covalent complexes in reaction with halides. There are no compounds K_2NiCl_6 or K_4FeCl_6.

The *spd* hybridization extends beyond the group of the Pt metals, as can be seen in the complex $KAuCl_4$ which has square groups and $AuCl_4^-$ is diamagnetic; the electron configuration with sixteen electrons is the same as that in K_2PtCl_4.

In the first subgroups, covalent bonds may be formed, too, but since here the *d* orbitals are completely filled, all complexes are diamagnetic and it is very difficult to ascertain what kind of bonds are formed. It was remarked before that, at the end of the periods, the complex formation may be due to completion of octets, as for example, in the complexes of the boron gallium group. In KBF_4 and $KGaCl_4$ eight electrons are available for the formation of an octet, but we do not know how strong is the competition of ionic forms like $Ga^{3+}Cl_4^-$. Covalency, finally, is the reason that PCl_5, SCl_4, $SeCl_4$ and $TeCl_4$ behave as strong Cl^- donors (*see* Section 54).

61. OXIDE COMPLEXES

The first indications of covalency in complexes of two metal oxides appear if one of the metals belongs to the platinum group. The oxide complexes in this group are not well known: only very recently a few complexes have been prepared and their magnetic properties measured. The compound Na_2IrO_3, that is formed when a mixture of the metal and Na_2CO_3 is heated in oxygen

$$Ir + Na_2CO_3 + O_2 \rightarrow Na_2IrO_3 + CO_2$$

has seventeen electrons available for bond formation, if it is assumed that each oxygen atom contributes two electrons, forming two bonds. Each Ir atom is surrounded by six O atoms: there evidently is s^2pd^3 hybridization, the configuration is the same as in K_2IrCl_6, the magnetic moment being due to one unpaired electron.

Very little is known of the complexes formed by the metals of the subgroups, but the complexes formed by the oxides of the non-metallic elements all show covalency.

With the exceptions of the oxides of fluorine, CO, N_2O and NO, all oxides of the non-metallic elements form complexes with metal oxides and with water. All complex groups formed in this way have a complete octet structure; as in the oxides, themselves, the ions CO_3^{2-}, NO_3^- and NO_2^- have double bonds

$$\left[\begin{array}{c} :\ddot{O}:\ddot{C}::\dot{O}\!\cdot \\ :\underset{..}{O}: \end{array}\right]^{2-}, \quad \left[\begin{array}{c} :\ddot{O}:\ddot{N}::\dot{O}\!\cdot \\ :\underset{..}{O}: \end{array}\right]^{-}, \quad \left[:\ddot{O}:N::\dot{O}\!\cdot\right]^{-}$$

but the remaining have such a composition that these formulae can all be written with semipolar bonds, only.

$$\left[\begin{array}{c} O^- \\ {}^-O:\ddot{Cl}:O^- \\ {}_-\ddot{O} \end{array}\right]^{-}, \quad \left[\begin{array}{c} O \\ O:\ddot{S}:O \\ \ddot{O} \end{array}\right]^{2-}, \quad \left[\begin{array}{c} O \\ O:\ddot{P}:O \\ \ddot{O} \end{array}\right]^{3-}$$

$$\left[\begin{array}{c} O:\ddot{Cl}:O \\ \ddot{O} \end{array}\right]^{-}, \quad \left[\begin{array}{c} O:\ddot{S}:O \\ \ddot{O} \end{array}\right]^{2-}$$

$$\left[O:\underset{..}{\ddot{Cl}}:O\right]^{-}$$

$$\left[:\underset{..}{\ddot{Cl}}:O\right]^{-}$$

Two of the complexes derived from chlorine are formed from oxides with a different valency: ClO_2 and O^{2-} ion form a mixture of chlorite and chlorate

$$2ClO_2 + K_2O \rightarrow KClO_2 + KClO_3$$

and Cl_2O_6 reacts to form perchlorate and chlorate

$$Cl_2O_6 + K_2O \rightarrow KClO_4 + KClO_3$$

Bromine forms the same type of compounds, viz. the very unstable hypobromites AOBr and the bromates $ABrO_3$. In all these reactions the double bonds in the oxides become semipolar bonds in the complex ions.

Besides the two complexes derived from sulphur, mentioned above, there are a large number of others, in which two or more sulphur atoms are bound together; the ions in these compounds again can all be formulated by assuming that the S—O bonds are semipolar, and the sulphur atoms have a complete octet.

$$\left[\begin{array}{c} O:\underset{..}{\ddot{S}}:\underset{..}{\ddot{S}}:O \\ O\;\;O \end{array}\right]^{2-}, \quad \left[\begin{array}{c} O \\ O:\underset{..}{\ddot{S}}:\underset{..}{\ddot{S}}:O \\ \ddot{O}\;\ddot{O} \end{array}\right]^{2-}, \quad \left[\begin{array}{c} O\qquad O \\ O:\ddot{S}:O:\ddot{S}:O \\ \ddot{O}\qquad\ddot{O} \end{array}\right]^{2-}$$

hyposulphite *pyrosulphite* *dithionate*

The polythionic acids have the formula

$$\begin{array}{ccccc} & O & & O & \\ & \cdot\cdot & & \cdot\cdot & \\ O : & S & : (S)_n : & S & : O \\ & \cdot\cdot & & \cdot\cdot & \\ & O & & O & \end{array}$$

with n ranging from 1 to 5.

The fact that in these compounds there are bonds between two sulphur atoms is a strong argument against ionic bonding in these compounds. There is another argument that the bonds in ClO^-, ClO_2^- and NO_2^- are not ionic. The N^{5+} ion in nitrates is so small that in ionic complex formation this ion would not be surrounded by more than three O^{2-} ions, and the low coordination in NO_3^- can therefore not be used as an argument against an ionic structure. Since, however, the N^{3+} ion would be larger than N^{5+}, the coordination in nitrites should be higher than in nitrates.

The structure analysis of nitrites, however, shows that they contain isolated NO_2^- groups; in complexes of trivalent metals, e.g. in the alkali aluminates ($KAlO_2$) that have the same bruto composition as the nitrites, the coordination, indeed, is higher. Here the Al^{3+} ions are surrounded by six oxygen ions, a coordination number that is as to be expected for a really ionic compound. Hypochlorites $AClO$, chlorites $AClO_2$, chlorates $AClO_3$, sulphites A_2SO_3, etc., all have coordination numbers that are smaller than those to be expected in ionic compounds.

Although the ions NO_3, PO_4, SO_4 and ClO_4 are not completely ionic, there is still an appreciable charge difference between the central atom and the oxygen atoms. Since, in all probability, the bonds are semipolar, the positive charges on the central atom are one for NO_3^- and PO_4^{3-}, two for SO_4^{2-} and three for ClO_4^-, and it can be understood that, in spite of the covalency, the rules for the acid strength can still be applied.

62. AMMONIA AND PHOSPHORTRICHLORIDE COMPLEXES

With some of the alkali- and alkaline-earth halides, ammonia forms complexes that, in their general behaviour, strongly resemble the hydrates. Since neither the positive nor the negative ions have unoccupied orbitals available for bond formation, it has to be assumed that in these ammoniates the ammonia is bonded by the electrostatic attraction of the ions of the halide on the dipole of the ammonia molecule.

In the ammoniates of the halides of elements beyond the aluminium group, this dipole ion attraction may be replaced by the formation of covalent bonds, the lone electron-pairs of the NH_3 molecules occupying the unoccupied *d* orbitals of the metal atoms.

There is good evidence that in the ammoniates of the platinum halides the bonding is of the covalent type. Counting the electrons in the $PtCl_4$ ammoniates, it is found that, in all of them, eighteen electrons are used in the bond formation. From the conductivity it can be concluded that in all of the ions formed, $Pt(NH_3)_6^{4+}$, $Pt(NH_3)_4Cl_2^{2+}$, $Pt(NH_3)_3Cl_3^{+}$, $Pt(NH_3)_2Cl_4$ and $Pt(NH_3)Cl_5^{-}$, the platinum atom has six ligands, as is to be expected for s^2pd^3 hybridization. The electron configuration, therefore, may be represented by

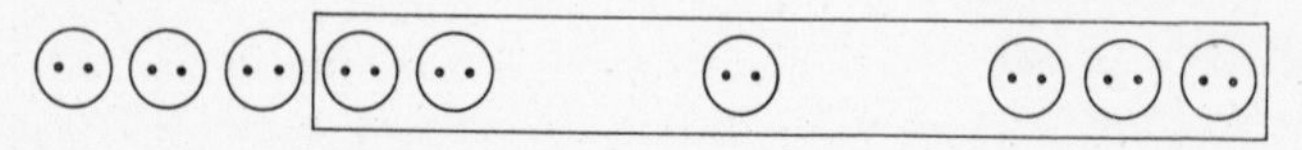

and with all orbitals occupied by two electrons, all these compounds must be diamagnetic.

There are ammoniates of $PtCl_2$, of halides of other platinum metals and of cobalt and nickel, too, some of which have been mentioned before in, Section 50. The cobalt complexes clearly show the importance of the completed *d* shells for the stability of the complex. Non complex compounds of trivalent cobalt are very unstable. Solutions of divalent cobalt in ammonia, however, are readily oxidized by air, because the NH_3 complex of trivalent cobalt $\{Co(NH_3)_6\}^{3+}Cl_3^{-}$ has eighteen electrons used in bond formation, whereas the ion $Co(NH_3)_6^{2+}$ would have nineteen electrons.

The complex ions like $\{Pt(NH_3)_6\}^{4+}$ and $\{Co(NH_3)_6\}^{3+}$ can be combined with all kinds of negative ions, single and complex, and thus give rise to an almost infinite number of compounds. By magnetic measurements it would be possible to decide how completely the ammoniates of the elements before the platinum group belong to the covalent complexes or have the NH_3 molecules bond by dipole ion interaction.

The ammonia molecule in complexes can be substituted by substitution products of NH_3, e.g. all kinds of amines. Very interesting compounds are formed by diamino aethane, which has two NH_2 groups and thus can replace two NH_3 molecules. WERNER found that compounds

$$\left\{Co\left(\begin{matrix} NH_2 & CH_2 \\ & | \\ NH_2 & CH_2 \end{matrix}\right)_3\right\}^{3+} Cl_3^{-}$$

can be obtained in two optical isomers (*see Figure 41 a* and *b*). By turning (*a*) over 180° it is seen that the two forms are not identical.

In (*a*) the amino groups are between 4 and 6 and between 3 and 5; in (*b*) they are between 4 and 5 and between 6 and 3. The broad lines represent the $NH_2.CH_2$ $CH_2.NH_2$ groups. From this it can be concluded that the six NH_2 groups must octahedrally surround the Co atom. In this way, the structure of the NH_3 complexes was determined, long before the application of x-rays to structural analysis.

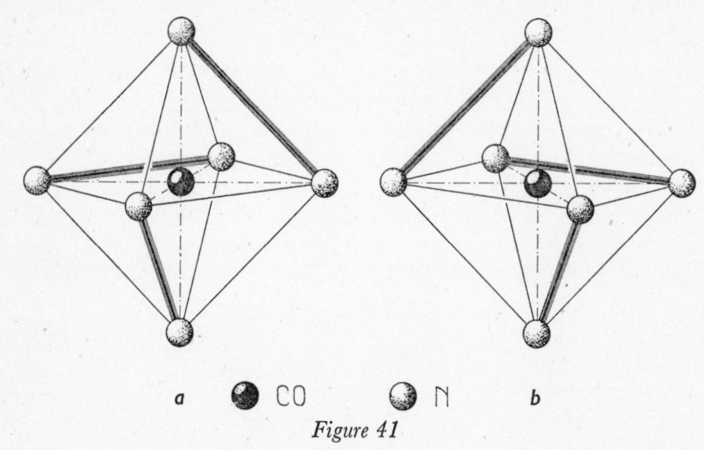

Figure 41

Ammonia will be able to complete the octet of boron. With BH_3 it reacts to form the compound $H_3N.BH_3$. With BCl_3 the reaction is more complicated, HCl being given off and BN eventually being formed. If $N(CH_3)_3$ reacts with BCl_3, a decomposition reaction is excluded, and the expected compound $(CH_3)_3N.BCl_3$ is formed.

Water, in its reaction with the alkali- and alkaline-earth metals, resembles ammonia, but the complexes with the halides of the platinum metals are different. The water molecule has two lone pairs of electrons, but these pairs seem to be less active in complex formation. There are many cases in which from the magnetic moment it can be concluded that the hydrates are still ionic, whereas in the corresponding NH_3 complex there is covalency, the NH_3 molecules sharing their lone electron-pairs with the metal atom.

Phosphine, PH_3, probably will form compounds analogous to the ammoniates, but such compounds have not been investigated in great detail.

PCl_3 *compounds*

When looking for other molecules with lone electron-pairs that perhaps will combine these electrons with *d* electrons of platinum metals, there are, first of all, the trihalides of the nitrogen-phosphor group of elements. Complexes formed from chlorides of the platinum metals and PCl_3 have been known for a very long time. In $PtCl_2.2PCl_3$ there are four ligands, and sixteen electrons are available for bond formation: the electronic configuration may be that of a spd^2 hybridization, with all d orbitals occupied

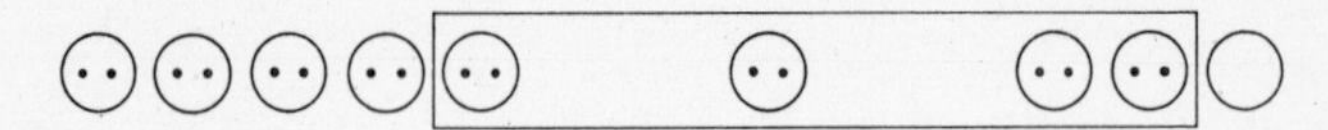

The four ligands then would be arranged in a square: this conclusion has been confirmed by recent x-ray work.

Up till now no explanation could be given for the difference in behaviour of NH_3 and PCl_3. PCl_3 does not react with $PtCl_4$. There are no compounds with six ligands. It might be argued that PCl_3 is so large that there is no room for six PCl_3 molecules around one Pt atom, but this argument is invalid, because CO, a small molecule, reacts like PCl_3, and not like NH_3. Theory clearly is not developed far enough to explain every detail.

Another remarkable difference between NH_3 and PCl_3 is that PCl_3, alone, is able to form compounds with some metals. Four PCl_3 molecules would be sufficient to complete an 18-electron configuration when reacting with nickel. Recently, by heating nickel carbonyl with PCl_3, a compound $Ni(PCl_3)_4$ has been prepared

$$Ni(CO)_4 + 4PCl_3 \rightarrow Ni(PCl_3)_4 + 4CO$$

and the corresponding fluoride and bromide have been obtained in a similar way.

The arsenic and the antimony halides, that have lone electron-pairs, too, form compounds similar to that of PCl_3, but less stable, and the bismuth halides do not react at all. The most probable explanation is that, in the series

$$PCl_3 \rightarrow AsCl_3 \rightarrow SbCl_3 \rightarrow BiCl_3$$

the bond in the halide is increasingly more ionic.

If, in $BiCl_3$, there is a strong positive charge on the Bi ion, it will not have a tendency to share its electron pair with another atom, because in this process the charge would further increase. No explanation can be given for the fact that covalent NCl_3 does not react with other halides.

It has been remarked earlier that the lone electron-pair in PCl_3 can be used for completion of an octet in boron compounds: with BCl_3 it forms the compound $Cl_3P.BCl_3$, the bromide and iodide have been prepared, a less stable compound is formed from BCl_3 and $AsCl_3$ and there is no reaction with $SbCl_3$.

63. CARBONYLS

The next group of molecules containing lone electron-pairs which are available to form complexes of the type of the PCl_3 complexes are NO, CO, and CN^-. It is not at once evident that these three groups have much in common, but if it is remembered that the nitrogen atom has one electron more than carbon, and one less than oxygen, it is evident that NO^+, CO and CN^- are *iso*electronic, i.e. have the same number of electrons, and thus may have the same electronic configuration and show analogous chemical behaviour. It will be seen below that NO and CN^- form compounds that, in their electronic configurations, strongly resemble the carbonyls.

Nickel, heated gently in a stream of CO, forms the carbonyl $Ni(CO)_4$. Carbonyls of other metals have been prepared by reduction of the halides with other metals in the presence of CO under high pressure. All carbonyls have 18-electron configurations: the formulae of the carbonyls of metals with even atomic numbers thus can be easily found, e.g. $Ni(CO)_4$, $Fe(CO)_5$, $Cr(CO)_6$ and $Mo(CO)_6$.

From an element with an odd number of electrons, e.g. cobalt, a simple carbonyl $Co(CO)_n$ cannot be derived, since the compounds with four CO molecules would be short one electron and the compound with five molecules would have one electron in excess.

The missing electron in $Co(CO)_4$ can be acquired in a large number of ways:

1. The molecule $Co(CO)_4$ can form a covalent bond between two Co atoms. It has been shown that the carbonyl with the composition $Co(CO)_4$ is actually dimeric, presumably with the formula $(OC)_4Co : Co(CO)_4$.
2. The missing electron can be provided by the formation of a covalent bond with a univalent atom, e.g. hydrogen or a halogen, in compounds like $ClCo(CO)_4$ and $HCo(CO)_4$.
3. The electron can be withdrawn from a metal, e.g. potassium. In this way a compound $K^+\{Co(CO)_4\}^-$ is formed, a typical complex with an isolated complex ion.
4. The 18-electron configuration may be completed by substituting one CO molecule by a NO group that, as will be shown below, can react with the participation of three electrons.

The hydrogen and halogen carbonyls and the nitroso carbonyls $Co(NO)(CO)_3$, in which all bonds are covalent, are non-polar compounds with relatively low boiling points. The dimeric carbonyl, too, is non-polar, but its boiling point is much higher than that of the monomeric carbonyls because of the larger size of the molecule.

The metal compounds of the carbonyls, e.g. the potassium compound, however, are quite different: as ionic complexes, they are not volatile, are insoluble in non-polar compounds and may be soluble in water.

A large number of halogen carbonyls has been prepared; some of them have not the 18-electron configuration: in $PtCl_2(CO)_2$, for example, there are only sixteen electrons. The carbonyls always have eighteen electrons, but the number of ligands is variable. It is therefore doubtful that they have d^2sp^3 hybridization.

64. NITROSO (NO) COMPLEXES

By giving off one electron, NO becomes *iso*electronic with N_2. The NO^+ ion, therefore, can form the stable electron configuration of the N_2 molecule, this stable configuration causing the NO molecule to be a strong electron donor. We have seen how, because of this property, it is able to form complexes, all containing NO^+ as a positive ion. If the negative ion does not contain a positive ion with a defective electron shell, there will be no tendency to form covalent bonds between the NO^+ ion and the negative group.

If, however, a NO^+ ion is combined with an ion that has a defective electron configuration, the lone electron-pair of NO^+ may react with the incomplete shell in the same way as toward the CO molecule. In such reactions, the NO molecule will donate three electrons, and NO compounds, similar to the carbonyls, may be formed, in which each NO molecule contributes three electrons instead of the two provided by CO. There are only a few compounds that merely contain NO groups. In carbonyls, part of the CO may be replaced by NO. If, in $Co(CO)_4$, one CO is replaced by a NO group, the number of electrons in $Co(CO)_3NO$ becomes equal to eighteen. This compound, then, will not dimerize like $Co(CO)_4$ to pair its unpaired electron. Monomeric $Co(CO)_3NO$ thus will not show the high boiling point of $Co(CO)_4$, but will have about the same boiling point as $Ni(CO)_4$. Iron forms a compound $Fe(CO)_2(NO_2)$, with a boiling point very nearly equal to that of $Ni(CO)_4$ and $Co(CO)_3NO$. The two nitroso compounds, $Fe(NO)_4$ and $Ru(NO)_4$, containing NO groups only, have not the low boiling point of the nitroso carbonyls: both are solids with very low vapour pressure.

If NO reacts with iron to form $Fe(NO)_3$, seventeen electrons are available for bond formation. If the compound really existed it probably would dimerize like $Co(CO)_4$, but what really happens is that the compound $Fe(NO)_4$ is formed. It seems reasonable to assume that the fourth NO molecule only contributes one electron, the structure being $NO^+\{Fe(NO)_3\}^-$. The partial ionic character of the bond explains the low vapour pressure of the compound, which can be compared with the metal carbonyl complexes, e.g. $A^+\{Co(CO)_4\}^-$.

65. CYANIDES

Substitution of O by N in N_2 leads to NO, which has one electron in excess and thus easily forms a positive ion: in CN there is one electron less than in N_2, and thus this compound becomes *iso*-electronic by attracting one electron and forming the negative ion CN^-.

As a univalent ion of medium size, CN^-, in simple compounds like K^+CN^-, behaves as a chlorine ion, especially if the positive ion has a rare-gas or an 18-electron structure, and covalent bonds cannot be formed. If, however, the positive ion is one of the transition elements, covalent bonds are formed by the lone electron-pair of the CN^- ion.

By double decomposition of $Ag_3Mo(CN)_8$ with KCN, a complex $K_4Mo(CN)_8$ is formed that is remarkable in many ways. In the first place, the reaction

$$8KCl + 2Ag_3Mo(CN)_8 \rightarrow 6AgCl + 2K_4Mo(CN)_8 + Cl_2$$

illustrates the stability of tetravalent molybdenum in complexes. In purely ionic complexes, a complex with a cation : anion ratio of 4 : 1 would not be stable, and would reduce this ratio by condensation of the complex group. If, however, the Mo—CN bond is covalent, the latter process is not possible: both the remarkable cation : anion ratio and the unusually high coordination are indications that the bond is covalent; by counting electrons it is found that the compound has an 18-electron configuration and the eight coordination may be an indication that this compound is an example of a rather seldom seen d^4sp^3 hybridization. The covalent nature of the ion $Mo(CN)_8^{4-}$ has been demonstrated by the diamagnetism of the compound.

Iron and cobalt both form complex cyanides: two well-known iron compounds are $K_4Fe(CN)_6$ and $K_3Fe(CN)_6$; the cobalt compounds are analogous to the iron salts, with formulae $K_4Co(CN)_6$ and $K_3Co(CN)_6$. By counting electrons, seventeen are found in $K_3Fe(CN)_6$ and nineteen in $K_4Co(CN)_6$, whereas the other two have eighteen, the number required for d^2sp^3 hybridization and complete filling of the *d* orbitals.

The $Fe(CN)_6^{3-}$ ion, in which one of the electrons of the stable 18-electron configuration is missing, can withdraw this missing electron from other compounds, and is thus a strong oxidizer, e.g.

$$2I^- + 2\{Fe(CN)_6\}^{3-} \rightarrow I_2 + \{Fe(CN)_6\}^{4-}$$

On the other hand, $K_4\{Co(CN)_6\}$ has one electron in excess, which can easily be withdrawn by other compounds, and the $Co(CN)_6^{4+}$ ion therefore has reducing properties.

Now it is very remarkable that cobalt, in ionic compounds, is unstable in the tervalent state, and that the divalent ion has no reducing properties. In a covalent complex ion, cobalt must be in the tervalent state in order to be able to form an 18-electron configuration. By the complex formation, the tervalent state, unusual in ionic compounds, is stabilized.

Otherwise, unusual valency states are often observed in cyanide complexes. A Mn complex $K_5Mn(CN)_6$ has been reported: here the stable 18-electron configuration causes the valency of manganese to take the very unusual value of one, and the compound is formed in spite of the extremely unfavourable cation : anion ratio. Still more remarkable are the complex nickel cyanides. KCN and $Ni(CN)_2$ form a complex $K_2Ni(CN)_4$, in which sixteen electrons are involved in the bond formation. The diamagnetism and the square structure of the $Ni(CN)_4$ ion show that the bonding is due to dsp^2 hybridization.

This ion now can be reduced to one with an 18-electron configuration. When treated with a solution of potassium in liquid ammonia it forms the compounds $K_3Ni(CN)_4$ (with seventeen electrons) and eventually $K_4Ni(CN)_4$, in which the ions have apparent valencies of 1 and 0, respectively. The latter compound is the full analogue of the carbonyl and the nickel—PCl_3 compounds. In the three compounds $Ni(:PCl_3)_4$, $Ni(:CO)_4$ and $Ni(:CN^-K^+)_4$, the 18-electron configuration is completed by four lone electron-pairs of molecules that are as different as CO, PCl_3 and CN^-K^+.

66. FURTHER GROUPS AS LIGANDS IN COMPLEXES

In this section we will try to find out which molecules or ions, besides those discussed in the preceding section, may occur as ligands in complexes.

All hydrogen compounds of the elements in the three last groups of the periodic system have lone electron-pairs, and thus, in principle, would be able to form complexes of the type of the ammoniates. However, the possession alone of a lone pair of electrons is not a sufficient condition for complex formation. The rare-gas atoms have lone electron-pairs too, but these pairs cannot be shared with other atoms. Evidently the 'activity' of the lone pairs decreases rapidly in the sequence NH_3, OH_2, FH, Ne. It was remarked before that the hydrates of compounds of the elements of the transition groups usually have the magnetic properties to be expected for ionic molecules. Obviously, in these compounds, the H_2O molecules do not share one of their lone electron-pairs with the central atom, and compounds in which this water is substituted by HF are not known. There is only one ion in which the electron pair of the fluorine atom is active in bond formation, viz. the fluoronium ion

$$H : \ddot{\underset{\cdot\cdot}{F}} : H^-$$

the analogue of H_3O and NH_4.

The rapidly decreasing stability of these ions in the sequence $NH_4^+ \rightarrow OH_3^+ \rightarrow FH_2^+$ may be used as an argument for the decreasing 'activity' of the electron pairs in this series.

With increasing size of the atoms there seems to be a further decrease: the molecules HCl, HBr and HI are not known to show any tendency to combine with protons: the proton affinity in the series $H_2O \rightarrow H_2S \rightarrow H_2Se \rightarrow H_2Te$ decreases, too, and even in the next group, $NH_3 \rightarrow PH_3 \rightarrow AsH_3$, PH_3 has a much lower proton affinity, and forms less stable bonds with electron-defective atoms than NH_3. It cannot be due to a less systematic investigation, alone, that, so far, only very few PH_3 complexes have been observed.

In the halide group the most active lone pair is found in the phosphortrihalides. The stability of the boron complexes $AX_3.BX_3$ decreases in the sequence $PX_3 \rightarrow AsX_3 \rightarrow SbX_3$, no antimony compounds being observed. The halides of the sulphur group do not form compounds at all: it seems improbable that the only reason for this behaviour is the disproportionation of these halides.

If SCl_2 reacts with $SbCl_5$, a strong Cl-acceptor, the former compound disproportionates according to

$$2SCl_2 \rightarrow S + SCl_4$$

and SCl_4 combines with $SbCl_5$ to form $SCl_3SbCl_6^-$.

Antimony compounds, e.g. $Ni(SbCl_3)_4$, analogous to the PCl_3 complexes of the transition elements, have been prepared, but they are not as readily formed as the compounds of PCl_3 and chlorides of the platinum metals, and thus it seems that in this group, too, the lone pair in PCl_3 is more active in complex formation than that of $AsCl_3$ or $SbCl_3$.

The stability of the complexes also depends on the halogen ion; in the boron compounds the fluorides are not stable, no compound being observed in the system BF_3—PF_3. The experimental data are too scarce to decide whether the bromides and iodides are more, or less, stable than the chlorides.

No explanation has been given for the remarkable fact that, whereas the hydrides of the second period, NH_3 and H_2O, have by far the strongest tendency to complex formation of the whole group, the halides, NCl_3 and OCl_2, do not show any tendency to complex formation at all. A compound of NCl_3 and BCl_3 could not be obtained from the mixture of the two compounds in CCl_4 solution.

The rules for the 'activity' of a lone pair of electrons can be summarized in the following simple way:

1. The pair should be a truly lone pair, i.e. the other six electrons should be used in bond formation. It is, therefore, active in PCl_3, but not in SCl_2, ClCl or A, active in NH_3 and not, or only to a small degree, in OH_2, HF or Ne.
2. The pair is activated if it is part of a simple negative ion, F^-, Cl^-, Br^-, I^-, O^{2-} and S^{2-} therefore able to share an electron pair with other atoms.
3. The activity of the lone electron-pair decreases if the compound becomes more ionic, decreasing in the sequence

$$PCl_3 \rightarrow AsCl_3 \rightarrow SbCl_3 \rightarrow BiCl_3$$

   being greater for the chloride PCl_3 than for the fluoride PF_3.
4. It has to be assumed that, in the atoms of the second period, the electrons are so strongly held by the atoms that NCl_3 and OCl_2 cannot share these electron pairs with other atoms.
5. For the great activity of NH_3, the following reasoning may apply:
   a. Comparing the compounds PCl_3 and PF_3, the electrons of the halogen atoms will be drawn more strongly in the direction of the P atom in PCl_3 than in PF_3, and the charge of P in PCl_3 thus will be more negative and the free electron pair in PCl_3 therefore more easily shared than in PF_3.
   b. In a hydride, the electrons will be drawn more easily towards the central atom of the molecule because of the low electron affinity of the hydrogen atom. Thus, the electron pair in NH_3 may be more active than in NCl_3.
   c. If NH_3 has ionic states, too, they will lay a negative charge on the central atom, and NH_3 will have a very active electron pair.

67. THE METALLIC BOND: TRANSITION BETWEEN THE THREE TYPES OF CHEMICAL BOND

It has been shown that molecular formation and crystal structure of elements in the last four groups of the periodic system are determined by the number of homopolar bonds which each atom can form. The elements of these groups have no metallic properties. The remaining elements, with the exception of boron and the noble gases, are truly metallic in character, but there is no relation between their normal valencies and the number of neighbours of each atom in the crystal. There are three main crystalline types:

1. The closest-packed cubic structure (*Figure 33*).
2. The closest-packed hexagonal structure (*Figure 36*).
3. The body-centred cubic structure.

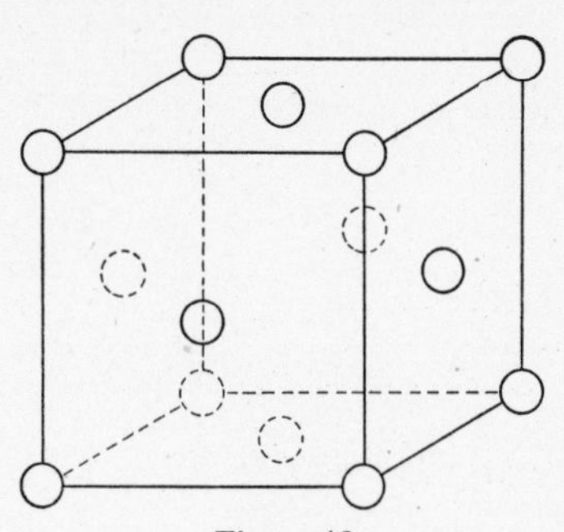

Figure 42

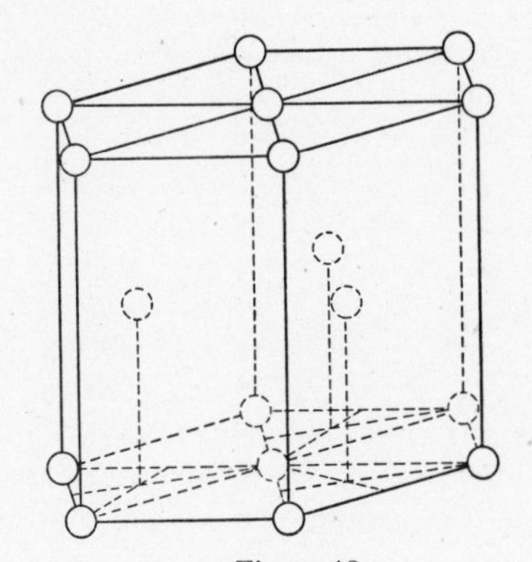

Figure 43

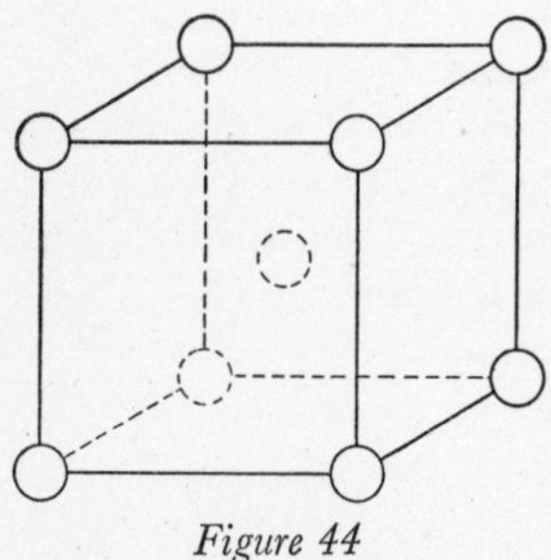

Figure 44

In the first two types, every atom is surrounded by twelve others (*see Figures 42* and *43*). In the third type, *Figure 44*, each atom has eight neighbours at a distance of $\sqrt{3}r/2 = 0{\cdot}86a$ (where a is the length of the side of the unit cell), followed by six more at a slightly greater distance. Therefore, each atom has fourteen neighbours.

As has been seen, there is no direct relation between valency and either position in the periodic system or coordination number. The following metals belong to the first structural type

Ca, Sr, Al, La, Ce, Pr, Th, Fe, Co, Rh, Ir, Ni, Pd, Pt,
Cu, Ag, Au, Hg*, Tl, Pb

while in the second are

Be, Mg, Ca, Y, La, Ce, Pr, Ti, Zr, Hf, Re, Ru, Os,
Co, Ir, Zn*, Cd*, Tl

and in the third

Li, Na, K, Rb, Cs, Ti, Zr, Hf, V, Cb, Ta, Cr, Mo, W, Fe

Some metals crystallize in more than one structural type, which means that there are two allotropic modifications. The metals marked * do not conform precisely to the closest-packed structure, but deviate slightly from it. Uranium, manganese, gallium and indium have very abnormal structures, and the last two are transitional between metallic and non-metallic elements of the carbon group. The picture presented by the metallic structures is utterly different from that of elements of the four last groups of the periodic system. The homopolar bonds of these latter strive to produce a state in which the number of neighbours of each atom is determined by its valency. In the other elements, however, forces appear to be acting that tend to surround each atom with as many other atoms as possible.

Occasionally, some residual homopolar bonds remain in metals, for example a small per cent of the molecules Li—Li, Na—Na, etc. are found in the vapours of these metals, analogous to the hydrogen molecule, but there is no trace of them in the solid state. The most characteristic property of metals, in which the smallest potential difference produces an electric current, is their electrical conductivity. Since no transport of mass takes place in a metallic conductor, a metal must contain free electrons, from which it follows that positive ions must also be present. The picture of a metal is therefore one in which the lattice is composed of positive ions held together by electrons which move freely in the space between. It is as though the ions were cemented together by an electronic gas.

In the homopolar bond, a pair of atoms are coupled together by two electrons while, in a metal, all the electrons hold all the ions together in the crystal. The theory of the metallic bond is even more complicated than that of the homopolar bond, as the subsequent discussion will show. In this section we shall only discuss how metallic properties are distributed in the periodic system.

The formation of a metal structure from free atoms must be associated with ionization, from which it follows that a high ionization energy in an element prevents it. Metallic properties are therefore found in the alkali- and alkaline-earth elements. Boron, the first element in the third group, is hardly metallic; in this group the element with the smallest ionic radius loses its metallic character.

In the fourth group, carbon and silicon are both non-metallic, while germanium has a very small electrical conductivity. It is only with white tin and lead that the electrical conductivity approaches the normal values for true metals. In the fifth group, arsenic and antimony are just on the limit between metallic and non-metallic properties, while of the elements of the sixth group, only polonium might be considered to have real metallic properties. The halogens, in the seventh group, show no trace of metallic properties.

The line dividing metals from non-metals in the periodic system runs from the left-hand top corner to the right-hand bottom one, parallel, in fact, to the line dividing the basic and acidic oxides, since the properties concerned depend on the sizes and charges of ions. The metallic bond is not confined to single elements and compounds can be formed between them. The composition of such compounds, however, cannot be predicted from the simple rules of valency, and the proportions of various atoms present are quite remarkable. Thus, lead and sodium form a compound with a composition very nearly corresponding to Pb_8Na_{31}, which can certainly not be expressed as $PbNa_4$, based on the normal valencies of the two elements. Mercury and sodium form no less than seven compounds Hg_4Na, Hg_2Na, $Hg_{13}Na_{12}$, $HgNa$, Hg_2Na_3, Hg_2Na_5 and $HgNa_3$. These examples suffice to show the complexity of the subject of metallic compounds. Can we now predict whether any two elements on reacting together will give an ionic, a homopolar or a metallic compound?

Let us begin with an element from the left-hand bottom corner of the periodic system with a low ionization energy, and one from the right-hand upper corner with a large electron affinity. An ionic compound is then obtained, the ideal example being CsF. If both elements are now chosen from the right-hand upper corner, they will have a high ionization energy and a large electron affinity, so that the ionization of one of the atoms does not arise. A coupling will then take place through the electron pairs. The best examples are, of course, the molecules of the elements themselves, further ones being the compounds OF_2, NF_3, OCl_2, S_2Cl_2, etc. If both elements are chosen from the left-hand bottom corner, they will have low ionization energies and metallic compounds will be formed.

There will, in addition, be transitions between all three types, for it was seen earlier that an ionic compound could take on the character of a homopolar one through polarization, and, further, that a homopolar bond could also assume the character of an ionic bond as a result of differences in ionization energy and electron affinity. If, for example, the ions in CsCl are successively replaced

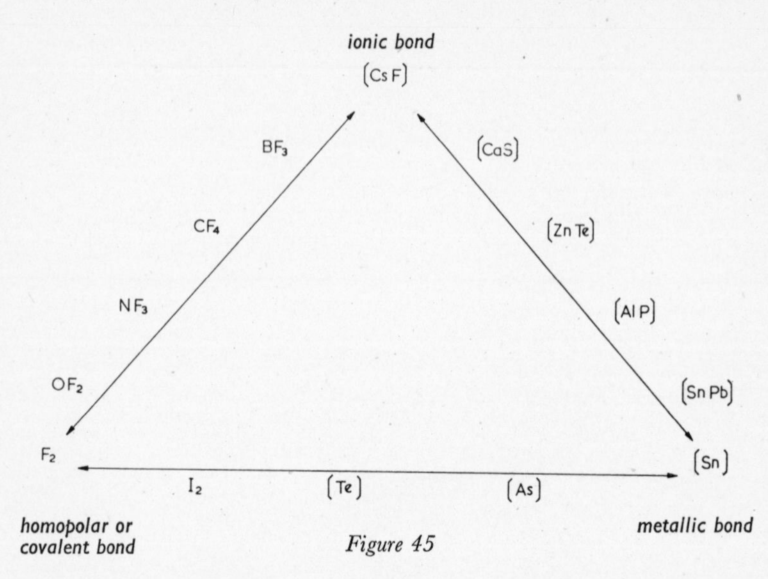

Figure 45

by others with steadily smaller differences in ionization energy and electron affinity, then the heteropolar character will gradually change over to the metallic (*see Figure 45*).

The compound ZnTe has metallic properties, and so far as the valency is concerned it can be thought of as heteropolar. The electron cloud is more concentrated around the tellurium atoms, so that they assume a negative charge with respect to zinc and, consequently, the metallic bond acquires the characteristics of an ionic one. Decreasing ionization energy causes the homopolar to change over into the metallic, as for example in the series

$$F_2 \rightarrow I_2 \rightarrow [Te] \rightarrow [As] \rightarrow [Sn]$$

Similarly, the series

$$C \rightarrow Si \rightarrow Ge \rightarrow Sn(grey) \rightarrow Sn(white) \rightarrow Pb$$

passes from the non-metallic diamond to the partly metallic germanium, and so to lead, which is completely metallic in character.

Tin occurs in two forms, the white being a typical metal. The grey variety of tin appears superficially to be metallic, although the more important property of electrical conductivity has not been measured.

In this connection it is worthy of note that graphite, one of the forms of carbon, has some electrical conductivity which is probably not caused by free electrons, as in metals, but by the shift of the bonds in the layers of C atoms (*see Figure 39*).

68. INTERSTITIAL COMPOUNDS

The hydrides, oxides and nitrides of the elements of the first three groups of the periodic system all behave as normal ionic compounds. They all show normal valencies, they crystallize in coordination lattices, do not show any metallic conductivity and, in so far as an estimate can be made of their heats of formation, they agree fairly well with the values to be expected for ionic compounds.

After the third group, however, the properties become rather different. In the first place, there is a strong tendency to form lower compounds. Thus titanium forms the compounds TiH_2, TiO and TiN. The halides of this element are found in *Table XXXIX*.

Table XXXIX

Halides of Titanium

—	—	TiF_4
$TiCl_2$	$TiCl_3$	$TiCl_4$
$TiBr_2$	$TiBr_3$	$TiBr_4$
TiI_2	TiI_3	TiI_4

The non-existence of the lower fluorides can be explained by the greater lattice energy of the fluorides that causes the V versus valency curve (*see Figure 16*, Section 29) to be convex towards the valency axis.

Now if the fluorides are compared with the oxides, the latter have a still greater lattice energy and the V versus n curve should be steeper for the oxides. Thus, if there were no lower fluorides, lower oxides would be still more unstable. From the existence of TiO, it can be concluded that this compound must be stabilized by some kind of non-ionic bonding. The same argument holds for the lower nitride TiN, and for the hydride TiH_2. Since the H^- ion is about the same size as the F^- ion, the lower hydride could not be stable if the fluoride is not.

A second argument, that the hydrides and nitrides of the metals beyond the third group are stabilized by non-ionic bond formation, runs as follows: If the heats of formation of these compounds are estimated from the values of the halides, taking into account the small electron affinities of hydrogen and nitrogen (the latter being strongly negative), very small, or even negative, values are obtained, and without some non-ionic bond formation these compounds could not be stable.

The structures of the hydrides, oxides and nitrides in this group are rather peculiar, for they can always be described as lattices, as found in pure metals, with the negative ions inserted in the octahedral holes of these structures. In the case of TiN, TiO and, in general, all compounds AB, all octahedral holes are occupied, and the structure is that of the sodium chloride type. There are nitrides of other types, too, e.g. A_2N, A_3N, etc., in which cases only a part of the octahedral holes are occupied.

Now the ions formed by hydrogen and the elements of the second period are so small that, on placing them in the octahedral holes of the metal, the distances between the metal atoms are not increased. There is practically no dilatation of the metal lattices and the metal atoms remain at the distances they were in the lattice of the metal, itself. Since, in the lower compounds, not all valency electrons of the metal are used in bond formation, there are electrons available to form the same kinds of bonds they form in the pure metal, or, in other words, in the formula for the heat of formation of the ionic compound

$$V = -S - I - D + E - U$$

the heat of sublimation of the metal S does not appear in total, since, in the formation of the compound, the metal atoms are not completely separated as in ionic compounds such as $TiCl_3$ and $TiCl_4$. Since the heat of sublimation of titanium is of the order of 150 kcal, the fact that the metal atoms are not separated will have a considerable influence on the heat of formation, and thereby on the stability of the compound.

It further becomes evident why these 'interstitial' compounds, as they are called, show metallic properties, e.g. metallic lustre, electron conductivity and often supraconductivity at low temperature. Because the metal atoms are still in the same positions as in the metals, and free electrons are available, as well, they must have the properties of metals.

Finally, there is another property of the interstitial compounds that should be mentioned. In contrast to the ionic halides of the same metal, they usually have not a stoichiometric composition, but form phases with broad regions of existence (*see* Section 24) with, many positions, available for negative ions, remaining unoccupied.

Let us imagine that in an ionic compound of the NaCl type a gap is formed by removing a negative ion. This is altogether impossible without a charge compensation that will be effected if the negative ion leaves behind its electron, which then becomes attached to the gap formed by the escape of the negative ion. However, it can be shown by calculation that even then the formation of the gap will cause a considerable increase in the energy of the crystal. So, even at high temperature, the alkali halides will only form a very small number of gaps, estimated at 1 in 10,000 negative ions. The situation is different for an interstitial compound, because in this case, if, for example, TiN gives off a nitrogen atom, the three remaining electrons can at once be used for the formation of metallic bonds. The formation of these metallic bonds may so far reduce the increase of energy due to the formation of a gap, that the total change in energy is small, and at a given temperature a large number of gaps can be formed.

The properties of the interstitial compounds thus can be explained by assuming a combination of metallic and ionic bonding. As in all ionic bonds, there may be some covalency. The question of how far the non-metallic bonds are still ionic, or partially covalent, will not be discussed.

The compounds with larger negative ions, like sulphides, selenides and phosphides, in many respect resemble the interstitial compounds. Like the latter, they often show metallic properties and have variable compositions, but their crystal structures are of quite a different type.

By inserting the large negative ions in the largest holes of the metallic structure, the metal atoms will become completely separated, and the metallic bonds will be broken. The lattice, however, can be changed in such a way that the metal atoms come nearer together, thus re-establishing their mutual bonds.

A lattice, very common among sulphides, selenides, phosphides, arsenides and antimonides of the metals beyond the aluminium group, is that observed in the mineral NiAs. Like the NaCl lattice, it is still a coordination lattice, each ion being symmetrically surrounded by six ions of opposite charge. However, whereas in NaCl each ion is surrounded by six ions forming the corners of an octahedron, in the NiAs structure the Ni^{-} ions are surrounded by six As^{3} ions, forming a somewhat distorted octahedral configuration and the six Ni ions that surround an As ion form a trigonal prism. This structure is hexagonal and the unit cell is as shown in *Figure 46*.

Obviously, the Ni atoms are nearer together when they form a trigonal prism around the As ions than when they are arranged as an octahedron. By changing the axial ratio C/a, the metal distances can be further reduced, and thus the metal—metal bonds in the NiAs type of lattice can be preserved. The bonds in compounds

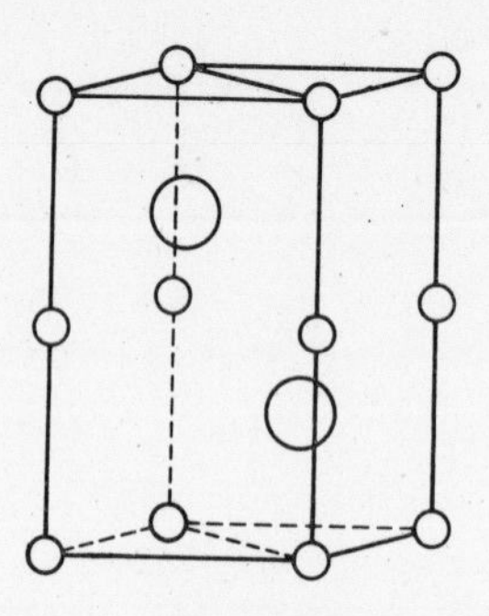

Figure 46

crystallizing in this structure are partially metallic and partially ionic, or ionic-covalent, and thus are intermediate between the true ionic and the true metallic compounds.

APPENDIX

69. COLLOIDS

WHEN dilute solutions of NaCl and $AgNO_3$ are mixed in approximately equivalent quantities, no silver chloride is precipitated. A colloidal solution is formed under these conditions, and microscopic examination shows that it contains small particles in rapid Brownian movement. From x-ray analysis it is found that the particles consist of small crystals of silver chloride. On electrolysis of the solution, the particles move towards one of the electrodes; the charge of the particles appears to be negative if the chlorine ions are in excess, but positive if the silver ions are in excess. If ions in which the solution is deficient are now added, then the charge disappears, movement in the electrical field ceases and the colloidal solution loses its stability. The particles then coalesce to larger aggregates which sink to the bottom of the vessel in the form of flocculent precipitates and the colloidal solution, or sol, is said to have deflocculated. Colloidal solutions, or sols, can be prepared from a variety of substances and, in nearly all, the particles carry an electric charge which can be destroyed by suitable electrolytes, although this does not always take place and there are colloidal solutions which contain uncharged particles.

We can now proceed to explain many phenomena in the realm of colloidal chemistry with the help of ideas based on the nature of the chemical bond. In Section 21 it was discussed how the extra field of the subgroup silver ion led to a large attraction for negative ions, especially when these ions were strongly polarizable (*see* Section 36). Since the silver ion is, itself, strongly polarizable, the van der Waals-London forces play an important part in still further strengthening the bond between the two ions. Due to the strong attraction between Ag^+ and Cl^- ions, the large lattice energy is not balanced by the hydration energy, with the result that silver chloride is insoluble in water. Therefore, as soon as solutions of NaCl and $AgNO_3$ are mixed together, the Cl^- and Ag^+ ions combine, and the growth of crystals starts at innumerable points throughout the solution, in a short time reaching their maximum size due to an insufficient supply of further ions. When neither Ag^+ nor Cl^- ions are present in excess then a small crystal can be represented diagrammatically as in *Figure 47*. NO_3^- ions are still present in the solution, but will not take part in the formation of the crystal. Since NaCl and $AgNO_3$ are both soluble, there is no reason why NO_3^- ions should combine with the Ag^+ ions on the surface of the crystal, nor why Na^+ ions should combine with the Cl^- ions.

If, on the other hand, there is a slight excess of silver ions, then they will certainly adhere to the chlorine ions and the crystal, thereby obtaining a positive charge. The number of silver ions which combine will not be large, since any further additions will be repelled by those already present. The free suspensoid of an AgCl crystal can

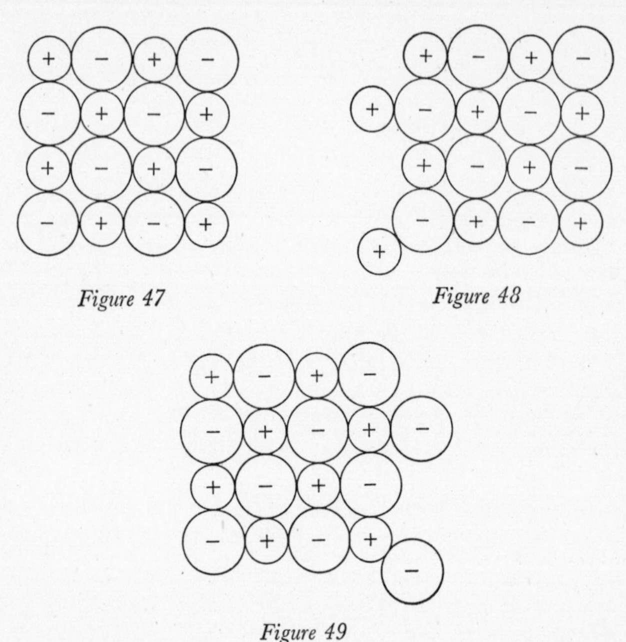

Figure 47

Figure 48

Figure 49

therefore be represented by *Figure 48* as a molecule built up of ions, but capable of taking up extra ions to form a complex. It is obvious that an excess of chlorine ions will equally well give the particles a negative charge (*see Figure 49*). The particles mutually repel one another, thus preventing coalescence of the crystals. When the charge is destroyed the crystals can join together, since ions of one crystal can come into contact with ions of opposite charge in the other crystal.

A positively charged AgCl particle can be discharged by ions other than those of chlorine; bromine and iodine ions have the same effect. In fact, these ions are held particularly strongly by the silver ions. Now it is to be noted that other negative ions, for example NO_3^-, can destroy the charge of a positive sol provided they are present in sufficient concentration, and this phenomenon can be explained in the following way: The positive colloid particle gives rise to an electric field which attracts all the negative ions in its immediate neighbourhood and repels all positive ones. The density of the positive charge therefore falls in the immediate neighbourhood of the particle. This effect will be unnoticeable in very dilute solutions, where there are very few ions and the thermal movement maintains the dispersion. In more concentrated solutions there is, however, a marked surplus of negative ions around this particle, which has the effect of weakening the field. At a given concentration the strength of the field is lowered to such an extent that the particles can join together and precipitate.

If the ions are particularly small, or have high charges, this effect will be correspondingly larger because of the stronger attraction exerted. Ions of high charge therefore cause precipitation at lower concentrations than do those of low charge. Negatively-charged colloids are very sensitive to the addition of highly-charged positive ions, and positively-charged colloids to highly-charged negative ones.

A number of other examples of colloidal solutions can be quoted. If H_2S is passed through a dilute solution of As_2O_3, a colloidal solution of As_2S_3 is formed; in this process S^{2-} ions, or rather SH^- ions, are in excess, and, consequently, the As_2S_3 crystals absorb them and the sol acquires a negative charge. The addition of highly-charged positive ions destroys the charge and precipitates the As_2S_3. The As_2S_3 sol has been investigated very thoroughly and its behaviour illustrates better than any other the influences of size and charge of ions on precipitation. It appears that the charge is by far the most important factor. Effects other than those of charge only occur when very large ions are added which can be absorbed as a result of dipole induction and polarization effects, as for example the organic ions which are included in *Table XL* under the univalent ions.

Suppose that to a solution of $FeCl_3$ dilute alkali is added and the precipitate of $Fe(OH)_3$ filtered off and washed carefully with distilled water. If a dilute solution of hydrochloric acid is now added to the precipitate, then the hydrogen ions will combine with the OH ions which are separated from the hydroxide particles and which therefore acquire an excess of Fe^{3+} ions and consequently a positive charge. The addition of $FeCl_3$ has the same effect when the Fe^{3+} ions are absorbed on the $Fe(OH)_3$ in exactly the same way as the Ag^+ ions are absorbed by AgCl. The effect of the addition of HCl can therefore be described by saying that the acid dissolves some of the $Fe(OH)_3$ to form $FeCl_3$. The sol of $Fe(OH)_3$ is particularly sensitive to highly-charged negative ions, and, naturally, to

OH^- ions as well. An excess of OH^- ions can, however, produce a negatively-charged $Fe(OH)_3$ sol, which is just as sensitive to highly-charged positive ions.

Positively-charged hydroxide sols can be prepared from many metals. To produce a colloidal solution from the precipitate, a process termed peptization, a solution of the salt, itself, is not

Table XL

Precipitation Values of an As_2S_3 *Sol*

electrolyte	*precipitation value*	*electrolyte*	*precipitation value*
univalent cations		*divalent cations*	
LiCl	58	$MgSO_4$	0·81
NaCl	51	$MgCl_2$	0·72
KCl	50	$CaCl_2$	0·65
KNO_3	50	$SrCl_2$	0·63
$\frac{1}{2}K_2SO_4$	63	$BaCl_2$	0·69
		$ZnCl_2$	0·68
HCl	31	$(UO_2)(NO_3)_2$	0·64
$\frac{1}{2}H_2SO_4$	30		
aniline chloride	2·5	*quinine sulphate*	0·24
strychnine chloride	0·5	*benzidine nitrate*	0·09
morphine chloride	0·4		
crystal violet	0·16		
fuchsine	0·11		
tervalent cations		*tetravalent cations*	
$AlCl_3$	0·093	$Th(NO_3)_4$	0·090
$Al(NO_3)_3$	0·095		
$\frac{1}{2}Al_2(SO_4)_3$	0·096		
$Ce(NO_3)_3$	0·080		

The precipitation values are given in millimol per litre.

necessarily required; $Fe(OH)_3$ can, for example, be brought into colloidal solution by the addition of Th^{4+} ions. In *Table XLI* are given the precipitation values for $Fe(OH)_3$ sol as an example of a positive sol. Here again the charge has the greatest influence on the precipitation values. The effect of the OH^- ion is much greater than that of any other univalent negative ion because it combines with the Fe^{3+} ion. It is incorrect to say that Fe^{3+} and OH^- combine because $Fe(OH)_3$ is insoluble; rather should it be said that the insolubility of $Fe(OH)_3$ is to be attributed to a very strong bond between Fe^{3+} and OH^-; therefore the OH^- are absorbed by particles with a superfluity of Fe^{3+} ions.

Colloidal solutions of metals can also be prepared, but only from the noble metals, since the others form hydroxides with water. A gold sol can be prepared by treating a weakly alkaline solution of a gold salt, such as $KAuCl_4$, with formalin or another reducing agent.

Table XLI

Precipitation Values for the $Fe(OH)_3$ *Sol*

electrolyte	*precipitation value*	*electrolyte*	*precipitation value*
univalent anions		*divalent anions*	
KI	16	K_2SO_4	0·20
KNO_3	12	Tl_2SO_4	0·22
KBr	12	$MgSO_4$	0·22
KCl	9	$K_2Cr_2O_7$	0·19
NaCl	9·2		
$\frac{1}{2}BaCl_2$	9·6		
$\frac{1}{2}Ba(OH)_2$	0·4		

The size of the particles formed is appreciably affected by the conditions of preparation and, since the colour of the sol is dependent on particle size, they vary in colour from yellow, red and violet to blue.

Platinum sols can be made in a similar manner, and such metal sols carry a negative charge. By drawing a spark between platinum or gold electrodes in water, the metal can be evaporated and the resulting vapour immediately condenses to small metal particles; in this way relatively stable metal sols can be prepared, provided the water is weakly alkaline. The negative charge of the metal sols is clearly caused by absorption of OH^- ions, but the combination of these ions is not so easily comprehended as in the earlier examples. It is, however, understandable that ions should be able to combine with a metal surface. A metal surface has the property of attracting an electric charge e at a distance r with a force e^2/r^2, the so-called image force. This is proved in the following way.

Let AB (*see Figure 50*), be an infinitely extended metal surface, and let there be a charge e at C. The lines of force from C must be at right-angles to the metal AB since this is an equipotential surface by virtue of the conductivity of the metal. These lines of force will not be affected if the metal is removed and replaced by a negative charge $-e$ at C', the lines of force from this point being denoted by broken lines. Since the two charges attract each other with a force e^2/r^2, the same force must be exerted by the metal. However, it is not clear why an OH^- ion is more attracted than a hydrogen ion. This would only be understandable if the hydrogen ions with their mantle of

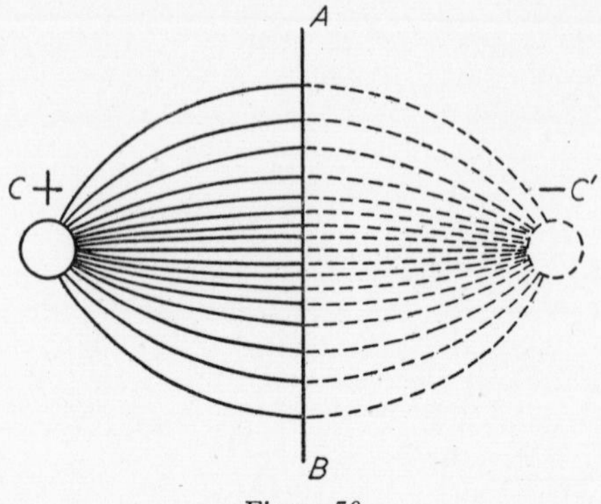

Figure 50

water molecules were larger than the hydroxyl ions, a point which has not yet been precisely determined.

Fine particles of carbon can be made into a colloidal solution in the same way by OH^- ions and always have negative charges. In view of the fact that graphite is a conductor, the image force may well be the cause. Very unstable colloidal solutions, so-called emulsions, can also be made by shaking water and oil together, but the oil droplets quickly combine to form larger droplets. It is possible, however, to make stable oil emulsions if a small amount of soap is added to the mixture of the two liquids. The particles acquire a negative charge, so that the fatty-acid ions are clearly adsorbed by the droplets. It was seen earlier that fatty acids with long chains, although insoluble in water, are soluble in hydrocarbons and oils. The long hydrocarbon chains of the fatty-acid ions will therefore try to separate from the water, which in this instance can only occur by their penetration into the oil droplets, thereby giving them negative charges. The difference in these oil emulsions from other sols that we have considered, is that the particles are liquid. This, however, makes little difference to their general behaviour, and, again, an oil emulsion can be discharged by positive ions. A fatty oil is also peptized by dilute alkali if the oil contains some free fatty acid.

Let us imagine that we have a very large organic molecule containing many NH_2 and COOH groups. If it is added to alkaline water, then the COOH group will change to COO^- and the molecules will acquire a negative charge. If the medium is acid, then the NH_2 will become NH_3^+, and the particles will acquire positive charges. Provided, therefore, the molecules are sufficiently large, the substance will behave as a positive colloid in an acid medium, whereas it will be negative in an alkaline one. Albumens are examples of substances which behave as colloids, although they are, in all probability, real solutions of very large molecules. There is, however, one important difference between them and the colloidal solutions previously considered. The albumen molecules have a mantle of strongly-held water molecules, presumably because of their active NH_2 and COOH groups. This mantle of water molecules permits the solution of many albumens, even when the charge of the particles is destroyed by addition of electrolytes. This covering of water molecules is also found in colloidal solutions of gum arabic, agar-agar and all other high molecular weight substances of animal or plant origin. These substances are known as hydrophilic colloids, in contrast to the previously considered hydrophobic ones. The covering of water molecules leads to very complicated reactions with solutions of electrolytes. We will not proceed any further with the discussion of the properties of hydrophilic colloids; the intention in this section was not to give a complete survey of colloid chemistry, but rather to show that the ideas put forward on the nature of the chemical bond could clarify many of the observed phenomena.

70. ADSORPTION PHENOMENA

The combination of foreign ions with the surfaces of colloidal particles is, in general, called adsorption. It goes without saying that this behaviour is not limited to small particles and that a large crystal of silver chloride can equally well adsorb positive or negative particles.

Chemical forces of various kinds can lead to such adsorption. Thus, the bond between ions and the AgCl molecule is due primarily to coulomb forces, but adsorption can equally well be caused by polarization forces alone, as for example when iodine is strongly adsorbed on the surface of CaF_2. The calcium ions create dipoles in the iodine molecules, and the attraction of these dipoles by the charges of the calcium ions gives rise to the bond. In the same manner, alkali atoms, particularly those of Cs, are adsorbed by metal oxides. Oxides with adsorbed alkali atoms are of the very greatest importance in the construction of photocells, used in instruments for measuring the intensity of light. Water molecules can be adsorbed on a surface when their dipoles are attracted by the ions on the surface. This is the reason why CaF_2 is always covered with a layer of water, which can only be removed with difficulty. The high charge of the positive ion in SiO_2 results in a strong adsorption

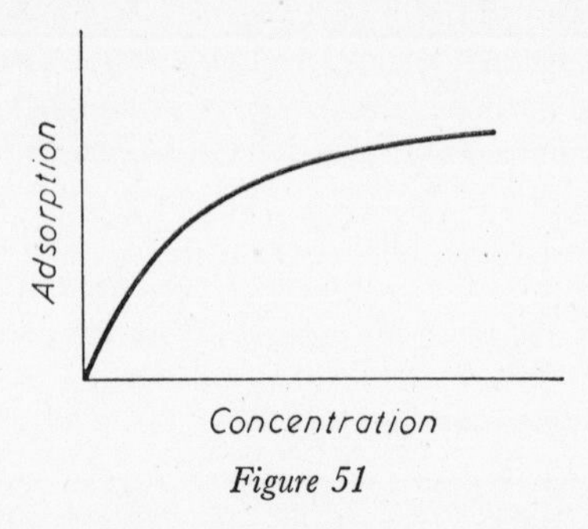

Figure 51

of water molecules; this adsorption is so strong that dry, finely divided SiO_2 is frequently used as a drying agent.

Calcium fluoride does not form a hydrate, yet the surface easily acquires a layer of water; this, however, is not formed on crystals which form hydrates. This at first sight appears to be somewhat paradoxical, but the explanation is quite simple. The water molecules are held very strongly by the calcium fluoride, due to the strong field of the ions which also holds the crystal together and at the same time prevents the penetration of water. Water can only penetrate those compounds which have weaker ionic fields, but it will then no longer be held so strongly and certainly not on the surfaces of the crystal.

It is a known fact that finely divided carbon can adsorb many gases, a property which is utilized in gas masks. Here the adsorption depends on the van der Waals-London forces, from which it follows that all strongly polarizable gases will be adsorbed, and, further, that a carbon mask is not suitable for the adsorption of CO. In practice, the efficacy of carbon for the adsorption of gases can be increased by adding other, usually ionic materials.

The quantity of material adsorbed will depend on its concentration, and the relation is shown in *Figure 51*. As the concentration is increased, more material is adsorbed, but as the surface of the adsorbent becomes more and more covered with molecules, the amount adsorbed will diminish. The theoretical implications of this adsorption curve will not be discussed further. As the temperature is increased, adsorption naturally decreases because the rise in temperature causes breaking of more and more bonds between the atoms. In oil emulsions, discussed in the previous section, it was seen that oil droplets have the property of adsorption. The phenomena which occur when fatty acids and higher alcohols are mixed together in water are of the very greatest interest and importance for a proper understanding of many biological problems. The fatty acids of lower molecular weight, such as acetic and propionic, are completely soluble in water, but solubility decreases as the length of the hydrocarbon chain is increased. Thus, an acid with six carbon atoms is still slightly soluble in water, that is to say, the COOH group dissolves well in water, while the hydrocarbon chain is insoluble. We therefore have two competing effects, one from the COOH group which tries to penetrate into the water, and one from the hydrocarbon residue which tries to separate from it. The net result of these two tendencies is for the molecules to concentrate at the surface of the water. As a result of thermal movement there will be some molecules which can penetrate into the water. In the liquid, therefore, there will be a low concentration of fatty-acid molecules, but at a small distance from the surface the concentration will increase and at the surface, itself, the concentration reaches a large value because here there are many molecules with their COOH groups in the water and their alkyl groups outside it. As the alkyl group becomes longer, the number of molecules that are lying on the surface becomes greater than the number of those which lie directly under the surface. In very long chains, when a small quantity of a substance is added to water, the remarkable phenomenon is found where all the molecules remain on the surface with their COOH groups dipping into the water. There will be a quantity of added fatty acid corresponding to complete coverage of the surface with molecules having their hydrocarbon groups directed away from the surface.

If now a small quantity of alkali is added to the water, then the hydrogen ions will be split off by dissociation from the COOH groups. This gives rise to a remarkable situation in which there is a monomolecular layer of fatty-acid ions having a negative electric charge with respect to the solution, while the solution which contains the hydrogen ions is positive. The hydrogen ions are naturally attracted by the negative charge but, owing to thermal movement, are driven back into the liquid. There will therefore be a high concentration of hydrogen ions immediately under the negative layer of COO^- groups in the liquid, which diminishes rapidly with distance. These electrical double layers play a particularly important part in colloid chemistry and in all kinds of biological problems.

71. SOME ADDITIONAL CALCULATIONS

Deformability of ions

It has been assumed throughout that the ions in a compound can be regarded as completely rigid spheres. At various points in the book, however, it has been pointed out that this is only an approximation, although no correction for deformability of the ions was applied. Such a correction can be applied by introducing a repulsion function which decreases rapidly with distance (*see Figure 1*), and BORN introduced a term b/r^n for the energy corresponding to repulsion of the electron clouds. This expression illustrates the fact that the repulsion decreases very rapidly with increasing distance. Some idea of the magnitude of n can be derived from the compressibilities of crystals; it has a value of approximately ten. PAULING assumes the following values of n for the types of ions tabulated:

ion	He	Ne	Ar	Cu^+	Kr	Ag^+	Xe	Au^+	Ra
n	5	7	9	9	10	10	12	12	—

We will now calculate the crystal energy of the compound NaCl with this correction included. The energy of one ion with respect to another at a distance r now becomes $-e^2/r + b/r^n$. The potential energy of one ion with respect to all the surrounding ones is found by a summation analogous to that given in Section 14, and the result is

$$-Ae^2/r + B/r^n$$

in which

$$B/r^n = b/r^n\{6 + 12/2^{n/2} + 8/3^{n/2} - \dots\}$$

The total crystal energy is therefore

$$U = -N'(Ae^2/r - B/r^n)$$

where there are N' ions in the crystal. This energy must have a minimum value in the crystal, and the condition for this to be so is that the energy shall be a minimum as a function of the mutual distance r between the ions. That is

$$\partial U/\partial r = 0$$

Then

$$\partial U/\partial r = N'Ae^2/r^2 - nN'Br^{n+1} = 0$$

Therefore, since $r = a$, the separation distance measured in the crystal

$$Ae^2/a^2 = nB/a^{n+1}$$

whence

$$B/a^n = Ae^2/an$$

and, substituting in the formula for U

$$U = \frac{n-1}{n}\left(-\frac{N'Ae^2}{a}\right)$$

a result which was used without proof in Section 14.

As a result of the repulsion, the distance between the atoms in a single molecule AB will be larger than it is in the lattice. If the crystal belongs to the NaCl type, then for n we have to take a value of 10; the second term, $12/2^5 = 0{\cdot}4$, is small compared with the first. As a first approximation, B can be replaced by bc/r^n where c is the lattice coordination number.

Again, if a is the equilibrium distance in the lattice and a_1 that in the free molecule, then the two conditions of equilibrium are

$$\partial U/\partial r = 0 \qquad \partial E/\partial r = 0$$

$$U = -N'(Ae^2/r - bc/r^n) \qquad E = -N'(e^2/r - b/r^n)$$

$$Ae^2/a^2 - nbc/a^{n+1} = 0 \qquad e^2/a_1^2 - nb/a_1^{n+1} = 0$$

whence, by eliminating b, the following relationship between a and a_1 is obtained

$$nb = Ae^2a^{n-1}/c = e^2a_1^{n-1}$$

so that

$$a_1 = a(A/c)^{1/(n-1)}$$

If we assume $n = 10$, $A = 1{\cdot}75$ and $c = 6$, then

$$a_1 = 0{\cdot}872a$$

This expression means that the distance in the molecule is approximately 13 per cent smaller than that in the crystal with a NaCl structure. This reduction in the distance has the effect of making the dipole moment of the molecule AB somewhat smaller than the value calculated from the formula

$$\mu = e(r_A + r_B)$$

in which r_A and r_B are the radii of the ions which are considered as rigid spheres.

Pauling's calculated values for the ionic radii are not really the radii of the rigid ions, but the values which these ions would have if they formed a lattice with the NaCl structure. In another lattice the distance will be somewhat different, so that the distance in the

CsCl lattice, which we can call a_8 if a_6 is the distance in the NaCl lattice, is equal to $a_6(8A_6/6A_8)^{1/(n-1)}$ where A_6 and A_8 are respective Madelung constants for the NaCl and CsCl lattices.

Since, from Section 13, the Madelung constant for the CsCl lattice is almost the same as that for NaCl, the equation can be written

$$a_8 = a_6(8/6)^{1/(n-1)} = 1{\cdot}04a_6$$

The distance in the CsCl lattice is therefore 4 per cent greater than that in NaCl.

As long as we only assume coulomb forces and repulsive forces of the type discussed, this contraction leads to the surprising result that the CsCl lattice can never be formed. It can only exist if the lattice energy of the CsCl lattice is smaller, or at least equal to that of the NaCl lattice. The conditions for the stability of the CsCl lattice are

$$U_8 < U_6$$

$$-(n-1)N'A_8e^2/nr_8 < -(n-1)N'A_6e^2/nr_6$$

$$r_8/r_6 < A_8/A_6$$

and since

$$r_8/r_6 = (8A_6/6A_8)^{1/(n-1)}$$

then

$$(8A_6/6A_8)^{1/(n-1)} < A_8/A_6$$

$$\text{or } (8/6) < (A_8/A_6)^n$$

Now A_8/A_6 differs little from unity, and therefore n must have a large value (about 35) to satisfy the equation. Since n is actually much smaller than 35 for all kinds of ions, the CsCl lattice cannot be stable. The introduction of non-rigid ions therefore has a serious effect on GOLDSCHMIDT's treatment. In KF, where the ions are of equal size, a CsCl structure is no longer to be expected. It is the van der Waals forces, described in Section 46, tending towards high coordination numbers, which lead to the formation of CsCl lattices, but only in the compounds CsCl, CsBr and CsI which are composed of strongly polarizable ions.

The corrections which have to be applied to the ionic radii are very large in molecules with high ionic charges and lead to very considerable contractions, but, when they are applied, there is agreement with the values observed for many compounds. Where a compound has a much smaller distance than the sum of the ionic radii, this does not prove that the compound concerned is not composed of ions; the contraction which takes place leads to a merging of values for the ionic and atomic radii.

Dipole and charge in an electric field

On pages 159 and 160 formulae have been derived for the energy of a dipole μ and a particle with polarizability α in the field of an ion a at a distance r. If the field of the ion is called F, these expressions become $-\mu F$ and $-\frac{1}{2}\alpha F^2$. It was noted before that the factor μ in the latter formula is due to the fact that the energy required to polarize a particle by a field F is equal to half the energy of the particle in that field.

The energy of the dipole can therefore be expressed as $-\mu F$ or, more generally, $-\mu F \cos \varphi$ if the dipole μ makes an angle φ with the direction of the field. We will now derive this formula. The dipole can again be considered as consisting of two charges, $-e$ and e, at a distance d apart. The distance AB is therefore $d \cos \varphi$ (*see Figure 52*). From the definition of potential, the energies of the two charges at A and B are $-eV_A$ and eV_B, respectively. But from the definition of F it follows that $V_A - V_B = aF$, where a is the distance between A and B. The energy of the dipole in the field is therefore

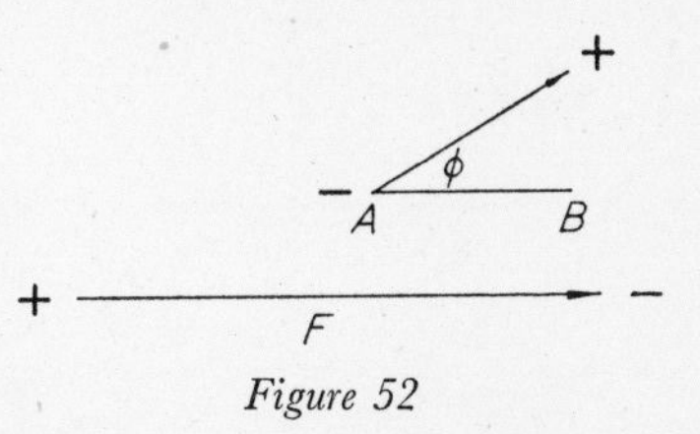

Figure 52

$$-eV_A + eV_B = -e(V_A - V_B) = -eaF =$$
$$-ed \cos \varphi = F = -\mu F \cos \varphi$$

If μ_α is the dipole caused by the field, then it follows that

$$\mu\alpha = \alpha F$$

As the induced dipole will necessarily lie in the direction of the field, the energy is equal to $-\alpha F^2$, keeping in mind that energy has been required for the creation of the dipole.

In order to calculate this energy, imagine that the field, containing the particle, increases slowly from a value of 0 to F. At a certain value F_x of the field, the dipole distance will be x. Now if the field increases by $\mathrm{d}F$, then the charges will be further displaced to a distance $x + \mathrm{d}x$, whereby the field does work corresponding to $e(F_x)\,\mathrm{d}x$. The total work from 0 to a distance d is therefore

$$\int_0^d eF_x \,\mathrm{d}x$$

and by substituting $F_x = \mu/\alpha = ex/\alpha$ the integral becomes

$$\int_0^d \frac{e^2 x \,\mathrm{d}x}{\alpha} = \frac{(ex)^2}{2\alpha} = \frac{\mu^2}{2\alpha} = \frac{\alpha F^2}{2}$$

The total energy of the polarizable particle in the field F is therefore

$$-\alpha F^2 + \tfrac{1}{2}\alpha F^2 = -\tfrac{1}{2}\alpha F^2$$

Energy of non-linear molecule AB_2

The following formulae are obtained when an exact calculation is made to determine whether a molecule of the type $A^{2-}B_2^+$ can become non-linear as a result of polarization of the ion A.

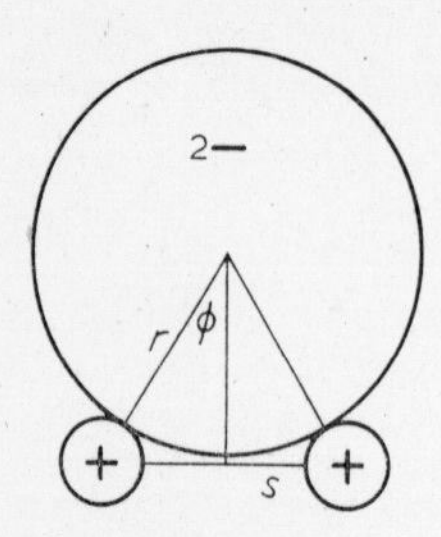

Figure 53

Let us suppose that the ion B is not polarizable. The problem then is to find the angle for which the energy of the molecule is a minimum. If r is the sum of the ionic radii (*see Figure 53*), then the energy of the molecule is

$$E = -2\frac{e^2}{r} + \frac{e^2}{s} - \frac{\alpha F^2}{2} + \frac{2B}{r^n}$$

in which the first term gives the energy of the two B ions with respect to the A ion, e^2/s the energy of the two B ions with respect to each other, and $-\alpha F^2/2$ that of the polarizable A ion in the field F, which is created by the B ions. Finally $2B/r^n$ is the Born repulsion energy between A and the two B ions.

If F is the resultant of the two field strengths e/r^2 of the two ions which make an angle 2φ with each other, then $F = 2e\cos\varphi/r^2$ and from the figure $s = 2r\sin\varphi$, so that

$$E = -2\frac{e^2}{r} + \frac{e^2}{2r\sin\varphi} - 2\alpha\frac{e^2}{r^4}\cos^2\varphi + \frac{2B}{r^n}$$

A value of φ must now be found which corresponds to minimum energy; this occurs when $\partial E/\partial\varphi = 0$. The condition for the minimum is therefore

$$-\frac{e^2}{2r\sin^2\varphi}\cos\varphi + 4\alpha\frac{e^2}{r^4}\cos\varphi\sin\varphi = 0$$

Two values of φ satisfy this equation, which are found from

$$\cos\varphi = 0 \qquad \text{and} \qquad -\frac{1}{2\sin^2\varphi} + \frac{4\alpha}{r^3}\sin\varphi = 0$$

The first relation gives a linear model for the molecule, and the second

$$\sin\varphi = (r^3/8\alpha)^{1/3}$$

giving the angle of the less symmetrical molecule which can only exist when $\sin \varphi < 1$ and therefore

$$(r^3/8\alpha) < 1 \qquad \text{or} \qquad \alpha > r^3/8$$

In order to determine whether the less symmetrical model is really stable, or that $\partial E/\partial \varphi$ really is a minimum, we must find $\partial^2 E/\partial \varphi^2$. We then have

$$\frac{\partial^2 E}{\partial \varphi^2} = \frac{e^2}{2r}\left(\frac{2\cos^2 \varphi}{\sin^3 \varphi} + \frac{1}{\sin \varphi}\right) + 4\frac{\alpha e^2}{r^4}(\cos^2 \varphi - \sin^2 \varphi)$$

$$= \frac{e^2}{2r}\left(\frac{1 + \cos^2 \varphi}{\sin^3 \varphi}\right) + 4\frac{\alpha e^2}{r^4}(\cos^2 \varphi - \sin^2 \varphi)$$

$$= \frac{e^2}{2r}\left\{\left(\frac{1 + \cos^2 \varphi}{\sin^3 \varphi}\right) + \frac{8\alpha}{r^3}(\cos^2 \varphi - \sin^2 \varphi)\right\}$$

For the linear model $\cos \varphi = 0$, $\sin \varphi = 1$, and it will only be stable when $\partial^2 E/\partial \varphi^2 > 1$ so that $(1 - 8\alpha/r^3) > 0$ and $(8\alpha/r^3) < 1$. Therefore, if we could allow the value $8\alpha/r^3$ of a molecule to increase continuously, when it reaches unity the molecule would begin to have lower symmetry. If we still wish to correct the energy for the change of r, then we must differentiate the expression for E with respect to r and eliminate B. At this point, however, the exact calculation can be taken no further because in hydrogen compounds no normal Born repulsion exists. The calculation can be carried through successfully for all molecules not containing hydrogen ions.

In more complicated molecules a value for μ cannot be found directly; E is then expressed as a function of μ, for example, for water

$$E = -2\frac{e^2}{r} - \frac{2e\mu \cos \theta}{r^2} + \frac{e^2}{s} + \frac{\mu^2}{2\alpha} + \frac{2B}{r^n}$$

In this expression the second term is the energy due to the interaction of dipoles with charges, and the fourth term is the energy required to form the dipole; μ can then be found from $\partial E/\partial \mu = 0$ which gives the value

$$\mu = \frac{2\alpha e}{r^2}\cos \varphi$$

The energy of two dipoles μ_1 and μ_2 is a function of the angles the dipole axes include with the line connecting the two centres of the dipole (*see Figure 54*).

We first consider three special cases

1. $\theta_1 = \theta_2 = 90°, \quad E = +\frac{\mu_1\mu_2}{r^3}$ or

$$\theta_1 = -\theta_2 = 90°, E = -\frac{\mu_1\mu_2}{r^3}$$

2. $\theta_1 = \theta_2 = 0, \quad E = -2\frac{\mu_1\mu_2}{r^3}$ or

$$\theta_1 = 0, \theta_2 = 180°, E = +2\frac{\mu_1\mu_2}{r^3}$$

3. $\theta_1 = 0, \theta_2 = 90°, E = 0$ or $\theta_2 = 0, \theta_1 = 90°, E = 0$

These formula can be easily derived by representing the dipole by two point charges at distances d_1 and d_2, respectively, and neglecting higher powers of d against higher powers of r, as in the example on page 171 where formula 2 was derived. With the aid of these three

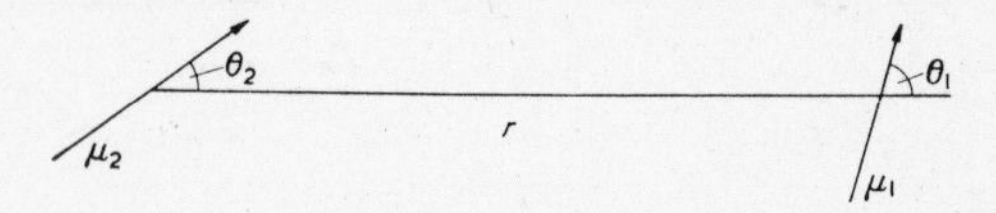

Figure 54

formulae the expression for the general case is easily derived. We first assume that the two dipoles lie in one plane. Then each of the two dipoles is resolved in its components, $\mu_1 \cos \theta_1$ and $\mu_2 \cos \theta_2$, parallel to the line connecting the centres, and $\mu_1 \sin \theta_1$ and $\mu_2 \sin \theta_2$, perpendicular to this direction. The energy of the two dipoles then is

$$-\frac{\mu^2}{r^3}(2 \cos \theta_1 \cos \theta_2 - \sin \theta_1 \sin \theta_2)$$

If one of the dipoles, e.g. μ_2, includes an angle Θ with the plane determined by the axis of the other and the line connecting the centres, the components perpendicular to the line connecting the centres have still to be projected on the plane, and we find

$$-\frac{\mu^2}{r^3}(2 \cos \theta_1 \cos \theta_2 - \cos \theta \sin \theta_1 \sin \Theta_2)$$

An important case is that in which the two dipoles are formed by the polarization of one charge at equal distance, as in symmetrical molecules AX_2. The dipoles then lie in one plane with the line connecting their centres and $\theta_1 = 180 - \theta_2$. Thus

$$E = -\frac{\mu^2}{r^3}(-2\cos^2\theta_1 - \sin^2\theta_1) = +\frac{\mu^2}{r^3}(1 + \cos^2\theta_1)$$

For a molecule *XAX* this reduces to

$$2\frac{\mu^2}{r^3}$$

TABLE OF KNOWN ELEMENTS

THE atomic numbers, names and chemical symbols of the known elements are given, together with the mean atomic weights to four figures, based on oxygen, O = 16·000. The sign ↕ indicates the places where the sequence of atomic weights of stable elements does not fall into line with that of the atomic numbers. Noble gases are italicized.

1	Hydrogen	H	1·008
2	*Helium*	He	4·003
3	Lithium	Li	6·940
4	Beryllium	Be	9·02
5	Boron	B	10·82
6	Carbon	C	12·01
7	Nitrogen	N	14·01
8	Oxygen	O	16·00
9	Fluorine	F	19·00
10	*Neon*	Ne	20·18
11	Sodium	Na	23·00
12	Magnesium	Mg	24·32
13	Aluminium	Al	26·97
14	Silicon	Si	28·06
15	Phosphorus	P	30·98
16	Sulphur	S	32·06
17	Chlorine	Cl	35·46
18	*Argon*	Ar	39·94 ↑
19	Potassium	K	39·10 ↓
20	Calcium	Ca	40·08
21	Scandium	Sc	45·10
22	Titanium	Ti	47·90
23	Vanadium	V	50·95
24	Chromium	Cr	52·01
25	Manganese	Mn	54·93
26	Iron	Fe	55·85
27	Cobalt	Co	58·94 ↑
28	Nickel	Ni	58·69 ↓
29	Copper	Cu	63·57
30	Zinc	Zn	65·38
31	Gallium	Ga	69·72
32	Germanium	Ge	72·60
33	Arsenic	As	74·91
34	Selenium	Se	78·96
35	Bromine	Br	79·92
36	*Krypton*	Kr	83·7
37	Rubidium	Rb	85·48
38	Strontium	Sr	87·63
39	Yttrium	Y	88·92
40	Zirconium	Zr	91·22
41	Columbium	Cb	92·91
42	Molybdenum	Mo	95·95
43	Technetium	Tc	99
44	Ruthenium	Ru	101·7
45	Rhodium	Rh	102·9
46	Palladium	Pd	106·7
47	Silver	Ag	107·9
48	Cadmium	Cd	112·4
49	Indium	In	114·8
50	Tin	Sn	118·7
51	Antimony	Sb	121·8
52	Tellurium	Te	127·6 ↑
53	Iodine	I	126·9 ↓
54	*Xenon*	Xe	131·3
55	Caesium	Cs	132·9
56	Barium	Ba	137·4
57	Lanthanum	La	138·9
58	Cerium	Ce	140·1
59	Praseodymium	Pr	140·9
60	Neodymium	Nd	144·3
61	Promethium	Pro	—
62	Samarium	Sm	150·4
63	Europium	Eu	152·0
64	Gadolinium	Gd	156·9
65	Terbium	Tb	159·2
66	Dysprosium	Dy	162·5
67	Holmium	Ho	163·5
68	Erbium	Er	167·6
69	Thulium	Tu	169·4
70	Ytterbium	Yb	173·04

No.	Element	Symbol	Atomic weight	No.	Element	Symbol	Atomic weight	
71	Lutecium	Lu	175·0	84	Polonium	Po	218·2	↑
72	Hafnium	Hf	178·6	85	Astatine	At	211	↓
73	Tantalum	Ta	180·9	86	*Radon*	Rn	222	
74	Tungsten	W	184·0	87	Francium	Fr	223	
75	Rhenium	Re	186·3	88	Radium	Ra	226·0	
76	Osmium	Os	190·2	89	Actinium	Ac	227	
77	Iridium	Ir	193·1	90	Thorium	Th	232·1	↑
78	Platinum	Pt	195·2	91	Protactinium	Pa	231	↓
79	Gold	Au	197·2	92	Uranium	U	238·1	
80	Mercury	Hg	200·6	93	Neptunium	Np	—	
81	Thallium	Tl	204·4	94	Plutonium	Pu	—	
82	Lead	Pb	207·2	95	Americium	Am	—	
83	Bismuth	Bi	209·0	96	Curium	Cm	—	

INDEX